THE ULTIMATE BOOK OF TRIVIA

PEOPLE

CINEMA

SCIENCE AND NATURE

PLACES

MUSIC

HISTORY

THE 20TH CENTURY

SPORT

TV AND RADIO

ART AND LITERATURE

GENERAL KNOWLEDGE

THE ULTIMATE BOOK OF TRIVIA

QUIZ 1

THE ULTIMATE
BOOK OF TRIVIA

This is a Parragon Book
First published in 2002

Parragon
Queen Street House
4 Queen Street
Bath BA1 1HE, UK

ISBN: 0-75259-140-1

Editorial, design and layout by
Essential Books, 7 Stucley Place, London NW1 8NS

Printed in Dubai by Oriental Press

THE ULTIMATE
BOOK OF TRIVIA

1 Who was president at the time of the 1929 stock market crash?

2 Which future president drafted the Declaration of Independence?

3 By what name is president Lyndon B Johnson's wife Claudia better known?

4 Who was the first president to be born in the twentieth century?

5 How many presidents have been assassinated while in office?

6 Who, at 69, was the oldest president to take the oath of office?

7 Which president had the nickname 'Old Hickory'?

8 After being shot in 1912, which former president said of the assassination attempt, 'It takes more than that to kill a Bull Moose'?

9 Who is the only president buried in Washington, DC?

10 From whose inaugural speech do these words come: 'There is nothing wrong with America that cannot be cured by what is right with America'?

11 Who was the only president to serve in both World Wars?

12 Which president gave the first televised State of the Union address?

13 Which president was elected four consecutive times?

14 In 1858, three years before becoming president, Abraham Lincoln became senator of which state?

15 Which future president was the United States Representative to the United Nations under the Nixon administration?

16 Who was the first president to visit all 50 states?

17 Why was the 23rd president, Benjamin Harrison, called the 'Centennial President'?

18 Who was the first president to win the Nobel Peace Prize?

19 Which president said in a *Playboy* interview that he had 'committed adultery in my heart many times'?

20 How many states existed when George Washington took office?

21 What is the significance of the play *Our American Cousin*?

22 Who was the only president to serve two non-consecutive terms in office?

23 Whose presidential competency was questioned when he insisted during a debate that there was no Soviet domination in Poland?

24 Between the years 1857 and 1861, during James Buchanan's presidency, what role was performed by his niece, Harriet Lane, and why?

25 Which ex-president died in 1973, five days before an agreement was signed in Paris ending the fighting in Vietnam?

25

15 Where was Errol Flynn born?

16 From which country do quesadillas originate?

17 What nationality would you be if you spoke Inuktitut?

18 Who speak Afrikaans?

19 Which nationalities are separated by the Khyber Pass?

20 What nationality are the Tamil Tigers?

21 What nationality are the Ashanti tribe, centred around Kumasi city?

22 What nationality is tennis player Kim Clijsters?

23 Which was the first country to legalize abortion?

24 What is the nationality of Gabriel Byrne?

25 What nationality is Frida from Abba?

1 Of which country was Edith Cresson prime minister?

2 Which countries were involved in the 1993 Downing St Declaration?

3 Of which country was Carlos Menem president?

4 Of which country was Golda Meir the first woman president?

5 Of which country is Aung San Suu Kyi the opposition leader?

6 Of which country did Mary McAleese become president?

7 Where did Tung Chee-Hwa become chief executive in 1997?

8 What nationality is the owner of the Paris Ritz?

9 Where is designer Catherine Walker from?

10 Where is author Thomas Keneally from?

11 If your currency is the lek, where are you from?

12 What nationality is a car marked 'LAR'?

13 Which nationality is the House of Bernadotte?

14 If you are from Abidjan, where are you from?

1 What was the name of Quint's boat in *Jaws*?

2 What is the name of the film company owned by Spielberg, Jeffrey Katzenberg and David Geffen?

3 What was the title of Spielberg's first feature film?

4 Which of Spielberg's films centres on a boy living in Shanghai at the outset of the Second World War?

5 What was the first Spielberg movie to be shot completely (exteriors as well as interiors) on soundstages?

6 Who came out of retirement to play the role of Richard Dreyfuss's spiritual guide in *Always*?

7 Who played the young Indy in *Indiana Jones and the Last Crusade*?

8 Which Spielberg movie featured the characters Sergeant Tree, Sitarski and 'Wild Bill' Kelso?

9 Which film director, much admired by Spielberg, played the role of a scientist in *Close Encounters of the Third Kind*?

10 Which of *The Color Purple*'s co-producers also wrote the music for the film?

11 Who played the part of Elliott's sister Gertie in *ET, The Extra-Terrestrial*?

12 During the shooting of *Schindler's List*, which other film was Spielberg editing from his hotel via satellite link?

13 Which film brought Spielberg his second Oscar for direction?

14 How was Spielberg 'credited' in the 1994 movie *The Flintstones*?

15 Which famous actress contributed some of the vocal effects to ET's voice?

16 Who played Dr Ellie Sattler in *Jurassic Park*?

17 In 1971, after two pilot episodes had been made, the then-23-year-old Spielberg directed the first regular instalment of which TV detective show?

18 Who played Indy's love interest in *Indiana Jones and the Temple of Doom*, later to marry Spielberg himself?

19 Who has composed the music for the vast majority of Spielberg's films?

20 Of which book did Spielberg say, 'I read it and felt that I had been attacked. It terrified me, and I wanted to strike back'?

21 Who played the title role in the film *Hook*?

22 Which book did producer Kathleen Kennedy describe as 'one of those projects that was so obviously a Spielberg film'?

23 Which then-local talk show host played the role of Sofia in *The Color Purple*?

24 Although Spielberg directed *Raiders of the Lost Ark*, he did not have the final cut. Who did?

25 To what was Spielberg referring when he said, 'This is the best drink of water after the longest drought of my life'?

1 Which 1956 film saw Gregory Peck as a captain obsessed with capturing a great white whale?

2 How did Hitchcock make his customary appearance in *Lifeboat*?

3 Who played the title role in 1951's *Captain Horatio Hornblower RN*?

4 Which actress starred alongside Nick Nolte and Robert Shaw in the 1977 film *The Deep*?

5 Who starred in *Sink the Bismarck*?

6 Which 1955 film featured Henry Fonda, James Cagney, William Powell and Jack Lemmon?

7 What was the subject of the 1958 British movie *A Night to Remember*?

8 Which 1995 brink-of-nuclear-disaster thriller, set aboard a submarine, starred Gene Hackman and Denzel Washington?

9 In the 1962 version of *Mutiny on the Bounty*, who played Captain Bligh and Fletcher Christian?

10 Who was the child star who appeared alongside Spencer Tracy in *Captains Courageous*?

11 Harrison Ford has twice played Jack Ryan in films of Tom Clancy's books, but who played him in *The Hunt for Red October*?

12 In which film is Sam Neill and Nicole Kidman's boat trip ruined by the appearance of Billy Zane?

13 Which James Cameron film, starring Ed Harris, won the 1989 Oscar for best visual effects?

14 What type of boat was featured in the German film *Das Boot*?

15 What was the name of Captain Nemo's submarine in the 1954 film *20,000 Leagues Under the Sea*?

16 Which Ernest Hemingway novel was filmed in 1958, starring Spencer Tracy?

17 What was the cinematic gimmick used in the third *Jaws* film?

18 Who starred in the 1940 pirate film *The Sea Hawk*?

19 Who was the technical wizard behind the special effects in *The Golden Voyage of Sinbad*?

20 In the 1955 film *It Came From Beneath the Sea*, what was 'it'?

21 What is the connection between the 1936 film *The Prisoner of Shark Island* and 1997's *Titanic*?

22 Who directed *Moby Dick* in 1956?

23 Which two stars fall in love aboard ship in the 1957 film *An Affair to Remember*?

24 Which actor, a former acrobat, starred in the 1952 swashbuckling spoof *The Crimson Pirate*?

25 Who starred in the 2000 film *The Perfect Storm*?

1 Which hormone regulates blood sugar level?

2 Where would you find carpal bones and tarsal bones respectively?

3 Caries is an extremely common disease. By what name is it better known?

4 In which organ are the hepatic arteries?

5 What is the condition called when an internal organ protrudes through the wall of the cavity in which it is normally contained?

6 Where in the body is the cochlea?

7 What is the essential difference between arteries and veins?

8 Where are the deltoid muscles?

9 What name is given to opacity in the lens of the eye?

10 Where is the pituitary gland?

11 What is the more common name for allergic rhinitis?

12 Of the two bones in the lower leg, the tibia and the fibula, which is the shinbone?

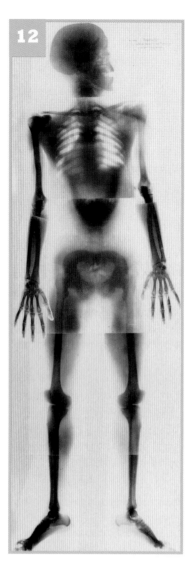

13 What are the pads of cartilage between spinal vertebrae commonly called?

14 Where are red blood cells formed?

15 Where is the temporal bone?

16 By what name is the tendon at the back of the ankle known?

17 Where is the coccyx?

18 Except for sex cells, all human cells contain 23 pairs of what?

19 What is the name given to an examination of a body by dissection to determine cause of death?

20 How many teeth should a person have?

21 Which sense is stimulated by the reaction of the olfactory cells?

22 What is the proper name for the kneecap?

23 Which gland produces hormones to control the body's metabolic rate?

24 Where is the carotid artery situated?

25 Which is the longest bone in the body?

1 Through which European capital city does the River Tagus flow?

2 In which city does the Blue Nile meet the White Nile?

3 Which river forms the border between Mexico and Texas?

4 On which river does Belfast stand?

5 The Orange river flows into the Atlantic Ocean between which two southern African countries?

6 Into which body of water does the River Volga flow?

7 On which river would you find the Victoria Falls and the Kariba dam?

8 The Putumayo, the Purus and the Madeira are three of the many tributaries of which great South American river?

9 Which Australian river forms most of the border between New South Wales and Victoria?

10 On which river do the cities of Florence and Pisa stand?

11 Which river featured in the musical *Showboat*?

12 At nearly 4,000 miles, Asia's longest river is the Chang Jiang. By what name is it better known in the West?

13 Into which body of water do the Tigris and the Euphrates flow?

14 Which rivers flow on the east and west of Manhattan Island?

15 Which river rises in Tibet and flows through China, Burma, Laos, Thailand, Cambodia and Vietnam before reaching the South China Sea?

16 From which South American country does the Orinoco flow into the Atlantic?

17 Which Asian capital city's airport is built at the mouth of the Tama-gawa?

18 Which two capital cities stand on the mouth of the Rio de la Plata, or River Plate?

19 On which river does Inverness stand?

20 Which river flows through the Grand Canyon?

21 The Mackenzie river in Canada's Northwest Territories flows north into the Beaufort Sea. What does it cross along the way?

22 In which country does the Rhine reach the sea?

23 Through which country does the River Dnieper flow before it reaches the Black Sea?

24 Which river is spanned by Britain's longest suspension bridge?

25 Which river flows between Lake Ontario and Lake Erie and forms part of the border between Canada and the United States?

1 What is the significance of the date 6 July 1957?

2 Which was the first single released by the Beatles on the Apple label?

3 On which Beatles song did George Harrison first play a sitar?

4 What is Paul McCartney's middle name?

5 Which was the first Beatles album to consist entirely of original material?

6 About whose sister is John Lennon's song 'Dear Prudence'?

7 Which sixties TV comedy show is mentioned on the *Sgt Pepper's Lonely Hearts Club Band* album?

8 From which band did the Beatles recruit Ringo Starr?

9 Who played lead guitar on George's 'While My Guitar Gently Weeps'?

10 Which single, when it peaked at number two in the UK charts in 1967, ended a run of eleven consecutive number ones?

11 In which American city did the Beatles play their last concert in 1966, vowing never to tour again?

12 Which album was at one time going to be called *Everest*?

13 What was the first Lennon–McCartney composition to feature Ringo on lead vocals?

14 Who were the Beatles accused of snubbing in Manila in 1966?

15 Which single was recorded at EMI's studios in Paris in 1964?

16 Who recorded a version of 'A Hard Day's Night' in the style of Laurence Olivier's *Richard III*?

17 Which song had the working title 'Scrambled Eggs'?

18 Which British prime ministers are mentioned in a Beatles song?

19 What was the title of John Lennon's second book?

20 Where did the Beatles appear on 30 January 1969?

21 Which one of the band's Hamburg friends designed the sleeve of the *Revolver* album?

22 Which Beatles song did Frank Sinatra describe as 'the greatest love song of the past fifty years'?

23 Who was the first Beatle to have a solo number one hit in the UK?

24 What contribution was made by Tony Gilbert, Sidney Sax, Kenneth Essex and Francisco Gabarro to the recording of the *Help!* album?

25 Which song from *The Beatles*, or 'The White Album' as it is commonly called, was originally titled 'Maharishi'?

1 Who wrote the music for *Shaft*?

2 The Celine Dion hit 'Because You Loved Me' stemmed from which film?

3 Who won a Grammy for the Best Original Film Song Score in 1970?

4 Name Mick Jagger's minor hit from *Performance*.

5 Which single was performed over the opening credits to *The Birdcage*?

6 Name Michael Sembello's *Flashdance* hit.

7 Who had the only hit from the soundtrack of *Midnight Cowboy*?

8 Who wrote all the songs for *The Lion King*?

9 Name the hit from *Rocky II*.

10 Which film song provided the UK's biggest-selling single of 1991?

11 Which ex-Beatle wrote the theme tune for a James Bond film?

12 Stevie Wonder appeared in *Muscle Beach Party* singing 'Happy Street'. True or false?

13 Which film provided Berlin's hit 'Take My Breath Away'?

14 Who sang the main theme to the Peter Sellers film *What's New, Pussycat?*?

15 In which film did Elvis Presley warble '[There's] No Room to Rhumba in the Back Seat of a Sports Car'?

16 Madonna sang this on the soundtrack to *Austin Powers: The Spy Who Shagged Me*.

17 Name Ronan Keating's *Notting Hill* hit.

18 Who sang the main theme to *Shaft In Africa*?

19 The Supremes provided the hit theme to a film starring Anthony Quinn, George Maharis and Faye Dunaway. What was the film?

20 Who wrote and sang the songs heard in *Jonathan Livingstone Seagull*?

21 Elton John wrote and performed the songs for a film about two kids, aged 14 and 15, who run off to a cottage to have a child of their own. What was it called?

22 Debbie Harry sang the title song to the Werner Herzog movie *Heart of Glass*. True or false?

23 *Play Misty For Me* was the title of the film in which Clint Eastwood portrayed a DJ. But whose version of Misty did he play?

24 In which film did Bill Haley's 'Rock Around the Clock' make its first sensational appearance?

25 David Bowie and Pat Metheny had a hit with 'This Is Not America'. Name the film from which it came.

WORLD WAR II

1 Who was voted out of power in July 1943 after the invasion of Sicily?

2 In which year was the Women's Land Army formed?

3 In which country is El Alamein?

4 What was Operation Overlord?

5 Which country was invaded by the Japanese in 1937?

6 When General Douglas MacArthur told the Australian press 'I shall return', to where was he referring?

7 Who started arriving in Britain in January 1942?

8 Which two European countries fought each other between November 1939 and March 1940?

9 Which battle in the Pacific was fought between 4 and 5 June 1942?

10 Which German city was devastated by 2,600 tons of British bombs in February 1945?

11 Who was appointed to command the US Pacific fleet shortly after Pearl Harbor?

12 Which country declared war on Japan the day before the bomb was dropped on Nagasaki?

13 What was Field Marshal Montgomery's first name?

14 Which Australian state capital was bombed by the Japanese in February 1942?

15 What happened aboard the USS *Missouri* on 2 September 1945?

16 What occurred between 26 May and 2 June 1940?

17 What was Operation Sealion?

18 Shostakovich's seventh symphony is named after which besieged Soviet city?

19 Who did Count Claus von Stauffenberg attempt to assassinate with a bomb on 20 July 1944?

20 Who replaced Winston Churchill at the Potsdam conference in July and August 1945?

21 Where did the British surrender to the Japanese in February 1942?

22 Which pilots were named after a typhoon which destroyed a Mongol invasion fleet bound for Japan in the Middle Ages?

23 Who succeeded Hitler as German leader?

24 What connected the countries of Eire, Portugal, Spain and Turkey during the war?

25 Which German word means 'lightning war'?

1 Which test batsman scored the most runs in the 1990s, with a total of 6,407?

2 Which wicket-keeper has a record 389 dismissals in test cricket?

3 Which future West Indies captain made his debut against England in the 1953–54 series at the age of 17 years and 245 days?

4 With 131 test appearances, who is India's most capped player?

5 Which bowler has taken the most wickets in matches between England and Australia?

6 Who is the only bowler to take hat-tricks in successive tests?

7 In which season did Sri Lanka and Zimbabwe first meet in test cricket?

8 Who was the last England captain to regain the Ashes?

9 Who is the only batsman to score centuries in each of his first three tests?

10 On 15 March 1877, which ground was the venue for the first-ever test match?

11 With an aggregate of 5,444 runs, who is New Zealand's highest scoring test batsman?

12 Which country did not play a test against England from 1965 to 1994?

13 Who is the only player to score a century and take five wickets in an innings on five separate occasions?

14 Of England's current test venues, which was the first to be used for test cricket?

15 Who scored a record 974 runs in a series against England in 1930?

16 In which season did India play their first series against Pakistan?

17 Who holds the record for the highest individual score in a test innings?

18 Which batsman has scored the most test centuries, with a total of 34?

19 Who scored a century off 56 deliveries for the West Indies against England in the 1985–86 series?

20 Which Indian bowler equalled Jim Laker's record of ten wickets in an innings when he dismissed Pakistan in the 1998–99 series?

21 Which currently available England player's father and grandfather both played for the West Indies?

22 Which country did Australia not play against between 1946 and 1973?

23 In the 1997–98 season, which country scored the highest ever innings total with 952 for 6 declared against India?

24 With 8,832 runs, who is Pakistan's leading test batsman?

25 Which two England players won their 100th caps in the same match against the West Indies in 2000?

1 What is the name of Barcelona's stadium?

2 Which Premier League team plays at The Stadium of Light?

3 Where was the disaster in 1985 involving Liverpool and Juventus?

4 Who is hosting the 2004 Olympics?

5 Who plays at the Olympic Stadium in Rome?

6 Which country will host the 2006 World Cup?

7 Who plays at Ibrox?

8 Where did Botham win the Ashes in 1981?

9 Which stadium held the 1998 World Cup final?

10 What happens at Walthamstow Stadium?

11 Who plays at Filbert Street?

12 Where did Roger Bannister break the four-minute mile?

13 Who played at The Stoop?

14 Where do Leicester Tigers play?

15 What did the Millennium Stadium replace?

16 Where is Britain's premier athletics stadium?

17 Who famously revealed all at Twickenham?

18 What is the capacity of the Sydney Cricket Ground?

19 Which other sport is played at the SCG?

20 Name four English Test cricket venues.

21 Who play at either end of the Seven Sisters Road?

22 Who plays at the Bernabau?

23 Where do Celtic play?

24 Where do the New York Mets play?

25 Which golf course is the home of golf?

1 What type of dead parrot did John Cleese take back to the pet shop?

2 Terry Jones played a man who claimed to have three what?

3 Which gang made Bolton 'a frightened city'?

4 On whose trail was Superintendent Harry 'Snapper' Organs?

5 What is it that 'nobody expects'?

6 In the Architects sketch, what did John Cleese's character propose instead of a block of flats?

7 What was the name of the cheese shop owner?

8 In the sketch involving Whistler, Wilde, Shaw and His Majesty, who played Oscar Wilde?

9 What does Michael Palin's lumberjack do on Wednesdays?

10 What did John Cleese try to sell from a tray in the cinema?

11 What did Graham Chapman complain about in the restaurant, provoking an over-the-top response from the entire staff?

12 What type of fish was John Cleese's character's pet, Eric?

13 Which pre-Python show was written by Eric Idle, Terry Jones and Michael Palin, in which they co-starred with Denise Coffey and David Jason?

14 Which member of the Python team was a doctor?

15 Which meat product was immortalised in song by the Pythons?

16 What did highwayman Dennis Moore demand from his victims?

17 What did the upper-class twits have to do to the dummies?

18 Who played the straight man to Eric Idle in the Nudge-Nudge sketch?

19 Which member of the Python team quit after the third series?

20 What is the significance of Bronzino's painting *Venus and Cupid*, which hangs in the National Gallery?

21 What character did Michael Palin change out of a superhero costume to become?

22 Which member of the team was responsible for Conrad Pooh's dancing teeth?

23 What is the title of the Monty Python theme tune?

24 In which town did Mr Hilter contest a local election?

25 What did Michael Palin's character want to be in the Vocational Guidance Counsellor sketch?

1 What is the name of Phoebe's identical twin sister?

2 Which of the characters had a relationship with Dr Richard Burke, as played by Tom Selleck?

3 What particular contribution is made to the show by Michael Skloff and Allee Willis?

4 What is the name of Chandler's ex-girlfriend with the irritating laugh?

5 What is Ross's profession?

6 When Joey moved to his own apartment, what was the name of Chandler's new room-mate?

7 At which famous department store did Rachel get a job?

8 Who did the cast prod with their giant poking device made from old chopsticks?

9 Whose parents are played by Christina Pickles and Elliott Gould?

10 What is the name of the coffee shop?

11 What is the title of Phoebe's best-known song?

12 What were Joey and Chandler's two unusual pets?

13 What are the names of Ross's first wife and her partner?

14 Which regular supporting character is played by James Michael Tyler?

15 What was the name of the soap opera in which Joey played the part of neurosurgeon Dr Drake Ramoray?

16 What type of animal was Marcel?

17 In the London episodes, who played the part of a souvenir vendor?

18 With which cast member was actor Tate Donovan romantically linked after appearing on the show?

19 Who were the two team captains for the Thanksgiving football match?

20 Who played the part of Emily's mother?

21 Where did Ross and Rachel finally consummate their relationship?

22 How did Chandler refer to his 'third nipple'?

23 Which one of the characters dated multi-millionaire Pete Becker?

24 What was the name of Ross's girlfriend who he met on his trip to China?

25 After Chandler moved in with Monica, who guested as Joey's new room-mate, Janine?

1 By what collective name were Moe Howard, Jerry 'Curly' Howard and Larry Fine better known?

2 Where were the three coins in Frank Sinatra's 1954 number one hit?

3 Who was the third man to set foot on the moon?

4 Who wrote *The Three Musketeers*?

5 Which chemical element has an atomic number of 3?

6 In the decathlon, which event comes third on the first day?

7 Where was the 1954 film *Three Coins in the Fountain* set?

8 Who directed the film *The Third Man*?

9 Which composer's third symphony is known as the *Eroica*?

10 Where does three appear between seventeen and nineteen?

11 Who had his only UK number one in 1960 with 'Three Steps to Heaven'?

12 Who was Henry VIII's third wife?

13 Who had a hit in 1977 with 'Three Times a Lady'?

14 What is the total of the three internal angles of a triangle?

15 Which disciple denied knowing Jesus Christ three times?

16 Which Philadelphia vocal group were favourites of Prince Charles?

17 Which cartoon character had three nephews called Huey, Dewey and Louie?

18 Where did Dawn singer Tony Orlando tell his loved one to 'knock three times' in the song of the same name?

19 Who was the third president of the United States of America?

20 Who wrote *Three Men in a Boat*?

21 Which rock music trio were filmed at their final concert at the Royal Albert Hall in 1968?

22 What is the world's third highest mountain?

23 In Shakespeare's play, who told Macbeth that he would eventually become king?

24 Who is third in line to the English throne?

25 Which three writers used the pseudonyms Currer, Ellis and Acton Bell?

1 After whom was the dessert 'pavlova' named?

2 In 'angels and devils on horseback', what are the angels and devils made of?

3 What is a 'vol-au-vent'?

4 In Scotland, which soup is traditionally served on Burns Night?

5 From where does the term 'chowder' for soup derive?

6 How did Toll House cookies get their name?

7 For which occasion was Vichyssoise soup created?

8 After whom is Caesar salad named?

9 How did jambalaya get its name?

10 What does chilli con carne mean?

11 How did garam masala get its name?

12 How did Eggs Benedict get its name?

13 What is the origin of the word 'gammon'?

14 Traditionally, how did Anadama bread get its name?

15 Where does Key Lime Pie come from?

16 Who invented muesli?

17 After whom was the sandwich named?

18 From where does spaghetti bolognese originate?

19 How did Caprese salad get its name?

20 What does the name of the veal dish 'saltimbocca' mean?

21 What French word is used for the water ice often served between courses to refresh the palate?

22 The name of which dish, literally translated, means 'outside the work'?

23 How did Pasta all'Alfredo get its name?

24 How did Spaghetti alla Puttanesca get its name?

25 How did chocolate get its name?

ANSWERS TO QUIZ 1

US Presidents
1 Herbert Hoover
2 Thomas Jefferson
3 Lady Bird
4 John F Kennedy
5 Four: Lincoln, Garfield, McKinley and Kennedy
6 Ronald Reagan
7 Andrew Jackson
8 Theodore Roosevelt
9 Woodrow Wilson
10 Bill Clinton
11 Dwight D Eisenhower
12 Harry S Truman
13 Franklin D Roosevelt
14 Illinois
15 George Bush
16 Richard Nixon
17 He was inaugurated 100 years after George Washington
18 Theodore Roosevelt
19 Jimmy Carter
20 Thirteen
21 Abraham Lincoln was assassinated while watching it
22 Grover Cleveland, 1885–89 and 1893–97
23 Gerald Ford
24 First Lady – Buchanan was a bachelor
25 Lyndon B Johnson

What Nationality?
1 France
2 Ireland and UK
3 Argentina
4 Israel
5 Burma (Myanmar)
6 Ireland
7 Hong Kong
8 Egyptian
9 France
10 Australia
11 Albania
12 Libyan
13 Swedish
14 Ivory Coast
15 Australia (Hobart, Tasmania)
16 Mexico
17 Canadian
18 South Africans and Namibians
19 Pakistanis and Afghans
20 Sri Lankan
21 Ghanaian
22 Belgian
23 Iceland
24 Irish
25 Swedish

Steven Spielberg
1 The Orca
2 Dreamworks
3 *Duel*
4 *Empire of the Sun*
5 *Hook*
6 Audrey Hepburn
7 River Phoenix
8 *1941*
9 Francois Truffaut
10 Quincy Jones
11 Drew Barrymore
12 *Jurassic Park*
13 *Saving Private Ryan*
14 'Steven Spielrock presents'
15 Debra Winger
16 Laura Dern
17 *Columbo*
18 Kate Capshaw
19 John Williams
20 *Jaws*
21 Dustin Hoffman
22 *Jurassic Park*
23 Oprah Winfrey
24 Executive producer George Lucas
25 His Oscar for *Schindler's List*

Films at Sea
1 *Moby Dick*
2 In a newspaper advert
3 Gregory Peck
4 Jacqueline Bisset
5 Kenneth More
6 *Mister Roberts*
7 The sinking of the *Titanic*
8 *Crimson Tide*
9 Trevor Howard and Marlon Brando
10 Freddie Bartholomew
11 Alec Baldwin
12 *Dead Calm*
13 *The Abyss*
14 A U-boat
15 The *Nautilus*
16 *The Old Man and the Sea*
17 It was shot in 3-D
18 Errol Flynn
19 Ray Harryhausen
20 A giant octopus
21 Gloria Stuart is in both films
22 John Huston
23 Cary Grant and Deborah Kerr
24 Burt Lancaster
25 George Clooney

The Human Body
1 Insulin
2 In the hands and feet
3 Tooth decay
4 The liver
5 A hernia
6 The inner ear
7 Arteries carry blood from the heart; veins return it
8 On the shoulder
9 A cataract
10 Under the brain
11 Hay fever
12 The tibia
13 Discs
14 In bone marrow
15 The side of the skull
16 The Achilles
17 At the base of the spine
18 Chromosomes
19 Autopsy
20 32
21 Smell
22 The patella
23 The thyroid
24 In the neck
25 The femur

Rivers
1 Lisbon
2 Khartoum
3 The Rio Grande
4 The Lagan
5 Namibia and South Africa
6 The Caspian Sea
7 The Zambesi
8 The Amazon
9 The Murray
10 The Arno
11 The Mississippi
12 The Yangtze
13 The Gulf (Persian)
14 The Hudson and the East River
15 The Mekong
16 Venezuela
17 Tokyo
18 Buenos Aires and Montevideo
19 The Ness
20 The Colorado
21 The Arctic Circle
22 The Netherlands
23 Ukraine
24 The Humber
25 The Niagara

The Beatles
1 It was the day John Lennon first met Paul McCartney
2 'Hey Jude'
3 'Norwegian Wood (This Bird Has Flown)'
4 Paul – his first name is James
5 *A Hard Day's Night*
6 Mia Farrow's
7 *Meet the Wife* (on 'Good Morning, Good Morning')
8 Rory Storm and The Hurricanes
9 Eric Clapton
10 'Penny Lane/Strawberry Fields Forever'
11 San Francisco
12 *Abbey Road*
13 'I Wanna Be Your Man'
14 Imelda Marcos
15 'Can't Buy Me Love'
16 Peter Sellers
17 'Yesterday'
18 Mr Wilson and Mr Heath in 'Taxman'
19 *A Spaniard in the Works*
20 On the roof of the Apple offices in Savile Row, London
21 Klaus Voormann
22 'Something'
23 George Harrison with 'My Sweet Lord'
24 They were the string quartet on 'Yesterday'
25 'Sexy Sadie'

Songs in Films
1 Isaac Hayes
2 *Up Close and Personal*
3 The Beatles for 'Let It Be'
4 'Memo From Turner'
5 Sister Sledge, 'We Are Family'
6 'Maniac'
7 Nilsson, with 'Everybody's Talkin''
8 Elton John, whose lyricist was Tim Rice
9 'Eye of the Tiger' by Survivor
10 Brian Adams's '(Everything I Do) I Do It For You' *from Robin Hood, Prince of Thieves*; a chart-topper for 16 weeks
11 Paul McCartney, for *Live and Let Die*
12 True, though he was Little Stevie Wonder in those days
13 *Top Gun*
14 Tom Jones
15 *Fun In Acapulco*
16 'Beautiful Stranger'
17 'When You Say Nothing At All'
18 The song was 'Are You Man Enough?' by the Four Tops
19 *The Happening*
20 Neil Diamond
21 *Friends*
22 False. Blondie's 'Heart of Glass' didn't stem from the Herzog flick
23 The version was by pianist Errol Garner

24 It opened the film *The Blackboard Jungle*, launching the whole rock 'n' roll revolution
25 *The Falcon and the Snowman*

World War II
1 Mussolini
2 1939
3 Egypt
4 The 1944 Allied landings at Normandy
5 China
6 The Philippines
7 American GIs
8 The Soviet Union and Finland
9 The Battle of Midway
10 Dresden
11 Admiral Chester W Nimitz
12 The Soviet Union
13 Bernard
14 Darwin
15 Japan formally surrendered
16 The Dunkirk evacuation
17 Hitler's proposed invasion of Britain
18 Leningrad
19 Hitler
20 Clement Attlee
21 Singapore
22 The kamikaze
23 Admiral Donitz
24 They remained neutral along with Switzerland
25 Blitzkrieg

Test Cricket
1 Alec Stewart, England
2 Ian Healy, Australia
3 Garfield Sobers
4 Kapil Dev
5 Dennis Lillee
6 Wasim Akram, Pakistan v Sri Lanka, 1998–99
7 1994–95
8 David Gower, 1985
9 Mohammad Azharrudin, India v England, 1984–85
10 Melbourne Cricket Ground, Australia v England
11 Martin Crowe
12 South Africa
13 Ian Botham, England
14 The Oval, 1880
15 Donald Bradman, Australia
16 1952–53
17 Brian Lara, West Indies, with 375
18 Sunil Gavaskar, India
19 Vivian Richards

20 Anil Kumble
21 Dean Headley
22 New Zealand
23 Sri Lanka
24 Javed Miandad
25 Michael Atherton and Alec Stewart

Venues
1 Nou Camp
2 Sunderland
3 Heysel
4 Athens
5 Lazio and Roma
6 Germany
7 Rangers
8 Headingley
9 Stade de France
10 Greyhound racing
11 Leicester City
12 White City
13 Harlequins
14 Welford Rd
15 Cardiff Arms Park
16 Crystal Palace
17 Erica Roe
18 120,000
19 Australian Rules Football
20 Trent Bridge, Old Trafford, Headingley, Edgbaston, Lord's and The Oval
21 Arsenal and Tottenham
22 Real Madrid
23 Parkhead
24 Shea Stadium
25 St Andrew's

Monty Python
1 A Norwegian Blue
2 Buttocks
3 Hell's Grannies
4 Doug and Dinsdale Piranha
5 The Spanish Inquisition
6 A slaughterhouse
7 Mr Wensleydale
8 Graham Chapman
9 He goes shopping and has buttered scones for tea
10 An albatross
11 A dirty fork
12 An halibut
13 *Do Not Adjust Your Set*
14 Graham Chapman
15 Spam
16 Lupins
17 Remove their bras
18 Terry Jones
19 John Cleese
20 It contains the foot used in the title sequence
21 Bicycle Repair Man
22 Terry Gilliam
23 'The Liberty Bell'

24 Minehead, which he spells Meinhead
25 A lion tamer

Friends
1 Ursula
2 Monica
3 Together they wrote the show's theme song
4 Janice
5 Palaeontologist
6 Eddie
7 Bloomingdales
8 Ugly naked guy
9 Ross and Monica
10 Central Perk
11 'Smelly Cat'
12 A chick and a duck
13 Carol and Susan
14 Gunther at Central Perk
15 *Days of Our Lives*
16 A monkey
17 Richard Branson
18 Jennifer Aniston
19 Ross and Monica
20 Jennifer Saunders
21 Under a rug at the museum
22 A nubbin
23 Monica
24 Julie
25 Elle Macpherson

The Number 3
1 The Three Stooges
2 In the fountain
3 Pete Conrad
4 Alexandre Dumas
5 Lithium
6 Shot put
7 Rome
8 Carol Reed
9 Beethoven
10 On a dartboard
11 Eddie Cochran
12 Jane Seymour
13 The Commodores
14 180 degrees
15 Peter
16 The Three Degrees
17 Donald Duck
18 On the ceiling
19 Thomas Jefferson
20 Jerome K Jerome
21 Cream
22 Kanchenjunga in the Himalayas
23 The three witches
24 Prince Henry
25 Charlotte, Emily and Anne Brontë

Food Names
1 The Russian ballet dancer Anna Pavlova
2 The angels are oysters and the devils are prunes
3 *Vol-au-vent* is French for 'flying on the wind' – they are puff pastry cases
4 Cock-a-leekie
5 The French *chaudière* – a huge copper pot for communal fish stew
6 When you had to pay a toll to cross the Mississippi, you could stop at the toll-man's house and buy his chocolate chip cookies
7 The opening of the roof garden at the old Ritz Carlton Hotel, New York City
8 Caesar Cardini, who would assemble it for his guests in Tijuana, Mexico in the 1920s
9 It was brought by Spaniards to New Orleans and *jamón* is the Spanish word for ham
10 It is the Spanish for 'meat with chilli powder'
11 It is Hindi for 'hot spice'
12 Created by a New York chef as a cure for a certain Mr Benedict's hangover
13 It was common in the French colony of Virginia and the French word for ham is *jambon*
14 A fisherman became so fed up with his wife's meals that he mixed a pile of luxury ingredients together while muttering 'Anna, damn her! This is what I like.'
15 It originated in Key West, Florida
16 Dr Muesli, who was Swiss
17 The Earl of Sandwich
18 Bologna
19 It came from the island Capri
20 Literally, 'jump in the mouth', in Italian
21 Sorbet
22 Hors d'oeuvre
23 It was created by a chef called Alfredo at a famous Roman restaurant
24 It is hot and spicy and '*puttanesca*' comes from the Neapolitan for prostitute
25 It was a Spanish imitation of the Aztec word *Tchocolatl*

THE ULTIMATE BOOK OF TRIVIA

OF TRIVIA

QUIZ

2

1 Which Oscar-winning actress was born Susan Tomaling in 1946 and is known by her former married name?

2 By what name is the 16th-century painter Domenikos Theotokopoulos better known?

3 What is Alice Cooper's real name?

4 By what shorter name do we better know Czech-born actor Herbert Charles Angelo Kuchacevich de Schluderpacheru?

5 Which cigar-smoking, wisecracking comedian was born Nathan Birnbaum?

6 Under what name did Nigel John Davies shape the early career of Twiggy?

7 By what name do we better know Marion Michael Morrison?

8 Who has written books under the name Barbara Vine?

9 Which less-than-cuddly punk rock star was born John Richie?

10 Which British actor, of Dutch descent, was born Derek Van Den Bogaerd?

11 Which singer/actor was born Dino Crocetti in 1917?

12 Which American writer was born Samuel Langhorne Clemens?

13 Which novelist was born Mary Ann Evans?

14 What was the well-known pseudonym of Gertrud Margarete Zelle, who was executed as a German spy towards the end of World War I?

15 Which Hollywood actress, whose face was praised by Madonna in the song 'Vogue', was born Margarita Carmen Cansino in 1918?

16 The folk trio of Yarrow, Stookey and Travers became famous using just their first names. What are they?

17 Which movie star was born Lucille le Sueur?

18 By what name was American civil rights campaigner Malcolm Little better known?

19 By what name did bodybuilder Angelo Siciliano become famous?

20 Actor Stewart Granger had to change his name because his real name was the same as which leading Hollywood star?

21 By what name was the British broadcaster William Joyce, a Nazi propagandist during World War II, known?

22 Remembered chiefly for his tough-guy roles, what was the screen name of Emanuel Goldenberg?

23 Which American actor was born Ramón Estevez in 1940?

24 Which Jamaican singer, who has had two UK number one hit singles, was born Orville Richard Burrell?

25 Which famous 19th-century author wrote under the name Ellis Bell?

17

1 British policemen were once known as 'peelers'. Why?

2 Which London station is named after a saint?

3 Who invented tarmac?

4 After whom were Germany's zeppelins named?

5 Which Austrian physicist devised a system of speed measurement using a series of numbers bearing his name?

6 Who gave his name to the vacuum cleaner?

7 Who originally gave his name to the toilet?

8 Who invented the first waterproof raincoat, made of vulcanized cloth?

9 Who gave his name to the first rocket?

10 What did Richard Arkwright give his name to?

11 What did Marconi give his name to?

12 What did a Mr Sadler open in London and give his name to?

13 Which building was named after David Garrick?

14 What takes its name from Pyrrhus?

15 To what did Dick Fosbury lend his name?

16 Who invented an international code for sending messages using only dots and dashes?

17 What was named after Martha Graham?

18 Which king had a dog named after him?

19 What piece of mining safety equipment did Sir Humphrey Davy give his name to?

20 Which bourbon originator still has a whiskey named after him?

21 Which Greek philosopher had a non-sexual relationship named after him?

22 What did Richard Jordan Gatling invent?

23 What did Sir Arthur Wellesley have named after him?

24 What was named after Mr Biro?

25 What did the Duke of Windsor give his name to?

1 In which two films did Emma Thompson win Oscars as leading actress and for adapted screenplay in 1992 and 1995 respectively?

2 In which year was an award for best sound first given?

3 Which Oscar winner lends his voice to the animated series *South Park*?

4 Which actor won two consecutive leading actor Oscars in the 1990s?

5 For which film did David Lean receive his first Oscar as director?

6 In which 1942 film did Irving Berlin's 'White Christmas' win the award for best song?

7 Which Alfred Hitchcock film won the best picture Oscar in 1940?

8 Which actress, mother of a British rock star, won a special Oscar in 1960 for outstanding juvenile performance in the movie *Pollyanna*?

9 For his performance in which film did Kevin Kline win the best supporting actor Oscar in 1988?

10 In 1948, which father and son won Academy Awards for the same movie, as supporting actor and director respectively?

11 Which two leading ladies tied for the best actress Oscar in 1968?

12 Which film, a mixture of live action and animation, won four Oscars in 1988?

13 Which British actress won two Oscars for leading roles in the 1970s?

14 What is the connection between 1981's best director and 1983's best leading actress?

15 For which animated short film did Nick Park win his first Oscar in 1990?

16 Gene Hackman won his second Oscar in 1996 as supporting actor in *Unforgiven*. For which 1971 movie did he win the best actor award?

17 Who famously broke down in tears during her acceptance speech at the 1998 awards ceremony?

18 For his role in which film did Michael Douglas receive the best actor award in 1987?

19 Which multi-Oscar-winning movie of the 1970s did Michael Douglas co-produce?

20 Jason Robards won his second consecutive Oscar as supporting actor in 1977 for *Julia*. For his role in which tense political thriller did he win in 1976?

21 For which 1970s movie did Francis Ford Coppola win the best director Oscar?

22 In which year were the supporting actor and actress categories introduced?

23 Which actor, born with the surname Coppola, won the best actor Oscar in 1995?

24 Which great singer won the best supporting actor award in 1953?

25 Which director won an Oscar for his first film in 2000?

1 Who directed the first James Bond film, *Dr No*?

2 What was the first film featuring James Bond not to star Sean Connery?

3 Which British actor played the villain Alec Trevelyan in *Goldeneye*?

4 Which character has been played in various films by Bernie Casey, Jack Lord, Cec Linder, Rick Van Nutter and Norman Burton?

5 Which French actress stars in *The World Is Not Enough*?

6 For his portrayal of which character is Harold Sakata remembered?

7 Which film was the first to feature Timothy Dalton in the lead role?

8 Who is Bond's leading lady in *From Russia with Love*?

9 Who sings the theme song in *For Your Eyes Only*?

10 Richard Kiel first appears as the enormous villain Jaws in *The Spy Who Loved Me*. In which film does he reappear?

11 To which organization does agent Ernst Blofeld belong?

12 Which Bond film was the first not to be based on an Ian Fleming story?

13 What was Roger Moore's Bond film debut?

14 Who plays Blofeld in *On Her Majesty's Secret Service*?

15 Which film features a spectacular car chase around Las Vegas?

16 In which film does Desmond Llewelyn first appear as 'Q'?

17 Which Bond villain is played by Joseph Wiseman?

18 Who took over the role of 'M' in *Goldeneye*?

19 Who plays Pussy Galore in *Goldfinger*?

20 Which film features an aerial battle between Bond in an armed autogyro and some helicopters?

21 Which film's title was the idea of Sean Connery's wife, Micheline?

22 What is the musical connection between *Goldfinger*, *Diamonds are Forever* and *Moonraker*?

23 In which film does Bond marry a girl called Tracy Draco?

24 Which two films are missing from this sequence: *Live and Let Die*, *The Spy Who Loved Me*, *Moonraker*, *For Your Eyes Only* and *A View to a Kill*?

25 What is Blofeld's trademark pet?

1 Why did William Penn, a Quaker, name the city that he founded 'Philadelphia'?

2 After what is Brazil named?

3 After whom was Rome named?

4 Which fruit gave its name to Thailand's capital city?

5 After whom was Barcelona named?

6 Why was 'Andalucia' so called?

7 How did Budapest get its name?

8 Why was Portugal so named?

9 What is the origin of the name 'Munich'?

10 What does the name 'Jerusalem' actually mean?

11 What is the origin of the name 'Mesopotamia'?

12 Why was the city of Alexandria so called?

13 When did New York get its name?

14 After whom was Bolivia named?

15 After whom was America named?

16 What is the origin of the name China?

17 How did Carthage, in Tunisia, get its name?

18 Why is Zimbabwe so called?

19 What is the origin of the name 'Canada'?

20 Why is Montreal so named?

21 What does Las Vegas mean?

22 Why is Ecuador so called?

23 What does Buenos Aires mean?

24 What is the literal meaning of 'Venezuela'?

25 What is the origin of the name of the Australian city of Adelaide?

1 What was special about Brooklyn Bridge?

2 How many times was Tower Bridge raised in 1990?

3 Which was the first suspension bridge in London?

4 Why is the Golden Gate Bridge painted in International Orange?

5 Which famous city bridge is known locally as 'The Coathanger'?

6 Which bridge was the first major suspension bridge in the world?

7 Constructed in 1333, which is the oldest wooden bridge in Europe?

8 Which bridge connects Europe with Asia?

9 Which bridge, opened in 1988, connected Japan's four main islands by high-speed rail for the first time?

10 Where is the original London Bridge now situated?

11 Which is the oldest surviving Thames crossing in London?

12 How many bridges are there in St Petersburg?

13 What type of shop predominates on the Ponte Vecchio in Florence?

14 In which country is the bridge over the River Kwai?

15 Which bridge in Scotland replaced the much-loved ferry at the Kyle of Lochalsh?

16 Which bridge connects Nepal to Tibet?

17 Which bridge in London was officially named William Pitt Bridge in 1769?

18 Which Cambridge bridge took its name from an architectural masterpiece in Venice?

19 What is the more famous name of the dancing 'St-Benezet' Bridge?

20 What record does the Second Lake Pontchartrain Causeway hold?

21 Which bridge had Van Gogh just finished painting before he cut off his ear?

22 Which London bridge had a gate over it on which the heads of criminals were displayed on spikes as a deterrent?

23 Which Cambridge bridge was put together in the 18th century without the use of a single nail?

24 Which bridge features on the poster for the Woody Allen film *Manhattan*?

25 What was so important about the Oresund bridge between Malmö and Copenhagen which opened in July 2000?

14

1 With which particular instrument would you associate Gerry Mulligan?

2 In which city would you find jazz clubs called Birdland, the Blue Note, and the Village Vanguard?

3 Who is generally credited with freeing the role of the jazz guitar to that of a solo instrument?

4 Whose trumpet was recognisable by the way it was bent out of shape?

5 Which band was formed in the 1970s by former Miles Davis band members Joe Zawinul and Wayne Shorter?

6 Written by Billy Strayhorn, what was the signature tune of the Duke Ellington band?

7 Which band featured among its members Joe Sample, Wayne Henderson and Wilton Felder?

8 With whom did Louis Armstrong sing about the virtues of jazz in the musical *High Society*?

9 With which instrument would you associate Lionel Hampton, Red Norvo and Gary Burton?

10 What was the name given to duels between soloists, where they would improvise head to head until one took a clear advantage?

11 Whose albums include *Kind of Blue*, *In a Silent Way*, *Bitches Brew* and *Tutu*?

12 Which saxophonist was known as 'Bird'?

13 What name is given to the type of singing that mimics an instrumental solo?

14 Over four decades, which drummer led a band called the Jazz Messengers?

15 With which instrument would you associate Tommy Dorsey, Glenn Miller and Trummy Young?

16 Which British guitarist fronted the Mahavishnu Orchestra?

17 Which trumpeter, born in 1961, enjoys equally successful jazz and classical careers?

18 Which singer was discovered in the 1930s after winning a singing contest at Harlem's Apollo Theatre?

19 Which keyboard player had an 'Arkestra' and claimed to have come from another planet?

20 James P Johnson wrote the signature to which 1920s dance craze?

21 Which band leader/composer/producer wrote the score for the 1967 movie *In the Heat of the Night*, featuring Ray Charles on the title song?

22 Who was the first black singer to host his own TV programme?

23 Which British sax player fronted the band Paraphernalia?

24 By what name is pianist Ferdinand Joseph Lemott remembered?

25 Which style of jazz was pioneered by Charlie Parker and Dizzy Gillespie?

1 Which record company had its first US hit with Carl Perkins's 'Blue Suede Shoes'?

2 What was the name of Bill Haley's best-known band?

3 Name Buddy Holly's Texas home town.

4 Which early rock 'n' roller is known as 'The Killer'?

5 For which famous rock 'n' roller did Scotty Moore play guitar in the 1950s?

6 Which Pennsylvania DJ helped launch rock by hosting live shows at the New York Paramount in the early 1950s?

7 The Rolling Stones' first single 'Come On' was a cover of a B-side by a famous US rock 'n' roller. Name him.

8 What is Bo Diddley's real name?

9 Name Fats Domino's home town.

10 Who led the Blue Caps?

11 Who formed the Million Dollar Quartet?

12 Who performed the main title song to the film *The Girl Can't Help It*?

13 Name the youthful singer who headed The Teenagers.

14 Which singer got his break when his band, the Shadows, deputized for Buddy Holly after the singer died in an air crash?

15 When Elvis Presley returned to civilian life after army duties, he appeared in a *Welcome Home Elvis* television spectacular. Who hosted the show?

16 Which group had hits with 'At the Hop' and 'Rock 'n' Roll Is Here to Stay'?

17 Which US songwriting team produced the hits 'Searchin'', 'Yakety Yak', 'Charlie Brown' and 'Poison Ivy' for the Coasters?

18 What are the Everly Brothers' Christian names?

19 Who wrote 'Great Balls of Fire', 'All Shook Up' and 'Don't Be Cruel'?

20 Name the owner of Sun Records.

21 Little Richard's early hits were recorded for a Los Angeles label. Which one?

22 Who produced the album *A Christmas Gift to You*, featuring seasonal favourites sung by his label's star acts?

23 Who is generally regarded as producing the first rock 'n' roll single, 'Rocket 88', in 1950?

24 Whose first record was a rocker called 'Ooby Dooby'?

25 Dion DiMucci headed a group named after an avenue in the Bronx. What was the group called?

1 What was special about the Iron Bridge at Coalbrookdale?

2 Where was the blast furnace first introduced?

3 What were Brunel's first names?

4 In 1851, the largest building the world had ever seen was erected in London. What was it?

5 Which newspaper had its own office on the second platform of the Eiffel Tower?

6 Which canal, the brainchild of Ferdinand de Lesseps, was opened, to great acclaim, in November 1869?

7 Which dam harnesses the Colorado River?

8 The spinning wheel arrived in Europe in the 13th century. From which country is it said to have come?

9 Which German chemist won the Nobel Prize for Chemistry in 1944 for discovering nuclear fission?

10 How far could you draw out one gram of gold?

11 Which metal expands the most when heated?

12 Where is the world's largest atomic establishment?

13 What was the Colossus, developed in Buckinghamshire in 1943?

14 Where were the world's first windmills?

15 In which country is Cherepovets, site of one of the world's largest blast furnaces?

16 Where is the world's biggest lathe?

17 In which country are the world's deepest mines?

18 Which country contains the world's biggest oil refinery?

19 Which port handles the greatest amount of trade in the world?

20 In the food processing industry, what do the initials MRM stand for?

21 By what abbreviated term is the Group of Eight Industrialized Nations known?

22 In which year was the Boeing 747 put into regular service?

23 What is Spain's largest port?

24 Which country is the world's main supplier of teak?

25 What is the principal crop of the United Arab Emirates?

1 Which English dramatist was stabbed to death in Deptford Tavern on 20 May 1593?

2 Martha Turner, Mary Ann Nicholls and Elizabeth Stride were three of whose victims during 1888?

3 The murder of which two princes led to the renaming of part of the Tower of London as the 'Bloody Tower'?

4 Whose murder was accompanied by a note which read: 'If you read his diary all will be explained. KH.'?

5 Which crucial primary had Bobby Kennedy just won moments before he was shot by Sirhan Sirhan in 1968?

6 Who directed the film depicting the story of the real-life murder of Nancy Spungeon by Sid Vicious?

7 On which day did Al Capone and his gang commit a gruesome, and not very romantic, massacre?

8 Which member of Marvin Gaye's family shot and killed him?

9 Where did Charlotte Corday murder the revolutionary leader Marat?

10 Who did Valerie Solanis attempt to murder in the Factory?

11 How was Rasputin murdered?

12 Which English painter killed his father?

13 Who took an axe and gave her mother forty whacks?

14 The emperor Nero murdered his mother. Who was she?

15 Whose assassination started the First World War?

16 Which Spanish poet and playwright was murdered by Falangist soldiers on 9 August 1936?

17 Who was assassinated in a Harlem ballroom in February 1965?

18 Which tsar murdered his son in a fit of rage?

19 Who assassinated Mahatma Gandhi?

20 Which 20th-century head of state survived the greatest number of assassination attempts?

21 Where did T S Eliot set his medieval play about murder?

22 Which Archbishop of Canterbury was executed during the English Civil War in 1645?

23 Which play was Abraham Lincoln watching when he was assassinated?

24 What happened in June 1994 at 875 South Bundy Drive, LA?

25 Which Indian politician was killed by an adolescent girl named Thanu?

1 For which team was Jean Alesi driving when he won the 1995 Canadian Grand Prix?

2 What connects the Spanish Grand Prix of 1981 with that of 1997?

3 Who won the first Malaysian Grand Prix?

4 Which Austrian driver made his debut in his home Grand Prix in 1971, driving for March?

5 Which female driver made twelve Grand Prix starts between 1974 and 1976?

6 Who retired from Formula One after winning his third Formula One title in 1973?

7 At which circuits would you find: a) Abbey Curve b) Adelaide and c) Clark Kurve?

8 Who is the only driver to win the Formula One title posthumously?

9 Who drove in 256 Grands Prix between 1977 and 1993, winning six races?

10 Which current TV presenter drove in the 1980 Belgian Grand Prix?

11 How many times did Graham Hill win at Monaco?

12 For whom did Italian-American Mario Andretti drive when he won the 1978 title?

13 Where did Juan Manuel Fangio win his first and his last Grand Prix?

14 How many Grand Prix wins did Damon Hill achieve?

15 Which Formula One driver, whose own team began racing in 1966 and is one of the major teams of today, was killed at Goodwood in 1970?

16 Who won all six races in the 1952 season?

17 In what way was Ireland successful in the 1961 United States Grand Prix?

18 Which German driver made his Formula One debut in Brazil in 1994, and won his first race at San Marino in 1997?

19 In which year was the Australian Grand Prix last staged at Adelaide, before being switched to Melbourne?

20 For which team did Michael Schumacher drive in his first Grand Prix in Belgium in 1991?

21 Between 1981 and 1991, which two Brazilian drivers won the Formula One title six times between them?

22 How many races did Nigel Mansell win in his championship-winning year of 1992?

23 Which driver drove a Lotus in all 25 of his Grand Prix victories in the 1960s?

24 Who was the only Formula One champion to have also been world motorcycling champion?

25 Who retired at the end of the 1993 season, having taken his fourth Formula One title?

1 Of which sport is Jun Sun world champion?

2 Who was the top female badminton player in 2000?

3 What does Turk Halil Mutlu do?

4 Who are women's volleyball champions?

5 Who are men's volleyball champions?

6 Who are world champions at table tennis?

7 Of which sport is Jonathon Power world champion?

8 Who is the only overseas player to have won the world championships at snooker?

9 Who in snooker is known as The Hurricane?

10 Who was known as The Whirlwind?

11 Who won back-to-back world snooker championships in the 1980s?

12 Who scored the first televised 147?

13 In 1990, who was the youngest snooker player to make a maximum in tournament play?

14 Who is Graham Randall?

15 Who is Alexei Yagudin?

16 Who is the women's ice-skating champion?

17 Who scored a perfect six with their ice dance 'Bolero'?

18 Who won ice-skating men's gold in 1978?

19 Which other Brit won ice-skating gold?

20 Who was Wayne Gretsky?

21 Who are the Olympic gymnastic champions?

22 Who is undisputed heavyweight champion?

23 Who is The Prince?

24 Who was Ali's trainer?

25 Which basketball player cross-dresses?

1 What is Obelix's favourite food?

2 What is the name of Harry Potter's school?

3 Pink Floyd's first album, *The Piper at the Gates of Dawn*, was named after a chapter title in which famous children's classic?

4 What kind of animal was H A Rey's 'Curious George'?

5 In Maurice Sendak's *Where the Wild Things Are*, what did Max wear to make mischief?

6 In the Hans Christian Andersen tale, with whom was the Tin Soldier in love?

7 What was the name of Captain Pugwash's mortal enemy?

8 What were A A Milne's first two names?

9 What is Bilbo Baggins's better-known alias?

10 Who wrote the *Just So Stories*?

11 Who illustrated Roald Dahl's *The BFG*?

12 In the Tintin books, what are the two identical policemen called?

13 Who wrote a book of fables based on animal characters?

14 Who owned Roald Dahl's Chocolate Factory?

15 Which Danish novelist and dramatist wrote the fairy tale *The Snow Queen*?

16 What was the hedgehog called in Beatrix Potter's tale?

17 Who originally wrote down the tale of Snow White?

18 What is the Tin Man searching for in *The Wizard of Oz*?

19 What happened to Hilaire Belloc's Matilda?

20 What were Wendy's brothers called in *Peter Pan*?

21 Who used the Dormouse as a pillow at the Mad Hatter's tea party?

22 Of which country did Peter, Susan, Edmund and Lucy become monarchs?

23 Who wrote *The Borrowers*?

24 In *The Jungle Book*, from whom was Mowgli saved as a baby?

25 What type of transport was featured in Sarah Ferguson's children's book?

1 What name is given to a person who shoes horses, and which can also be another name for a veterinary surgeon, or a non-commissioned officer who looks after horses in a cavalry regiment?

2 What is a lepidopterist?

3 What was the name given to a boy who carried a torch for pedestrians in dark streets?

4 In which branch of medicine does an oncologist work?

5 What does a lapidary do?

6 What is the colloquial term for a travelling salesman for a firm specialising in hire purchase?

7 A person employed to do all sorts of work is given what Latin-based name?

8 A medical practitioner specialising in the diagnosis and treatment of eye diseases used to be called an oculist. What is the name used now?

9 What is a bonze?

10 In which occupation might you be called a bluejacket?

11 What would a lithologist study?

12 What does a funambulist walk on?

13 What would a hagiologist write about?

14 What slang term is used for a criminal who specialises in safecracking?

15 In America he is called a longshoreman. What is the UK equivalent?

16 What occupation was used by Lennon and McCartney for the name of one of their early bands?

17 What was once sold by a colporteur?

18 What does a dendrologist study?

19 Why is a colour-sergeant so called?

20 What term is used for a person who illegally makes and/or smuggles distilled liquor?

21 What familiar word, sometimes humorously associated with lightning, describes a person who rides the near horse of a team of horses drawing a coach?

22 What does a milliner make?

23 Who would be involved in the scientific study of the origin, history, structure and composition of the Earth?

24 What word for a labourer originates from the days of canal building when it was important that the labourers knew where they were going?

25 In which country does a gaucho herd cattle?

1 Who was defeated at El Alamein in 1942?

2 Which Carthaginian general led his army across the Alps with a contingent of elephants?

3 Who opposed the Communists in China and started his own government in Nankin in 1927?

4 Who was the second US president to be assassinated?

5 Which general took Argentina into the Falklands War?

6 In June 1940 who rallied the French troops against the German armies?

7 Who signed the 1918 armistice for the Allies?

8 Who directed Israel's Sinai campaign against Egypt in 1956?

9 Which American general joined up with the Russian army on the Elbe in 1945?

10 Who did Napoleon Bonaparte famously defeat at the Battle of Borodino in 1812?

11 Who died in a plane accident, probably due to sabotage, in 1943?

12 Which Venezuelan-born general led Colombia to independence from Spain in 1825?

13 During the American Civil War, who organized the 'march to the sea' through Georgia?

14 On 4 May 1945, who received the capitulation of the German armies fighting in Holland and Denmark?

15 Which general is more famous in England for the biscuits named after him than for his reunification of Italy?

16 Who took part in the Franco-Prussian War of 1870 and committed suicide in Belgium in 1891?

17 Whose American Seventh Army landed in Sicily in 1943?

18 Who was stabbed to death in Rome in March, AD 44?

19 Which British general was killed at Khartoum in 1885?

20 Whose arrival in Fachoda spelled the end for the French in the Sudan?

21 Who was made King of Macedonia at the age of 20 and led his country to victory in Asia?

22 Which general was known as 'Old Blood and Guts'?

23 Who served in Morocco, took the title of 'caudillo' and died in 1975?

24 Which fearsome lady organized a revolt against the Romans in AD 60?

25 Which Chief Commander of the Allies received the German Capitulation in Berlin in May 1945?

ANSWERS TO QUIZ 2

Real Names

1 Susan Sarandon
2 El Greco
3 Vincent Furnier
4 Herbert Lom
5 George Burns
6 Justin de Villeneuve
7 John Wayne
8 P D James
9 Sid Vicious
10 Dirk Bogarde
11 Dean Martin
12 Mark Twain
13 George Eliot
14 Mata Hari
15 Rita Hayworth
16 Peter, Paul and Mary
17 Joan Crawford
18 Malcolm X
19 Charles Atlas
20 James Stewart
21 Lord Haw-Haw
22 Edward G Robinson
23 Martin Sheen
24 Shaggy
25 Emily Brontë

Gave Name to

1 After Sir Robert Peel, founder of the British police force
2 St Pancras
3 John Macadam
4 Count Ferdinand von Zeppelin
5 Ernst Mach
6 Hoover
7 Thomas Crapper
8 Charles Macintosh
9 Stephenson
10 A type of spinning machine
11 The transmitter
12 Sadler's Wells
13 The Garrick Theatre
14 Pyrrhic victory
15 The Fosbury flop
16 Samuel Morse
17 The Graham technique
18 King Charles (Spanish)
19 The Davy lamp
20 Jack Daniels
21 Plato
22 The Gatling gun
23 Wellington boots
24 The Biro pen
25 The Windsor knot

The Oscars

1 *Howards End* and *Sense and Sensibility*
2 1930
3 Isaac Hayes
4 Tom Hanks (*Philadelphia* in 1993, *Forrest Gump* in 1994)
5 *The Bridge on the River Kwai*
6 *Holiday Inn*
7 *Rebecca*
8 Hayley Mills

9 *A Fish Called Wanda*
10 Walter and John Huston (*The Treasure of the Sierra Madre*)
11 Katharine Hepburn (*The Lion in Winter*) and Barbra Streisand (*Funny Girl*)
12 *Who Framed Roger Rabbit?*
13 Glenda Jackson (*Women in Love* in 1970 and *A Touch of Class* in 1973)
14 They are brother and sister; Warren Beatty and Shirley MacLaine
15 *Creature Comforts*
16 *The French Connection*
17 Gwyneth Paltrow
18 *Wall Street*
19 *One Flew over the Cuckoo's Nest*
20 *All the President's Men*
21 *The Godfather, Part II*
22 1936
23 Nicolas Cage (*Leaving Las Vegas*)
24 Frank Sinatra (*From Here to Eternity*)
25 Sam Mendes (*American Beauty*)

Bond Films

1 Terence Young
2 *Casino Royale* (with David Niven as Sir James Bond)
3 Sean Bean
4 Felix Leiter
5 Sophie Marceau
6 Oddjob, in *Goldfinger*
7 *The Living Daylights*
8 Daniela Bianchi
9 Sheena Easton
10 *Moonraker*
11 SPECTRE
12 *Goldeneye*
13 *Live and Let Die*
14 Telly Savalas
15 *Diamonds Are Forever*
16 *From Russia with Love*
17 *Dr No*
18 Judi Dench
19 Honor Blackman
20 *You Only Live Twice*
21 *Never Say Never Again*
22 The theme songs are all sung by Shirley Bassey
23 *On Her Majesty's Secret Service*
24 *The Man with the Golden Gun* and *Octopussy* (all seven starred Roger Moore)
25 A white cat

Name Origins

1 It means 'City of Brotherly Love' and, in 1682, became the first city in the US to sign a treaty of peaceful coexistence

with the American Indians
2 Pau brasil, a tree the wood of which produces a red dye
3 After the twins Romulus and Remus. Romulus killed his brother over who should govern the city and then named it after himself
4 Bangkok was originally named Ban-cok or 'the city of the wild plum'
5 From Hamilcar Barca, Hannibal's father
6 Muslim invaders of Spain named it Al-Andalus ('country of light') in the 8th century
7 In 1873, the two cities of Buda and Pest, on opposite sides of the River Danube, were administratively united
8 In the mid-800s it became known as Portucale or the 'gateway to Cale', a county of the kingdom of Leon
9 Being founded as a monastery, it was called 'Zu den München' or 'to the monks'
10 From the two Hebrew words 'yeru' and 'shalom', meaning 'city of peace'
11 From the Greek words 'meso' (middle) and 'potamus' (river)
12 After its founder, Alexander the Great
13 In 1664, the Dutch colony of New Amsterdam was invaded by the English, who renamed it after the Duke of York
14 Simon Bolívar, who led the country to independence
15 Amerigo Vespucci, a navigator from Florence
16 The Qin dynasty (pro-nounced 'chin'), founders of modern China
17 Carthage is the Phoenician for 'new city'
18 It is named after a complex of stone ruins in that country
19 When French explorer Jacques Cartier discovered the Bay of St Lawrence in 1530, locals told him he had found 'Canada' meaning 'a village'
20 It was founded around its main hill, the Mount Real
21 The Meadows: a Mormon settler named it in the 1850s
22 It lies on the equator
23 'Good Air': the Spanish were relieved to get there after months of plagued voyaging
24 'Little Venice'
25 Named, in 1836, after Queen Adelaide, wife of King William IV

Bridges

1 It was the world's first steel suspension bridge
2 460 times
3 Hammersmith Bridge
4 The colour helps visibility in the frequent early morning fog
5 Sydney Harbour Bridge
6 The Menai Strait bridge in Wales
7 The Kapellbrucke in Lucerne, Switzerland
8 The Galata Bridge over the Bosphorus in Istanbul
9 The Seto Ohashi Bridge
10 At Lake Havasu, Arizona
11 Richmond Bridge
12 365
13 Jewellers have had the monopoly since 1593
14 Burma (Myanmar)
15 The Skye bridge
16 The Friendship Bridge
17 Blackfriars Bridge, London
18 The Bridge of Sighs (St John's College)
19 Le Pont d'Avignon
20 It is the longest bridge in the world, at 23.9 miles (38.4 km)
21 The Langlois Bridge in Arles
22 London Bridge
23 The Mathematical Bridge (Queens' College)
24 Queensboro Bridge
25 Because it was the first permanent link between Europe and the Swedish peninsula

Jazz

1 Baritone sax
2 New York
3 Charlie Christian
4 Dizzy Gillespie
5 Weather Report
6 'Take the "A" Train'
7 The Crusaders
8 Bing Crosby
9 Vibraphone
10 Cutting contests
11 Miles Davis
12 Charlie Parker
13 Scat singing
14 Art Blakey
15 Trombone
16 John McLaughlin
17 Wynton Marsalis
18 Ella Fitzgerald
19 Sun Ra
20 The Charleston
21 Quincy Jones
22 Nat 'King' Cole
23 Barbara Thompson
24 Jelly Roll Morton
25 Bebop

Rock 'n' Roll

1 Sun Records
2 The Comets
3 Lubbock
4 Jerry Lee Lewis
5 Elvis Presley
6 Alan Freed
7 Chuck Berry
8 Elias Bates (or Elias McDaniel)
9 New Orleans
10 Gene Vincent
11 Elvis Presley, Jerry Lee Lewis, Carl Perkins and Johnny Cash
12 Little Richard
13 Frankie Lymon
14 Bobby Vee
15 Frank Sinatra
16 Danny and the Juniors
17 Jerry Leiber and Mike Stoller
18 Don and Phil
19 Otis Blackwell
20 Sam Phillips
21 Specialty
22 Phil Spector
23 The Kings of Rhythm (featuring Ike Turner)
24 Roy Orbison
25 The Belmonts

Industry

1 It was the world's first major iron construction
2 France, around 1400
3 Isambard Kingdom
4 Crystal Palace
5 *Le Figaro*
6 The Suez Canal
7 The Hoover Dam
8 India
9 Otto Hahn
10 2,400 metres
11 Caesium
12 Underground at CERN, between Switzerland and France
13 An electronic computer to help break codes during the Second World War
14 In Iran, in the 7th century
15 In Russia, at the Cherepovets works
16 In Rosherville, South Africa. It can machine components weighing 300 tonnes
17 South Africa, near Carletonville; they are 3,777 m deep
18 Venezuela
19 Rotterdam, the Netherlands
20 Mechanically recovered meat
21 G8
22 1970
23 Barcelona
24 Burma (Myanmar)
25 Dates

Murders

1 Christopher Marlowe
2 Jack the Ripper
3 The boy king Edward V and his brother, the Duke of York
4 Joe Orton
5 California
6 Alex Cox
7 St Valentine's Day, 1929
8 His father
9 In his bath
10 Andy Warhol
11 He was poisoned, then shot, then thrown into an icy river
12 Richard Dadd
13 Lizzie Borden
14 Agrippina
15 Archduke Ferdinand of Austria
16 Federico García Lorca
17 Malcolm X
18 Ivan the Terrible
19 Nathuram Godse
20 Charles de Gaulle (31)
21 Canterbury Cathedral
22 William Laud
23 *Our American Cousin*, by Tom Taylor
24 Nicole Simpson (O J's wife) and Ron Goldman were murdered
25 Rajiv Gandhi

Formula One

1 Ferrari
2 They were won by father and son, Gilles and Jacques Villeneuve
3 Eddie Irvine
4 Nikki Lauda
5 Lella Lombardi
6 Jackie Stewart
7 a) Silverstone b) Magny-Cours c) Hockenheim
8 Jochen Rindt, 1970
9 Riccardo Patrese
10 Tiff Needell
11 Five: 1963, 1964, 1965, 1968 and 1969
12 John Player Lotus
13 Monaco 1950 and Germany 1957
14 22
15 Bruce McLaren
16 Alberto Ascari
17 The winning driver was Innes Ireland
18 Heinz-Harald Frentzen
19 1995
20 Jordan
21 Nelson Piquet 1981, 1983, and 1987; and Ayrton Senna 1988, 1990, and 1991
22 Nine
23 Jim Clark
24 John Surtees
25 Alain Prost

Indoor Sports

1 Badminton
2 Camilla Martin
3 Weightlifting
4 Cuba
5 Russia
6 China
7 Squash
8 Cliff Thorburn
9 Alex Higgins
10 Jimmy White
11 Steve Davies
12 Cliff Thorburn
13 Ronnie O'Sullivan
14 A judo champion
15 An ice-skater
16 Maria Bulyrskaya
17 Torvill and Dean
18 John Curry
19 Robin Cousins
20 An ice-hockey player
21 China
22 Lennox Lewis
23 Naseem Hamed
24 Gus d'Amato
25 Dennis Rodman

Children's Books

1 Wild boar
2 Hogwarts School of Witchcraft and Wizardry
3 Kenneth Grahame's *The Wind in the Willows*
4 A monkey
5 His wolf suit
6 The dancer
7 Cut-throat Jake
8 Alan Alexander
9 *The Hobbit*
10 Rudyard Kipling
11 Quentin Blake
12 Thompson and Thomson
13 Aesop
14 Willy Wonka
15 Hans Christian Andersen
16 Mrs Tiggywinkle
17 The Brothers Grimm
18 His heart
19 She told lies and was burned to death
20 John and Michael
21 The March Hare and the Hatter
22 Narnia
23 Mary Norton
24 Shere Khan, the tiger
25 A helicopter

Occupations

1 Farrier
2 One who studies butterflies or moths
3 A linkboy
4 Cancer/tumour treatment
5 Works or deals in precious stones
6 A tallyman
7 A factotum
8 Ophthalmologist
9 A (Japanese or Chinese) Buddhist priest
10 A sailor
11 Rocks/stones
12 A tightrope
13 Saints
14 Peterman
15 A stevedore
16 Quarrymen
17 Books, especially Bibles
18 Trees and shrubs
19 He has responsibility for carrying a regimental/national flag
20 Moonshiner
21 Postillion
22 Hats
23 A geologist
24 Navvy (from navigator)
25 Argentina

Generals

1 Erwin Rommel
2 Hannibal
3 Chiang Kai-Shek
4 James A Garfield, in 1881
5 General Galtieri
6 Charles de Gaulle
7 Ferdinand Foch
8 Moshe Dayan
9 Omar Bradley
10 Mikhail Koutouzov
11 Wladyslaw Sikorski
12 Simon Bolívar
13 William Sherman
14 Bernard Montgomery
15 Giuseppe Garibaldi
16 Georges Boulanger
17 General Patton
18 Julius Caesar
19 General Charles Gordon
20 Horatio Kitchener
21 Alexander the Great
22 George Patton
23 Francisco Franco
24 Boudicca
25 Dwight Eisenhower

THE ULTIMATE BOOK
OF TRIVIA

QUIZ

3

1 The novel *Children of the New Forest* by Captain Marryat was set during which conflict?

2 Who is the eldest of actor John Mills's three children?

3 What relation is Princess Beatrice to Peter Phillips?

4 How old was Shirley Temple when she appeared in her first short film?

5 What was the brand name of the unsuccessful Ford car that was named after Henry Ford's son?

6 Caesarion was the child of Julius Caesar and which famous woman?

7 Peter, Phyllis and Roberta were collectively known as what in the title of a book by E Nesbit?

8 What was the real name of the man whose son was known as Baby Doc?

9 What was the forename of William Shakespeare's son?

10 Which rock star named his daughter Moon Unit?

11 In Dickens's *A Christmas Carol*, who was Tiny Tim's father?

12 Actor Martin Sheen has two sons. What are their names?

13 Christabel was one of suffragette leader Emmeline Pankhurst's two daughters. What was the name of the other?

14 What was the name of Pinocchio's creator-cum-father?

15 Which musical gangster movie had a cast made up entirely of children?

16 In which children's book will you meet Charlie Bucket?

17 What was the name of the ill-fated Czar Nicholas II's youngest daughter?

18 Which British actor is the son of a former Attorney General?

19 Cedric Errol was the given name of which eponymous child hero of a 19th-century novel?

20 Which film star thoughtfully named his daughter Sage Moonblood?

21 Whose daughter was nicknamed 'Thunderthighs'?

22 Which band had a hit with 'Little Children' in the 1960s?

23 Which daughter of James V of Scotland met an untimely death?

24 Who was the famous son of Jennie Jerome?

25 His hair is on the long side but he certainly doesn't come from Liverpool. Who is he?

25

1 Which actress who has played a TV cop was christened Ilynea Lydia Mironoff?

2 In its title, what TV programme shows life on the streets?

3 Edgar Allan Poe's *The Murders in the Rue Morgue* featured which early literary detective?

4 What was the name of the detective portrayed by Gene Hackman in *The French Connection*?

5 What was Don Johnson's character called in *Miami Vice*?

6 Who was Michael Knight's computer buddy?

7 Which literary New Scotland Yard detective regularly called on Sherlock Holmes for advice?

8 Who played the television *Avengers* role played by Uma Thurman on film?

9 *Se7en* has two detectives on the trail of a serial killer. On what theme are his murders based?

10 Which famous 1970s big-screen detective was played by Richard Rowntree?

11 Who was Starsky and Hutch's boss?

12 Why did Peter Sellers not appear in *The Curse of the Pink Panther*?

13 In which series was Frank Farillo the chief?

14 Which TV cop did Peter Falk play?

15 Which 19th-century classic featured a detective named Petrovitch?

16 Why was TV cop Ironside so called?

17 Which Hollywood star made his name in *The Streets of San Francisco*?

18 What was the title of the 1970s series based on the exploits of LAPD vice detective Sergeant Pepper Anderson?

19 What was the name of Sherlock Holmes's more intelligent brother?

20 Which actor played the only employee of the Rockford Detective Agency?

21 Meg Foster and Sharon Gless both played the part of a TV detective that had previously been played by *M*A*S*H*'s Loretta Swit. What was the character called?

22 How long did the *Inspector Morse* episodes usually last?

23 *The Mysterious Affair at Styles* introduced which famous literary detective?

24 Who sucked a lollipop?

25 Which detective did Basil Rathbone play?

1 Which Edith Wharton novel has been filmed three times, most recently by Martin Scorsese in 1993?

2 What was the title of Milos Forman's 1989 film based on the novel *Les Liaisons Dangereuses*?

3 Which writer/director adapted *The Great Gatsby* for the 1974 film version?

4 What was the title of the Stanley Kubrick film based on the novel *Red Alert*?

5 The movie *One Flew Over the Cuckoo's Nest* was made in 1975. In which year was Ken Kesey's novel published?

6 In 1971 Doubleday publishers received an outline of a novel called *A Stillness in the Water*. What was the book, and film, eventually called?

7 By what title do we know the 1979 film based on Joseph Conrad's novel *Heart of Darkness*?

8 In 1939 *Heart of Darkness* was supposed to have been the directorial debut of which actor/writer/director?

9 On which Jane Austen novel was the 1996 comedy *Clueless* based?

10 Who played author Paul Sheldon in the film of Stephen King's *Misery*?

11 The title role in which controversial story was played by Sue Lyon in 1962 and by Dominique Swain in 1997?

12 Which James M Cain novel was turned into a film in 1944 by director Billy Wilder and starred Fred MacMurray, Barbara Stanwyck and Edward G Robinson?

13 Which Alfred Hitchcock film, from a Robert Bloch book, did director Gus Van Sant remake virtually shot-for-shot in 1998?

14 Which actor made his final screen appearance in 1984 in the film *1984*?

15 What was the full title of the H G Wells story that formed the basis of the film *Things to Come*?

16 What was Stephen King's first novel, published in 1974 and made into a film by Brian de Palma two years later?

17 Which film did Ridley Scott make from Philip K Dick's novel *Do Androids Dream of Electric Sheep?*?

18 In the context of this section, what connects directors George Cukor, David Lean, Ronald Neame and Carol Reed?

19 What connects the films *The Bridge on the River Kwai* and *Planet of the Apes*?

20 What was the title of Quentin Tarantino's film based on Elmore Leonard's book *Rum Punch*?

21 Which Herman Melville novel was first filmed in 1926 as *The Sea Beast*?

22 Which Alexandre Dumas novel has featured, in three of its filmed versions, Douglas Fairbanks, Louis Jourdan and Gabriel Byrne as d'Artagnan?

23 Which 1960 Pulitzer Prize-winning novel spawned a 1962 movie in which Gregory Peck gave an Oscar-winning performance?

24 Which science fiction movie was based on an Arthur C Clarke short story called 'The Sentinel'?

25 Which film is based on a James Jones novel set in Honolulu prior to the attack on Pearl Harbor?

1 In which film did Brando make his debut in 1950?

2 Which historical figure did he play in the 1954 movie *Desirée*?

3 Brando starred as Terry Malloy in *On the Waterfront*. Who played his brother Charlie?

4 In which film was Brando directed by Charles Chaplin?

5 After filming *Mutiny on the Bounty*, Brando purchased Tetiíaroa. What is it?

6 Which part did Brando play in the 1953 film of *Julius Caesar*?

7 What did American Indian Sacheen Little Feather do on Brando's behalf at the 1973 Academy Awards?

8 In which 1958 film did Brando bleach his hair and play a Nazi officer?

9 For which movie was he first awarded an Oscar?

10 Where was Marlon Brando born?

11 Jessica Tandy played Blanche Dubois opposite Brando's Stanley Kowalski in the Broadway production of *A Streetcar Named Desire*. Who played her in the 1951 film?

12 What did Brando do, without warning director Francis Coppola, to enhance the appearance of Colonel Kurtz in *Apocalypse Now*?

13 What is Don Corleone doing immediately before his death in *The Godfather*?

14 Why did Brando choose the name 'Pennebaker' for his own film production company?

15 What is Brando's only film as a director?

16 In which Western did he star with Jack Nicholson?

17 In which film did Brando play a lawyer hired to defend a wrongly accused black man in South Africa?

18 Brando played Vito Corleone in *The Godfather*. Who played him as a young man in *The Godfather, Part II*?

19 In which film did Brando play a character called Jor-El?

20 Who directed Brando in the 1971 British-made film *The Nightcomers*?

21 In *Bedtime Story* Brando and David Niven play a couple of con men preying on women on the French Riviera. What was the remake called and who were its two stars?

22 At the end of *On the Waterfront* Terry (Brando) has a brutal fight with gang boss Johnny Friendly, played by whom?

23 In which musical did Marlon Brando star with Frank Sinatra and Jean Simmons?

24 What make of motorcycle does Brando ride in *The Wild One*?

25 Of which film did Brando say, 'all I could see were my mistakes and I hated it. But years later, when I saw it on television from a different perspective, I decided it was a pretty good film'?

1 What is the name for a line on a weather map which connects points of equal temperature?

2 What is the central area of a hurricane called?

3 What is an anemometer?

4 Which warm, dry wind is prevalent along the eastern edge of the Rocky Mountains, and has a name that means 'snow eater'?

5 What does the abbreviation CFC stand for?

6 Which gas is most prevalent in the earth's atmosphere?

7 In which desert does the wind known as the Sirocco originate?

8 What occurs between a negatively charged cloud base and positively charged earth below?

9 What is the common name for wispy cirrus clouds?

10 What name is given to the dividing line between advancing cold air and a mass of warmer air?

11 Which vital part of the atmosphere makes up about seven millionths of its volume?

12 Occurring twice yearly, what name is given to a day that consists of twelve hours of daylight and twelve hours of darkness?

13 What name is given to westerly winds found in the southern hemisphere between 40 and 50 degrees latitude?

14 Usually occurring in summer, what name is given to a mass of cloud that is fractured into a pattern of ripples?

15 Which Pacific Ocean weather condition brings unusually high water temperature and was given its name by Peruvian fishermen?

16 What nationality was Anders Celsius, who devised the Centigrade scale of temperature measurement?

17 What is the name given to the weather feature in which the atmospheric pressure is lower than that of the surrounding air?

18 In India, what name is given to the period between June and September when about 75 per cent of the region's annual rainfall arrives?

19 Which layer of the atmosphere lies between heights of approximately six-and-a-half miles and 30 miles above the earth's surface?

20 According to the Beaufort Scale, how many miles per hour must a wind reach to be classified as a hurricane?

21 When lightning strikes, the air along its path heats up very quickly and very intensely. What is produced by this sudden expansion of air?

22 What name is given to a prolonged period of unusually hot weather well above the average for a particular region?

23 How far above the earth's surface do cirrus clouds usually form?

24 What name is given to the layer of ground that remains permanently frozen despite seasonal changes in temperature?

25 At what temperature does the Fahrenheit scale give the same reading as the Celsius, or Centigrade scale?

21

1 Which water bird has brown and black feathers with a white flank slash and a red beak shield?

2 Which bird is renowned for taking over the nests of other species?

3 Which bird is resident of the American Southwest and has been immortalised in a cartoon series?

4 What colour are the eggs of the redstart?

5 What colour is the beak of a mature mute swan?

6 Which continent is the natural habitat of the ostrich?

7 For how long does a female turkey incubate her eggs?

8 What is meant by a low wing bearing?

9 Which bird, sometimes called the peewit, has dark green plumage with white neck and underside, and a distinctive green crest?

10 Which curved-billed bird is the largest European wader?

11 Which has a black bill, the crow or the rook?

12 Which bird was depicted on the rear of the farthing coin?

13 Which is the smallest of all birds?

14 What type of bird is a teal?

15 How many are in a clutch of blackbird's eggs?

16 Which is the largest species of penguin?

17 To which family does the jay belong?

18 Where do swallows go when they migrate from Britain for the winter?

19 Which bird is the emblem of the United States?

20 Which bird of prey can often be seen hovering above hedges and ditches at the roadside?

21 Native to America, what type of bird are Lewis's red-bellied, ladder-backed and Nuttall's?

22 Which sea bird has a black and white body and a very large, bright yellow and red beak?

23 Which is the largest owl found in Britain?

24 Which lays blue eggs, the song thrush or the mistle thrush?

25 Which country is the natural habitat of the emu?

1 Which singing cowboy was born Leonard Slye, and whose early career was as part of the Sons of the Pioneers group?

2 Who wrote the song 'Coat of Many Colours', about a girl ridiculed for the coat her mother made for her from fabric scraps?

3 How old was LeAnn Rimes when she had her first number one country album?

4 With which band is Raul Malo the lead singer?

5 Which successful solo artist is the regular host of the Country Music Awards?

6 Which guitarist replaced Bernie Leadon in the Eagles in 1975?

7 Who was the first woman to be inducted into the Country Music Hall of Fame in 1973, ten years after her death?

8 Which singer is known as 'The Man in Black'?

9 Which fiddle-playing singer is backed by the band Union Station?

10 Which singer started as a session guitarist, working with the likes of Bobby Darin, Frank Sinatra, Dean Martin and the Beach Boys?

11 Who was declared dead on New Year's Day 1953, at the age of 29?

12 Who wrote the songs 'Oh, Lonesome Me', 'Sweet Dreams' and 'I Can't Stop Loving You'?

13 Which female trio released the multi-platinum album *Wide Open Spaces* in 1998?

14 Who released an album in the guise of a fictitious singer entitled *In the Life of Chris Gaines* in 1999?

15 Which singer/songwriter appeared in the movie *The Player*, where he met his wife-to-be Julia Roberts?

16 Which guitarist joined RCA in 1947 and was put in charge of the label's Nashville studio in 1955, where he helped further the careers of, among others, Jim Reeves, Don Gibson and Elvis Presley?

17 Which singer is the younger sister of Loretta Lynn?

18 With which instrument is Earl Scruggs associated?

19 Which country singer had a song named after him on Prefab Sprout's 1985 album *Steve McQueen*?

20 Which member of the Monkees went on to front the First National Band?

21 Which two singers married in 1969, divorced in 1975, and recorded one last album together in 1995?

22 Whose albums include *Copperhead Road*, *Guitar Town* and *Train A Comin'*?

23 Born Roberta Streeter, whose first single was the strange 'Ode to Billy Joe', about a young man's suicide?

24 The song 'Crazy' is synonymous with Patsy Cline, but who wrote it?

25 Who was a member of the Byrds and the Flying Burrito Brothers, and recorded the solo albums *GP* and *Grievous Angel*?

1 What was the instrument that produced the weird noises on the Beach Boys' 'Good Vibrations'?

2 With which instrument is Les Paul associated?

3 Name the instrument played by Larry Adler.

4 What is the connection between swing bandleaders Woody Herman, Artie Shaw and Benny Goodman?

5 What did Adolphe Sax invent?

6 'Let There Be ——' was a hit for Sandy Nelson.

7 Bösendorfer, Steinway and Bechstein are all makes of which instrument?

8 Instrumentally, what's the connection between Jimmy Smith, Booker T. and Billy Preston?

9 Name the instrument connected with Guy Barker.

10 Herbie Mann is best known for playing which instrument?

11 Name the three greats who played guitar with The Yardbirds.

12 Musician Ray Brown was married to Ella Fitzgerald. Which instrument did he play?

13 Name the country music instrument that looks like a guitar, has a resonator and was invented by the Dopera brothers of California.

14 Name the orchestral instrument that lent its name to Mike Oldfield's best-known album.

15 What is the connection between Jean-Luc Ponty, Stéphane Grappelli and Jerry Goodman?

16 Which instruments were duelling on the *Deliverance* film soundtrack?

17 '—— Rain' was a minor hit for Bruce Hornsby in 1987.

18 Rockin' Dopsie, Queen Ida and Clifton Chenier are all cajun music legends. How are they connected instrumentally?

19 Which was the main instrument used by Vangelis on his film score for *Chariots of Fire*?

20 Which guitar manufacturer was responsible for the Stratocaster?

21 'Mr —— Man' was a hit single for The Byrds.

22 What are maracas?

23 Name the instrument most readily associated with Gary Burton, Milt Jackson and Lionel Hampton.

24 Conga, bongos and tabla are all forms of which instrument?

25 Which instrument connects Glenn Miller and Tommy Dorsey?

1 What two-word term is given to a simulated three-dimensional environment using computer graphics?

2 Which stock control system was introduced in American supermarkets in 1974?

3 Which German company introduced the interrupter gear, enabling a machine gun to fire through an aeroplane's propeller?

4 What fundamental part of computer technology was patented in the US in 1961?

5 In which country was the portable domestic electric room heater first marketed in 1912?

6 In 1937 American engineer Chester Carlson invented a process called xerography. What is its more common name?

7 In which country did polyethylene plastic go into commercial production in 1939?

8 In which decade did the British Post Office introduce a telex service?

9 Which Dutch company began marketing compact disc players in 1982?

10 Developed in the United States in 1930, by what name is polyvinyl chloride plastic better known?

11 What diameter floppy disks were introduced by IBM in 1970?

12 In which country was fuel injection for cars introduced in 1954?

13 In 1976 JVC introduced the VHS video format. What do the initials stand for?

14 What widely used kitchen item was first marketed by the General Electric Company in 1909?

15 What advance in sound recording was made by British engineer Alan Blumlein in 1933?

16 Which American architect/engineer invented geodesic dome construction?

17 What type of hook and eye fastening was invented by Swiss engineer Georges de Mestral in 1948, and introduced commercially in 1956?

18 In which year were tissue cells first grown outside the body by US biologist Ross Harrison?

19 What vehicular safety device was first patented by E J Claghorn in 1885?

20 In computing, what does HTTP stand for?

21 Scotch tape was invented in 1930 by American Richard Drew. For which company did he work?

22 Name the kitchen development patented by American radar engineer Percy Spencer in 1945.

23 The lightweight portable electric drill was first marketed in 1917 by two American inventors with the first names Duncan and Alonso. What were their surnames?

24 What type of engine was invented by German Felix Wankel in the mid-1950s?

25 What communication aid was invented in 1905 by American undertaker Almon Strowger?

1 Which scandal was uncovered by journalists Bob Woodward and Carl Bernstein?

2 Which Hollywood actor was charged with, and acquitted of, three rape charges in 1943?

3 Which rock 'n' roll singer shocked Britain in 1958 when he arrived with his thirteen-year-old wife?

4 In which year did King Edward VIII abdicate from the British throne?

5 Which entertainer sued the *Daily Mirror* in 1959 for publishing an article implying that he was a homosexual?

6 Who was the Queen's art adviser exposed in November 1979 as a spy for the Russians?

7 Who was prime minister during the Profumo scandal?

8 Which titled lady was pictured in a compromising position with a 'headless' man?

9 Which Conservative MP admitted in 1983 to having an affair with his secretary, Sara Keays, who went on to have his child?

10 With which pop star do you associate allegations involving a child named Jordan Chandler?

11 What was the name of the Arkansas property development with which the Clintons were involved?

12 Which star of the silent screen was accused of the rape and manslaughter of actress Virginia Rappe in 1920?

13 Germans Konrad Kujau and Gerd Heidemann were arrested in May 1983 for their part in which fraudulent publication?

14 In which year did National Guardsmen open fire on student demonstrators at Kent State University, Ohio, killing four?

15 In which year did Palestinian terrorists kill members of the Israeli Olympic team?

16 Who was sentenced to ten days in prison and fined $500 for 'indecent behaviour' on the Broadway stage in 1927?

17 What rank was Oliver North at the time of the 'Irangate' hearing?

18 Nick Leeson was held responsible for the fall of which merchant bank in 1995?

19 Which American TV evangelist was involved in a sex and money scandal in 1987?

20 Which skater allegedly had rival Nancy Kerrigan attacked at the 1994 Winter Olympics?

21 The subject of a Robert Redford film, what was the name of the 1950s American TV quiz show in which Charles Van Doren received questions in advance to keep his winning run going?

22 In which year was hostage-turned-terrorist Patti Hearst arrested by FBI agents?

23 Who wrote a report on the misconduct of President Clinton in the wake of the Monica Lewinsky affair?

24 What was the name given to the scandal involving disc jockeys or radio stations being bribed to play certain records?

25 Which South African township saw riots in 1976 that resulted in around 175 deaths?

1 Which Spanish team plays at the Vicente Calderón stadium?

2 Who is the older, by about fifteen minutes, of the Dutch twins Ronald and Frank De Boer?

3 Which German team won the European Cup three years in succession from 1974?

4 From which Italian team did Tottenham Hotspur sign Jimmy Greaves in 1961?

5 Which English manager once played his home games at the Volksparkstadion on the outskirts of Hamburg?

6 Who did eventual winners Denmark replace just before the start of the 1992 European Championships?

7 Which Scotsman managed Turkish club Galatasaray in the mid-1990s?

8 Which club's stadium has the largest capacity in Europe?

9 Who did France beat in the semifinal of Euro 2000?

10 What is meant by the name Steaua, as in Steaua Bucharest?

11 Which Norwegian club plays in the city of Trondheim?

12 By what score did Hungary, featuring Ferenc Puskas, beat England in their first-ever Wembley defeat in 1953?

13 Which company is the sponsor of Dutch club PSV Eindhoven?

14 To what did Dinamo Zagreb change their name after independence in 1992?

15 Who did Borussia Dortmund beat in the final to lift the European Cup for the first time in 1997?

16 Sunderland's Stadium of Light takes its name from that of which other European team?

17 Whose arrival at Napoli spurred the team on to its first Italian league title in 1987?

18 Slovan Bratislava last won the Czechoslovakian league title in 1992. Which league title did they win in 1994?

19 Which two Englishmen scored in the 1999 and 2000 European Cup finals?

20 Which European city has teams with the names CSKA, Dynamo, Spartak and Torpedo?

21 Which player moved from Barcelona to Real Madrid for a record transfer fee in the summer of 2000?

22 Which French side has its home at the Parc des Princes?

23 Who had Manchester United been playing prior to the Munich air disaster in 1958?

24 What nationality is Jean-Marc Bosman, after whom the transfer ruling is named?

25 With which Italian club do you associate Welshman Ian Rush, Irishman Liam Brady, and Frenchman Michel Platini?

1 When did United first win the European Cup?

2 Who preceded Sir Alex Ferguson as manager?

3 In which year did they win the unique treble?

4 Which player went on to manage Coventry City?

5 Which of two famous brothers played for United?

6 Who did United beat 9–1 in 1998?

7 For which country did George Best play?

8 Where was David Beckham born?

9 What was Andy Cole's first club?

10 Which player went on to manage Crystal Palace?

11 In which city did the Busby Babes plane crash take place?

12 Which ex-City player became assistant to Alex Ferguson?

13 Which controversial manager was at the club in the 1970s?

14 What is the capacity of Old Trafford?

15 Who scored the goal to put United through to the 1999 Cup Final?

16 What is the Neville brothers' sister's claim to fame?

17 Who is the chairman of the club?

18 Who sponsors the first-team shirts?

19 Which member of the *Have I Got News For You* team is a fanatical United fan?

20 Which band is named after the club's colours?

21 Which Danish goalkeeper played for seven seasons?

22 Where did the Cantona karate incident take place?

23 Who is the current club captain?

24 Who scored the winning goal in the Champions' League final?

25 Who was voted the best player ever to play for United?

1 Who originally starred alongside Dennis Franz in *NYPD Blue*?

2 In the British-made *Sherlock Holmes* series shown in the 80s and 90s, who played the title role?

3 Which programme's lead character was detective Steve McGarrett?

4 What is Chief Inspector Morse's Christian name?

5 Who had a 1981 hit with the theme tune from *Hill Street Blues*?

6 Name one of the two future Munsters who starred in the 1960s cop comedy *Car 54, Where Are You?*

7 In which show were the assembled officers advised by Sergeant Esterhaus to 'be careful out there'?

8 Who played the part of Stavros in *Kojak*?

9 Which TV cop had a US and UK number one with 'Don't Give Up On Us'?

10 Who played the lead role in the early 1970s American show *Dan August*?

11 Which 1987 film saw Columbo's Peter Falk narrating an unconventional fairy tale to a bed-ridden boy?

12 Which 1970s TV cop show made a star of Michael Douglas?

13 Which musical police show was the brainchild of writer/producer Steven Bochco?

14 Which series starred Larry Wilcox and Erik Estrada as officers Jon Baker and Frank 'Ponch' Poncherello?

15 Which well-known TV series about crime-fighters was brought to the big screen in 1987, starring Kevin Costner?

16 From which 1970s cop show does the catchphrase 'Book 'em, Dan-O' hail?

17 What was the setting for the series *Magnum, PI*?

18 Who were the best known subordinates of Chief Inspector Frank Haskins in a British series of the 1970s?

19 What 1971 film saw Paul Michael Glaser as suitor to one of Topol's daughters?

20 Which of *Columbo* star Peter Falk's eyes is the false one?

21 Who played opposite Tyne Daly in the pilot episode of 1980s series *Cagney and Lacey*?

22 Which wheelchair-bound policeman was played by Raymond Burr from 1967 to 1975 in the USA?

23 Which show had central characters called Maddie Hayes and David Addison?

24 In the TV version of *In the Heat of the Night*, who played the role of Police Chief Bill Gillespie, made famous by Rod Steiger in the original film?

25 Which police comedy series spawned the *Naked Gun* movies?

1 Which educational programme, first shown in the 1960s, was the creation of Television Workshop co-founder Joan Ganz Cooney?

2 Former Mr Universe Lou Ferrigno played TV's The Incredible Hulk, but who played his alter ego, mild-mannered scientist Bruce Banner?

3 Which cartoon series, starring a drawling dog, was the first to win an Emmy for Outstanding Achievement in Children's Programming?

4 Hong Kong Phooey's cases were usually solved by his accomplice, whose efforts were never recognised. What was his name?

5 What was the Littlest Hobo's name?

6 Taking its cue from *The Flintstones*, which 1960s cartoon series featured a suburban US family of the late 21st century?

7 Where did the Hair Bear Bunch live?

8 What was Mike Judge's animated follow-up to *Beavis and Butthead*?

9 *Gilligan's Island* star Alan Hale Jr appeared as an heroic train driver in which 1950s TV series?

10 Which character played the drums in the Muppets band?

11 Which cartoon series revolved around the antics of the inhabitants of Jellystone National Park?

12 Francine Pascal's novels, set in a Californian high school, became a popular 1990s TV series. What was it called?

13 What is the name of the *South Park* character who is regularly killed?

14 What kind of animals are Rocky and Bullwinkle?

15 Who did the voices of Batman and Robin in the 1970s cartoon series called *The New Adventures of Batman*?

16 What kind of animal was My Friend Flicka?

17 TV's McCloud, Dennis Weaver, played the part of a game warden in a 1960s series about a bear cub. What was it called?

18 The Flintstones' daughter and the Rubbles' adopted son became inseparable. What were their names?

19 Which famous pop star narrated *Thomas the Tank Engine*?

20 What does 'Daktari' mean?

21 George Dolenz played TV's The Count of Monte Cristo. His son became a TV star himself in the 1960s. In what TV programme?

22 What was the name of Rin Tin Tin's eleven-year-old master?

23 Who played Robin Hood in the 1950s TV series?

24 What was the name of Champion the Wonder Horse's German shepherd dog companion?

25 Which myopic cartoon character had two nephews called Prezley and Waldo?

1 Which member of the British royal family helped popularise items such as Fair Isle sweaters, suede shoes and dinner jackets?

2 Which British designer popularised the minidress in the 1960s?

3 Born in Saumur, France in 1883, by what name is Gabrielle Bonheur better known?

4 In which decade did Giorgio Armani establish his own company?

5 Who was appointed dressmaker to the Queen in 1955?

6 In 1947 whose first collection under his own name was dubbed the New Look?

7 Who presented a collection called Pirate in 1981, with her then partner Malcolm McLaren?

8 Which designer was responsible for the trend of slogan-bearing T-shirts in the 1980s?

9 In 1985 which designer loaned Bruce Springsteen and his then wife, Julianne, his Lake Como villa for their honeymoon?

10 Who was the most famous recipient of a David and Elizabeth Emanuel creation?

11 What do the initials DKNY stand for?

12 Which fashion model has appeared in advertisements for Citroën cars?

13 Born in Hamburg in 1938, which former design director at Chanel is best known for his sophisticated day and evening wear?

14 In which year were nylon stockings introduced?

15 Which British designer was appointed dressmaker to the royal family in 1938?

16 Whose work has included sweatshirts trimmed with lace and satin, and shoes with upside-down Eiffel Towers as heels?

17 Which family firm started in the north of Italy in 1960, specialising in inexpensive yet fashionable knitwear?

18 Who is most associated with the concept of 'designer' jeans?

19 Who wrote the book *Men Without Ties*?

20 Which American president popularised the Panama hat?

21 Which Italian designer, born in 1890, liked to shock and amuse with her creations, which included hats in the shapes of ice cream cones and lamb cutlets?

22 Which French ex-tennis player was known as 'Le Crocodile' because of his aggressive style of play, which led to the crocodile being used as an emblem on his sportswear?

23 What nationality is designer Issey Miyake?

24 In which year did Levi Strauss take out a patent on his denim workpants?

25 Who directed the movie *Prêt à Porter*?

1 Whose motto was 'Tune in, Turn on, Drop out'?

2 Which famous novelist coined the phrase 'Go to work on an egg'?

3 Whose motto is '*Honi soit qui mal y pense*'?

4 Whose epitaph is '*Si monumentum requiris circumspice*' – 'if you want a monument, look around'?

5 What is the motto of Eton College?

6 What is the BBC's motto?

7 Which country's motto is '*E pluribus unum*' ('one out of many')?

8 Complete this motto used by John Lewis: 'Never knowingly ——'?

9 On whose grave is it marked 'BULA MATARI'?

10 What does it say underneath the lion on the MGM symbol?

11 Whose epitaph was 'A brave life and a heroic death. Be British'?

12 Whose grave bears the words '*Homo sum!* The adventurer!'?

13 What is the motto of the Prince of Wales?

14 Who penned his own epitaph, 'Here lies one whose name was writ in water'?

15 Of whom was it said, on her gravestone, that 'Wit can never be Defence enough against Mortality'?

16 Who was famously buried under the words 'Workers of all Lands Unite'?

17 Which movement's motto is 'Be prepared'?

18 'Here lies ——, the once and future king'. Who was he?

19 Of whom was it written on his gravestone, 'savage indignation can tear his heart no longer'?

20 Which country's motto is '*nemo me impune lacessit*' ('no one provokes me with impunity')?

21 Which sculptor was said, on his gravestone, to be 'a loss to the Café Royal'?

22 Which shop's motto was 'Don't ask the price – 'tis a penny'?

23 Whose gravestone describes him as 'like the cover of an old book, its contents torn out'?

24 What is the motto of the Stock Exchange?

25 Whose gravestone bears the words 'His sins were scarlet but his books were read'?

16

ANSWERS TO QUIZ 3

Children
1 English Civil War
2 Juliet
3 (First) Cousin
4 Three
5 Edsel
6 Cleopatra
7 The Railway Children
8 François Duvalier
9 Hamnet
10 Frank Zappa
11 Bob Cratchit
12 Charlie Sheen & Emilio Estevez
13 Sylvia
14 Gepetto
15 *Bugsy Malone*
16 *Charlie and the Chocolate Factory*
17 Anastasia
18 Nigel Havers
19 Little Lord Fauntleroy
20 Sylvester Stallone
21 Aristotle Onassis
22 Billy J Kramer and The Dakotas
23 Mary, Queen of Scots
24 Winston Churchill
25 Little Jimmy Osmond

Detectives
1 Helen Mirren
2 *Homicide*
3 Auguste Dupin
4 Popeye Doyle
5 Sonny Crockett
6 Kitt
7 Inspector Lestrade
8 Diana Rigg
9 The Seven Deadly Sins
10 Shaft
11 Captain Dobey
12 Because he had died
13 *Hill Street Blues*
14 Columbo
15 *Crime and Punishment*
16 He was wheelchair-bound
17 Michael Douglas
18 *Police Woman*
19 Mycroft
20 James Garner
21 Detective Christine Cagney, from *Cagney and Lacey*
22 2 hours
23 Hercule Poirot
24 Kojak
25 Sherlock Holmes

Films of Books
1 *The Age of Innocence*
2 *Valmont*
3 Francis Ford Coppola
4 *Dr Strangelove, or How I Learned to Stop Worrying and Love the Bomb*
5 1962
6 *Jaws*
7 *Apocalypse Now*
8 Orson Welles
9 *Emma*
10 James Caan
11 *Lolita*
12 *Double Indemnity*
13 *Psycho*
14 Richard Burton
15 *The Shape of Things to Come*
16 *Carrie*
17 *Blade Runner*
18 They have all directed films of Charles Dickens novels
19 They were from books by the same author, Pierre Boulle
20 *Jackie Brown*
21 *Moby Dick*
22 *The Man in the Iron Mask*
23 *To Kill a Mockingbird*
24 *2001: A Space Odyssey*
25 *From Here to Eternity*

Marlon Brando
1 *The Men*
2 Napoleon
3 Rod Steiger
4 *A Countess from Hong Kong*
5 An island near Tahiti
6 Mark Antony
7 She declined his Oscar for *The Godfather*
8 *The Young Lions*
9 *On the Waterfront*
10 Omaha, Nebraska
11 Vivien Leigh
12 He shaved his head
13 Playing with his grandchild
14 It was his mother's maiden name
15 *One-Eyed Jacks*
16 *The Missouri Breaks*
17 *A Dry White Season*
18 Robert De Niro
19 *Superman*
20 Michael Winner
21 *Dirty Rotten Scoundrels* (Steve Martin and Michael Caine)
22 Lee J Cobb
23 *Guys and Dolls*
24 Triumph
25 *The Godfather*

The Weather
1 An isotherm
2 The eye
3 A device for measuring wind speed
4 Chinook
5 Chlorofluorocarbons
6 Nitrogen, 78.08%
7 The Sahara
8 Fork lightning
9 Mares' tails
10 A cold front
11 The stratosphere
12 Equinox
13 The Roaring Forties
14 Mackerel sky
15 El Niño
16 Swedish
17 A depression – also called a low or a cyclone
18 Monsoon season
19 Ozone
20 74 mph
21 Thunder
22 A heatwave
23 Between five and ten miles
24 Permafrost
25 Minus 40 degrees

Birds
1 Moorhen
2 Cuckoo
3 Roadrunner
4 Usually blue with a greenish tinge
5 Orange
6 Africa
7 Approximately 28 days
8 A low body weight to wing area ratio
9 The lapwing
10 Curlew
11 Crow
12 Wren
13 Bee hummingbird, weighing 2 grams
14 Duck
15 Usually between 3 and 5
16 Emperor
17 Crow
18 South Africa
19 Bald eagle
20 Kestrel
21 Woodpeckers
22 Atlantic puffin
23 Snowy owl
24 Song thrush
25 Australia

Country & Western
1 Roy Rogers
2 Dolly Parton
3 Thirteen
4 The Mavericks
5 Vince Gill
6 Joe Walsh
7 Patsy Cline
8 Johnny Cash
9 Alison Krauss
10 Glen Campbell
11 Hank Williams
12 Don Gibson
13 Dixie Chicks
14 Garth Brooks
15 Lyle Lovett
16 Chet Atkins
17 Crystal Gayle
18 The banjo
19 Faron Young
20 Mike Nesmith
21 George Jones and Tammy Wynette
22 Steve Earle
23 Bobbie Gentry
24 Willie Nelson
25 Gram Parsons

Instruments
1 Theremin
2 Guitar
3 Harmonica
4 They all led on clarinet
5 Saxophone
6 Drums
7 Piano
8 Organ
9 Trumpet
10 Flute
11 Eric Clapton, Jeff Beck and Jimmy Page
12 Bass
13 Dobro
14 Tubular bells
15 Violin
16 Banjos
17 Mandolin
18 Accordion
19 Synthesizer
20 Fender
21 Tambourine
22 Shaken Latin percussion instruments made from gourds with beans or peas inside them
23 Vibraphone
24 Drums
25 Trombone

Technology
1 Virtual reality
2 Bar codes
3 Fokker
4 The silicon chip
5 England
6 Photocopying
7 Britain
8 1930s (1932)
9 Philips
10 PVC

11 Eight-inch
12 Germany
13 Video home system
14 The electric toaster
15 Stereophonic sound
16 Buckminster Fuller
17 Velcro
18 1905
19 Seat belt
20 Hypertext transport (or transfer) protocol
21 3M
22 The microwave oven
23 Black & Decker
24 Rotary internal combustion engine
25 The dial telephone

Scandals
1 Watergate
2 Errol Flynn
3 Jerry Lee Lewis
4 1936
5 Liberace
6 Sir Anthony Blunt
7 Harold Macmillan
8 The Duchess of Argyll
9 Cecil Parkinson
10 Michael Jackson
11 Whitewater
12 'Fatty' Arbuckle
13 The Hitler Diaries
14 1970
15 1972
16 Mae West
17 Lieutenant Colonel
18 Barings
19 Jim Bakker
20 Tonya Harding
21 *Twenty-One*
22 1975
23 Kenneth Starr
24 Payola
25 Soweto

European Football
1 Atlético Madrid
2 Ronald
3 Bayern Munich
4 AC Milan
5 Kevin Keegan
6 Yugoslavia
7 Graeme Souness
8 Barcelona
9 Portugal
10 Star
11 Rosenborg BK
12 6-3
13 Philips
14 Croatia Zagreb
15 Juventus
16 Benfica
17 Diego Maradona
18 The Slovakian
19 Teddy Sheringham and Steve McManaman
20 Moscow
21 Luis Figo
22 Paris Saint-Germain
23 Red Star Belgrade
24 Belgian
25 Juventus

Man Utd
1 1959
2 Ron Atkinson
3 1999
4 Gordon Strachan
5 Bobby Charlton
6 Notts Forest
7 Northern Ireland
8 Leytonstone
9 Arsenal
10 Steve Coppell
11 Munich
12 Brian Kidd
13 Tommy Docherty
14 63,000
15 Ryan Giggs
16 She is an England netball player
17 Martin Edwards
18 Vodafone
19 Angus Deayton
20 Simply Red
21 Peter Schmeichel
22 Crystal Palace
23 Roy Keane
24 Ole Gunnar Solskjaer
25 George Best

Police Shows
1 David Caruso
2 Jeremy Brett
3 *Hawaii Five-O*
4 Endeavour
5 Mike Post
6 Fred Gwynne and Al Lewis
7 *Hill Street Blues*
8 Telly Savalas's brother George
9 David Soul
10 Burt Reynolds
11 *The Princess Bride*
12 *The Streets of San Francisco*
13 *Cop Rock*
14 *CHiPs*
15 *The Untouchables*
16 *Hawaii Five-O*
17 *Hawaii*
18 Regan and Carter in *The Sweeney*
19 *Fiddler on the Roof*
20 The right eye
21 Loretta Swit
22 Chief Robert T Ironside
23 *Moonlighting*
24 Carroll O'Connor
25 *Police Squad*

Children's TV
1 *Sesame Street*
2 Bill Bixby
3 *Huckleberry Hound*
4 Spot the cat
5 London
6 *The Jetsons*
7 Wonderland Zoo
8 *King of the Hill*
9 Casey Jones
10 Animal
11 *Yogi Bear*
12 *Sweet Valley High*
13 Kenny
14 A flying squirrel and a moose
15 Adam West and Burt Ward
16 A black stallion
17 *Gentle Ben*
18 Pebbles and Bam-Bam
19 Ringo Starr
20 Doctor, in Swahili
21 *The Monkees*
22 Rusty
23 Richard Green
24 Rebel
25 Mister Magoo

Fashion
1 The Duke of Windsor
2 Mary Quant
3 Coco Chanel
4 1970s
5 Hardy Amies
6 Christian Dior
7 Vivienne Westwood
8 Katharine Hamnett
9 Gianni Versace
10 Lady Diana Spencer
11 Donna Karan New York
12 Claudia Schiffer
13 Karl Lagerfeld
14 1940
15 Norman Hartnell
16 Jean-Paul Gaultier
17 Benetton
18 Calvin Klein
19 Gianni Versace
20 Theodore Roosevelt
21 Elsa Schiaparelli
22 René Lacoste
23 Japanese
24 1872
25 Robert Altman

Mottos and Epitaphs
1 Timothy Leary
2 Fay Weldon
3 The British Royal Family
4 Sir Christopher Wren
5 *'Floreat Etona'*
6 'Nations shall speak peace unto nations'
7 The United States
8 'Never knowingly undersold'
9 Sir Henry Stanley ('breaker of rocks')
10 *'Ars Gratia Artis'* ('art for art's sake')
11 Edward Smith – captain of the *Titanic*
12 D H Lawrence
13 *'Ich Dien'* ('I serve')
14 John Keats
15 Aphra Behn
16 Karl Marx
17 The Boy Scouts, Girl Guides and Brownies
18 King Arthur
19 Jonathan Swift
20 Scotland
21 Jacob Epstein
22 Simon Marks's Penny Bazaar (the original Marks & Spencer)
23 Benjamin Franklin
24 'My word is my bond'
25 Hilaire Belloc

THE ULTIMATE BOOK OF TRIVIA

QUIZ 4

1 Which former prime minister of France became his country's president after the resignation of Charles de Gaulle?

2 Which politician enrolled in the law faculty of Havana University in 1945, at the age of nineteen?

3 Who was Russian president after Yuri Andropov and before Mikhail Gorbachev?

4 Who caused uproar in Britain in 1968 with his 'rivers of blood' speech on the immigration issue?

5 Which American chaired the Good Friday agreement in Ireland in 1998?

6 Who was deemed to have made a breach of protocol when he touched the Queen's arm during a visit to Australia?

7 Which English prime minister signed the infamous Munich agreement with Hitler in 1938?

8 Who replaced Ehud Barak as Israel's prime minister in early 2001?

9 Who was Bertie Aherne's predecessor as Prime Minister of Ireland?

10 Which communist leader, who died in 1969, once worked as a pastry cook in London?

11 Who was replaced by Peter Mandelson as Secretary of State for Northern Ireland in 1999?

12 Which Soviet president famously banged his shoe on the table while Harold Macmillan was speaking to the United Nations in 1960?

13 In which year was Mikhail Gorbachev awarded the Nobel Peace Prize?

14 Who became the first British Labour prime minister in 1924?

15 How did President Sadat of Egypt die in 1981?

16 Which German Chancellor resigned in May 1974 after a spy was discovered working in his office?

17 In 1967, 41-year-old Svetlana Alliluyeva defected from the Soviet Union. Who was her father?

18 Which Democratic candidate ran against Ronald Reagan in the 1984 US election?

19 Who became British Prime Minister in 1783 in his 25th year?

20 Which future French President lost the 1974 election to Valéry Giscard d'Estaing?

21 Of which political party in Northern Ireland is John Hume a member?

22 Which former British prime minister died in 1986 at the age of 92?

23 Which two Middle East leaders shared the 1978 Nobel Peace Prize?

24 Which British politician of the 1970s disappeared in Miami, Florida, leaving clothes on the beach, and reappeared in Australia?

25 Who was British Prime Minister during the Suez crisis in 1956?

1 Who is the young Spanish number one golfer?

2 Who was German chancellor during the 1990s?

3 Who was the French prime minister through the 1980s and early 1990s?

4 Which media tycoon was president of Italy?

5 Who is head of the French Nationalists?

6 Who led France in the 1998 World Cup?

7 Which Spaniard wrote *Don Quixote*?

8 What is the Basque terrorist organization called?

9 Who led the French at Trafalgar?

10 Who won an Oscar for *Life Is Beautiful*?

11 Which French director made *Léon*?

12 Who played the lead in *Mon Père Le Héros*?

13 Which Italian actress became Hollywood's sexiest woman in 1973?

14 Which German film is about a U-boat?

15 Who scored the winning goal in Euro '96?

16 *Battleship Potemkin* was the work of which European film director?

17 Which 20th-century impresario owned a company called the Ballets Russes?

18 Who nailed 95 theses on indulgences to the door of a church in Wittenberg, precipitating the Reformation?

19 Who managed France to World Cup success?

20 Who moved the Russian capital from Moscow to St Petersburg?

21 Who was France's prime minister in the early 1990s?

22 Who is king of Spain?

23 Which Italian wrote *Madama Butterfly*?

24 Who wrote *The Outsider*?

25 Which 19th-century British statesman wrote the novel *Sybil: or, the Two Nations*?

1 What is Michael Caine's real name?

2 In which 1988 comedy did Caine and Ben Kingsley play Sherlock Holmes and Dr Watson respectively?

3 In which Peter Sellers film did Caine appear in 1962?

4 Who starred with Caine in the 1982 thriller *Deathtrap*, playing a young playwright who Caine's character intends to murder?

5 In which Len Deighton story did Caine first star as agent Harry Palmer in 1965?

6 For which film did he receive his first Academy Award as supporting actor?

7 With which other young British actor did Caine share an apartment in London in the 1960s?

8 Apart from starring in the 1987 film of Frederick Forsyth's *The Fourth Protocol*, what was Caine's other involvement in the film?

9 Why did he choose the surname Caine?

10 In which year was *Educating Rita* released?

11 In which film did Caine play Dr Wilbur Larch, in a performance that gained him a second Academy Award?

12 Who starred alongside Caine in the 1988 film *Dirty Rotten Scoundrels*?

13 Which British actress won an Oscar for her role as Caine's wife in the 1978 comedy *California Suite*?

14 Which American actress starred with Caine in *Alfie*?

15 What significant event in Caine's life took place on 16 June 2000?

16 In which 1988 film did he play a sleazy talent agent who meets an agoraphobic young woman with a brilliant talent for singing?

17 Caine played a villain in *Mona Lisa* opposite which other leading British actor?

18 What was the title of the 1980 Brian De Palma murder thriller in which Caine starred as psychiatrist Dr Robert Elliott?

19 Which 1971 gangster film was based on Ted Lewis's novel *Jack's Return Home*, about a man going up to Newcastle to investigate his brother's death?

20 Which 1964 film is generally regarded as the film that made Caine a star?

21 Who co-starred with Caine in the 1972 thriller comedy *Sleuth*?

22 Which flamboyant British director was at the helm of Caine's third film as Harry Palmer, *Billion Dollar Brain*?

23 Which film, based on a Kipling short story, was directed by John Huston who, decades after wanting to make the film with Humphrey Bogart and Clark Gable, finally made it in 1975 with Caine and Sean Connery?

24 In 1997 Caine played support in the film *Blood and Wine*, as an ex-con. Who played the lead role in that film?

25 Michael Caine has long been known as a trivia fan. What phrase of his became popular as a result?

1 Who directed Peter Sellers in *Dr Strangelove*?

2 ... and which three roles did Sellers play in the film?

3 Who is his co-star in *The Millionairess*?

4 What is the 'Pink Panther'?

5 In which film does Swedish actress Mai Zetterling star with Sellers?

6 In which spoof thriller did Sellers star as one of a number of great sleuths who were invited by a criminal mastermind to spend the weekend together in a house and solve a murder that would take place at midnight?

7 Which 1979 film earned Sellers an Oscar nomination?

8 What is the title of the second *Pink Panther* movie?

9 For which film did he win a BAFTA in 1960?

10 Which actress became Sellers's second wife on 19 February 1964?

11 In *Dr Strangelove*, what was the fourth role originally earmarked for Sellers to play?

12 With which actress does he star in *There's a Girl in My Soup*?

13 Which classic black comedy paired Sellers with Alec Guinness as two members of a gang of bank robbers intent on a murderous mission?

14 On which of his comic heroes did Sellers base the character of Chance the gardener in *Being There*?

15 Who plays Clouseau's long-suffering boss Inspector Dreyfus in the *Pink Panther* films?

16 What was the last film completed by Sellers?

17 In which film does he play a character called Clare Quilty?

18 Who beat Sellers to the Oscar for best actor in 1964, the year in which he was nominated for *Dr Strangelove*?

19 As played by Burt Kwouk, what is the name of Clouseau's manservant in *the Pink Panther* movies?

20 In which film does Sellers appear as an Indian called Hrundi Bakshi?

21 What was the name of the hit song from *The Millionairess*?

22 In which Sellers film does Ringo Starr appear?

23 Which character is portrayed by Sellers in the 1972 film *Alice's Adventures in Wonderland*?

24 In which 1959 film does he play three roles: a prime minister, a field marshal and the Grand Duchess Gloriana?

25 After whose withdrawal did Sellers originally get the part of Inspector Clouseau in *The Pink Panther*?

1 Which 'hall of arts and sciences' was built with the profits from the Great Exhibition of 1851?

2 Which famous central London landmarks did Sir Edwin Landseer design?

3 Which 19th-century engineer designed Paddington Station?

4 What did Sir Giles Gilbert Scott rebuild after it had been devastated by bombs in the Second World War?

5 The author of *The Castle of Otranto* had a suitably Gothic house at Strawberry Hill. Who was he?

6 Who founded the London Library?

7 What is the origin of the name 'London'?

8 Who built the Tower of London?

9 What is believed to be the derivation of the name Soho?

10 Which animal was the cause of the Great Plague of 1665?

11 Who heard London Calling in 1979?

12 Where did the Queen Mother live?

13 What did Baedeker describe as 'the first hotel in London' in 1860?

14 In which street did the Great Fire of London begin?

15 London's first playhouse was build in East London by James Burbage in 1576. What was it called?

16 The Italian croquet-like game *pallo a maglio* gave its name to which central London area?

17 Which wobbly London landmark was designed by Sir Norman Foster?

18 Who was the first poet to be buried at Poet's Corner in Westminster Abbey?

19 The author Henry Fielding established six volunteer 'thief-takers' that became the prototype for the British police force. By what name were they known?

20 To which reformer is Eros in Piccadilly a tribute?

21 Where was the first permanent London gallows set up?

22 Which playwright was both a shareholder and a player at the Globe Theatre?

23 In which London cemetery are Michael Faraday, Christina Rossetti and Karl Marx buried?

24 Who founded the Metropolitan Police?

25 What historical fact distinguishes Hammersmith Bridge in west London?

1 What is the largest urban park in the world?

2 Which famous rocker released the album *Greetings from Asbury Park N.J.*?

3 Which famous architect lived for a while in Barcelona's Parc Güell?

4 Which park features the 'Strawberry Fields' of Beatles fame?

5 Who wrote the novel *Gorky Park*?

6 What is the name of the only real park in Florence, Italy?

7 Which park in Rome is situated in the palace garden of its most notorious family?

8 In which European city are the Tivoli Gardens?

9 Which park in New York houses the Lefferts Homestead, one of the city's oldest buildings?

10 Which park features El Angel Caido, the world's only public statue to Lucifer?

11 Which park in Spain houses the Joan Miró Foundation?

12 In which national park is the lowest point in the Western hemisphere?

13 What is the world's largest marine park?

14 For whom was 'Itchycoo Park' a big hit in 1967?

15 Which group had a big hit with 'Parklife'?

16 Who designed Central Park?

17 How many flamingos live in Lake Nakuru National Park, Kenya?

18 In which country is Serengeti National Park?

19 Until the 1930s, which was the only national park in the United States east of the Mississippi?

20 The construction of which dam almost destroyed Yosemite National Park?

21 Which was the first designated national park in the United States?

22 Who founded the national parks movement in India?

23 Which national park contains the highest peak in Spanish territory?

24 What is the largest enclosed public park in Europe?

25 Which park in Berlin houses both the Zoo and a memorial to Rosa Luxemburg?

1 Which Patti Smith album featured a cover shot by controversial photographer Robert Mapplethorpe?

2 Born James Osterburg, who is called the 'Godfather of Punk'?

3 According to the title of their 1979 hit, where did The Leyton Buzzards spend Saturday Night?

4 With which band was David Johansen lead singer?

5 By what name did Marion Elliott become famous, fronting the band X-Ray Spex?

6 Which legendary New York punk club saw appearances by the Ramones, Television and Blondie, among others?

7 Who did Sid Vicious replace in the Sex Pistols?

8 Which ex-member of Television fronted the Voidoids?

9 What is Johnny Rotten's real name?

10 Who had a hit in 1977 with 'Roadrunner'?

11 Whose 1979 debut album was called *Inflammable Material*?

12 Who did the Stilettoes go on to become?

13 Which American band comprised Jeffrey Hyman, John Cummings, Douglas Colvin and Tommy Erdelyi, although all were known professionally by the same surname?

14 Which member of The Velvet Underground produced Patti Smith's debut album, *Horses*?

15 By what archetypal punk name was drummer Chris Miller known?

16 Which famous fashion designer was co-owner of Malcolm McLaren's Sex clothes shop in London's Kings Road?

17 On which label was the Sex Pistols' first single, 'Anarchy in the UK'?

18 With which mod revival band did Style Council's Mick Talbot play keyboards?

19 By what name is John Graham Mellor, born in Ankara, Turkey in 1952, better known?

20 Which member of the Buzzcocks went on to form the band Magazine?

21 Who sang with the Attractions?

22 Which product was advertised using The Clash's 'Should I Stay Or Should I Go', making the record a UK number one hit in 1991?

23 Which American band had their biggest UK success with a spiky version of The Rolling Stones' 'Satisfaction'?

24 Whose albums included *Plastic Letters* and *Parallel Lines*?

25 Which band featured ex-New York Dolls guitarist Johnny Thunders?

1 Name the record company formed by Berry Gordy.

2 On which label did Elvis Presley launch his career?

3 Who was the star behind Rocket Records?

4 Barry Manilow's 'Mandy' was the first hit for which label?

5 Name one of the three record labels the Sex Pistols were on.

6 Neil Young was once the only artist on Reprise. True or false?

7 Name the UK label associated with a dog named Nipper.

8 Of which record label was Ahmet Ertegun the co-founder?

9 Name the production genius behind Philles Records.

10 Blue Note Records began in a) 1938, b) 1948, or c) 1958?

11 Which label shares its name with a famous Hollywood tower?

12 Mary Hopkins's 'Those Were the Days' and The Beatles' 'Hey Jude' were early hits for which label?

13 Name the label owned by Madonna.

14 Brother Records was formed by which group?

15 Elvis Costello's 'Watching the Detectives' was the first hit for which label?

16 Who founded Reprise records?

17 Name the company originally started (and later sold) by Richard Branson.

18 Which label is associated with a palm-tree logo?

19 All of Connie Francis's hit singles appeared on one label. Which one?

20 What do the initials RCA stand for?

21 Chuck Berry, Bo Diddley, Howlin' Wolf. Name the label that linked them.

22 Which label turned down The Beatles but signed the Rolling Stones?

23 Frank Zappa launched two labels of his own. Name one.

24 Name the label that links Joy Division, Durutti Column, OMD, A Certain Ratio, New Order and Happy Mondays.

25 On which label did Oasis rise to fame?

25

1 Where was the first successful steam engine installed?

2 When was the first transcontinental railroad in North America completed?

3 Which is the longest railway line in the world?

4 Which steam locomotive won the prize for providing the first regular passenger service?

5 Which was the first international airline to launch a service?

6 Which nationality was the man who built the first bicycle propelled by pedals?

7 Where did Wilbur Wright demonstrate flight in public for the first time in August 1908?

8 And where did his brother, Orville, repeat the experiment a few days later?

9 Who designed the VW Beetle?

10 Who designed the Mini and the Morris Minor?

11 What type of fuel is usually used in jet aircraft engines?

12 Who invented the hovercraft?

13 What road safety device was invented by Percy Shaw in 1943?

14 What was the name of Alexander the Great's famous horse?

15 What large animals did Hannibal bring with him across the Alps?

16 Who built the first tunnel under the River Thames?

17 In 19th-century Britain, who was 'The Railway King'?

18 What was the name of the first ship to sail around the world?

19 What was Don Quixote's faithful horse called?

20 Whose report led to a much reduced British national rail system in the 1960s?

21 Whose son flew too close to the sun on waxen wings?

22 In which city is the oldest metro system in the world?

23 What is the world's longest man-made waterway?

24 Which road runs from Alaska to Chile?

25 Which two towns were linked by the world's first commercial railway?

1 In 1789, what was the approximate population of France?

2 Who is the French Revolution's most famous painter?

3 How many prisoners were there in the Bastille when it was pulled down?

4 What was the motto of the French Revolution?

5 Which execution device was invented to kill aristocrats during the French Revolution?

6 What did Marie Antoinette famously say of the poor citizens of France, on being told that they had no bread?

7 Why did the women of Paris march to Versailles on 5 October 1789?

8 Which famous Dickens novel is set during the French Revolution?

9 Which English hero, created by Baroness Orczy, famously risked his life to save French aristocrats?

10 Who were the sans-culottes?

11 What was the name of the dung-cart in which victims of the Revolution were carted to the guillotine?

12 Who was Robespierre's great rival?

13 Who was guillotined on 21 January 1793?

14 A revolutionary calendar was invented during the Revolution. How many days did each week have?

15 How was France administratively reorganized as a result of the Revolution?

16 How were weights and distances modified as a result of the Revolution?

17 Which prestigious decoration was created towards the end of the Revolutionary period?

18 Which general put an end to the French Revolution?

19 What was the Sainte Alliance?

20 Which popular revolutionary song became the national anthem?

21 With which war did Revolutionary France get involved, by which it was financially crippled?

22 Where was the first National Assembly formed?

23 Where was Marie Antoinette imprisoned before her execution?

24 What was the name of the public prosecutor at the Revolutionary Tribunal?

25 Where was the guillotine that killed Marie Antoinette, Louis XVI and Robespierre situated?

1 Where did Roger Bannister run the first sub-four-minute mile in 1954?

2 How long did his time of 3m 59.4sec stand as a world record?

3 Which future women's 10,000 metre record holder represented the USA at the age of fourteen?

4 Who was the first man to jump eight feet in the high jump?

5 Which American discus thrower won four consecutive Olympic titles in addition to being a four-time world record holder?

6 Jesse Owens set the record for the long jump in 1935 with 8.13m. Who bettered this in 1960?

7 Florence Griffith-Joyner broke the 200 metres world record in the semifinals at the Seoul Olympics on 29 September 1988. What happened under two hours later?

8 Which three British athletes broke the mile and 1,500 metres records a total of eleven times between 1979 and 1985?

9 After dominating the 400 metres for so long, who finally broke Harry 'Butch' Reynolds' 1988 world record in 1999?

10 In which event did Christos Papanikolau become the first Greek to set an athletics world record in 1970?

11 In the final at which world championships did Sally Gunnell break the 400 metres hurdles world record?

12 Moses Kiptanui of Kenya broke the 3,000 metres steeplechase world record twice in Zurich, in 1992 and 1995. Why was the second occasion remarkable?

13 Jumping 18 m for the first time, who broke the men's triple jump world record twice in the same competition in 1995?

14 Which Polish woman was the first to break the 50-second barrier for the 400 metres in 1974?

15 Why was German Klaus Tafelmeier's 1986 javelin world record nineteen metres shorter than the previous record throw?

16 Whose outlawed time of 9.79 seconds for the 100 metres did American Maurice Greene equal when he set the world record in Athens in 1999?

17 What nationality was Chi Cheng, who set world records for women's 100 metres, 200 metres and 100 metres hurdles in 1970?

18 At which Olympics did Daley Thompson set his fourth and final world record in the decathlon?

19 Which city's marathon was won by Norwegian Greta Weitz nine times in total?

20 Which Finnish runner held the 5,000 and 10,000 metres world records and won both in the 1972 and 1976 Olympic games?

21 Kenyan-born Wilson Kipketer finally beat Sebastian Coe's 1981 time for the 800 metres in 1997. Which country does he now represent?

22 Which Ukrainian athlete has held and improved the pole vault world record since 1984?

23 Which heptathlete won two Olympic and two world titles in addition to breaking the world record four times between 1986 and 1988?

24 How many times did Romanian Iolanda Balas break the women's high jump world record between 1956 and 1961?

25 Which 400-metre hurdler, a four-time world record holder, won 122 consecutive races between 1977 and 1987?

1 Who said, 'They think it's all over.'?

2 Who said, 'Where are the Germans and frankly who cares?'?

3 Which sport does Clive Everton commentate on?

4 Who is Sid Wadell?

5 Who, known as the voice of rugby, retired in 2002?

6 Who commentates on rugby and hockey?

7 Which Irishman is Radio Five's football commentator?

8 Who moved from Five Live to BBC Television's *On Side*?

9 Who is famous for his sheepskin coat?

10 Who was the voice of ITV football?

11 Which former athlete presented *A Question of Sport* until he was replaced by Sue Barker?

12 Who is currently ITV's main football commentator?

13 Who went from commentator to religious guru?

14 Which athletics voice passed away in the 1990s?

15 Which Geordie ex-world-champion runner now works for BBC Sport?

16 Which Olympic 400 metre silver medallist commentates for the BBC?

17 Which country's commentator made the famous comment 'We gave you one hell of a beating'?

18 Who commentated on the boat race for over 40 years?

19 Which former Aussie leg spinner is the voice of cricket?

20 Who was the voice of *Test Match Special*?

21 Who took over *TMS*?

22 Which cricket broadcaster is famous for his observations of passing traffic?

23 Which cricket commentator's son is a professional cricketer?

24 Where did Brian Johnston live?

25 Who notoriously gets it wrong in Formula one?

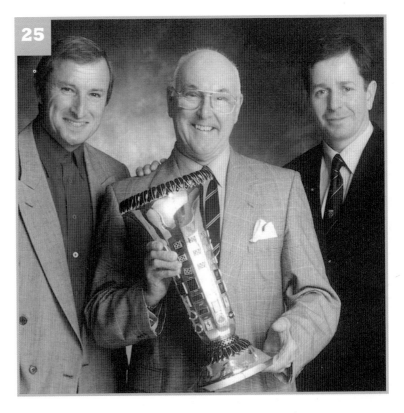

1 With which other artist did Van Gogh live from October until his breakdown in December 1888?

2 Which restaurant in Notting Hill Gate features models of DNA by Damien Hirst?

3 Which leading pointillist used his technique to paint women haymaking?

4 Which artist, philosopher and poet worked on a new method of printing in order to illustrate his *Songs of Innocence*?

5 Which French artist is best known for repeatedly painting his wife in a bath tub?

6 Which Dutch painter's real name was Jerome van Aken?

7 Which French artist was exhibited at the Louvre in 1961 – the first time a living artist had ever received such an accolade?

8 Which German painter was Burgomeister of Wittenberg and specialized in both erotic nudes and biblical woodcuts?

9 Which Swiss sculptor's elongated models of people allegedly stemmed from problems with his eyesight?

10 The culmination of whose career was *Las Meninas* (1656), which now hangs in the Prado?

11 Which famous couple's personal collection did much to bring the work of Cézanne, Renoir and Matisse into the public eye?

12 Which city's National Palace is decorated with a series of historic murals by Diego Rivera?

13 Which famous artist was married to Diego Rivera?

14 Which great German engraver and painter decorated the altar at his home town of Nuremberg?

15 Which Italian artist of the 17th century is best known for his homoerotic still lifes?

16 Which revolutionary surrealist short was Salvador Dalí's first film?

17 What did Michelangelo paint on the ceiling of the Sistine Chapel?

18 Where is the Musée Picasso?

19 Whose *Bigger Splash* takes place in a swimming pool in California?

20 Whose progress did William Hogarth chart in eight etchings in 1735?

21 Which 18th-century Italian artist declined an offer to decorate the Royal Palace in Stockholm because the fee was too small?

22 His wife was Saskia, his son Titus and his most famous painting *The Night Watch*. Who is he?

23 Which famous statue was found on the island of Melos and signed by Andros of Antioch?

24 Which famous erotic work by Fragonard is exhibited in the Wallace Collection, London?

25 Where did Joseph Wright's *Experiment on a Bird* take place?

1 Dickens's first published work was *Sketches by* —?

2 Who said, 'Please, sir, I want some more'?

3 To whose manor house is Pip sent in *Great Expectations*?

4 To which prison was Dickens's father sent with his family?

5 What did Dickens do while the rest of his family were in prison?

6 In *A Christmas Carol*, who says 'Bah, humbug!'?

7 Which novel begins with 'Fog everywhere'?

8 Whose film version of *Oliver Twist* starred Alec Guinness as Fagin?

9 Chapters of which novel were the first to appear in print?

10 In which novel does John Harmon feign death?

11 Who states that 'Father is rather vulgar, my dear. The word Papa, besides, gives a pretty form to the lips'?

12 Which of Dickens's novels is dedicated to 'Miss Burdett Coutts'?

13 Which tragic heroine dies in *The Old Curiosity Shop*?

14 Which novel is subtitled 'A tale of the riots of 'Eighty'?

15 Whose annual income of twenty pounds and annual expenditure of nineteen pounds nineteen and six results in happiness?

16 'It was the best of times, it was the worst of times.' When were the times?

17 Whose interminable law case is finally resolved at the end of *Bleak House*?

18 Who loved Estella?

19 Which was Dickens's last, uncompleted novel?

20 In which novel is it stated that 'He had one eye and the popular prejudice runs in favour of two'?

21 On which newspaper did Dickens first get a full-time job as a journalist?

22 Of whom is it said, 'he'd make a lovely corpse'?

23 In which magazine was *Oliver Twist* serialized?

24 At whose Academy, at the delightful village of Dotheboys, are there 'no extras, no vacations and diet unparalleled'?

25 Where is Dickens buried?

1 What is the origin of the word 'biscuit'?

2 The Greek words for 'beautiful', 'appearance' and 'I behold' converge to give us which word?

3 What was the name of the Swiss physician who induced a trance-like state in his patients, a condition which now bears his name?

4 Which word, a mixture of Norse and Anglo-Saxon, means son of, or belonging to, a creek or inlet?

5 Which pasta dish has a name that means 'little worms'?

6 The Arabic expression 'shah mat' signifies 'the king is dead'. How do we know this expression in relation to a popular game?

7 Which term is used to describe words such as 'chit-chat', 'helter-skelter' and 'tittle-tattle'?

8 Which word originated at Eton boys' school, as a result of the shortness of the school jackets?

9 Which word, meaning guilty, has passed out of common usage, although its opposite is still in everyday use?

10 Which type of hat takes its name from the Prussian town in which it was originally made?

11 Which mode of transport gets its name from the old Dutch 'jachtim', meaning to speed or to hunt?

12 Which drink gets its name from Jerez in Spain?

13 Where does the word 'ginormous' come from?

14 The name of which political party translates as 'we ourselves'?

15 Which type of transport got its name during the Second World War because it was used as a general purpose vehicle?

16 To which writer does the word 'Shavian' apply?

17 Which word, describing unintelligible talk, is derived from the sound made by a turkey?

18 Which musical instrument got its name from the Latin for 'soft' and 'loud'?

19 Which record label got its name because it was based in Detroit, an important centre of the automobile industry?

20 The Romans paid their soldiers *salarium*, or 'salt money'. Which word do we get from this?

21 What is the meaning of the word 'rabbi'?

22 Which expression, meaning to be in financial straits, comes from the practice of tradesmen marking 'query' against the name of a customer who couldn't pay?

23 Which adjective do we get from the Latin 'punctum', meaning 'point'?

24 Which ancient country was named from the Greek 'mesos' and 'potamos' because it lay between two rivers?

25 What contraction of the word 'grandfather' is used as a slang term to describe someone in charge?

1 With which scandalous tale of student life did Martin Amis launch his career?

2 Why was *Afrique sur Seine* a significant debut?

3 Why was John Rice and May Irwin's cinema debut significant?

4 Which member of the British Royal Family made his screen debut opposite John Cleese in *Grimes Goes Green*?

5 Who made her screen debut in Charlie Chaplin's *Limelight* in 1952?

6 Whose first novel was a pseudonymous parody called *An Apology for the Life of Mrs Shamela Andrews*?

7 Tony Richardson gave his two daughters, Natasha and Joely, their screen debuts in the same film. Which one?

8 Whose first play appeared in a double bill with T S Eliot's *Sweeney Agonistes*?

9 Which film marked the cinema debut for a cast of Laplanders?

10 In 1959, who gained international recognition for his first novel, the 'autobiography' of Oskar Matzerath?

11 In 1944, what was unusual about a film called *Days of Glory*?

12 Whose subsequently disowned first novel was *The Man Within* (1925)?

13 Which English actor, born in 1904, made his screen debut in *Who is the Man?*?

14 In which film did Vivien Leigh make her screen debut?

15 Who celebrated the completion of his debut novel, *Swami and Friends*, by treating his friends to a coffee at the Hundred Feet Road restaurant in Mysore, India?

16 Which Dame made her stage debut as Ophelia opposite John Neville's Hamlet at the Old Vic in 1957?

17 Who made his screen debut in *Porky's Hare Hunt* in 1938?

18 What was the name of Mickey Mouse's debut outing?

19 Who first appeared on the stage in 1885 under the name Bella Delmere?

20 In which film did Lawrence Fishburne make his screen debut?

21 Whose debut novel was set in San Francisco and written entirely in verse?

22 Which was James Joyce's first collection of short stories, published in 1914?

23 Whose first play starred John Gielgud as the retiring headmaster of a minor public school?

24 Whose first (and only) novel was *Le Grand Meaulnes*?

25 Whose directorial debut was *Lock, Stock and Two Smoking Barrels*?

ANSWERS TO QUIZ 4

Politicians
1 Georges Pompidou
2 Fidel Castro
3 Konstantin Chernenko
4 Enoch Powell
5 Senator George Mitchell
6 Paul Keating
7 Neville Chamberlain
8 Ariel Sharon
9 John Bruton
10 Ho Chi Minh
11 Mo Mowlam
12 Nikita Krushchev
13 1990
14 Ramsay MacDonald
15 He was shot during a military parade
16 Willy Brandt
17 Joseph Stalin
18 Walter Mondale
19 William Pitt the Younger
20 François Mitterrand
21 Social Democrat and Labour Party
22 Harold Macmillan
23 Anwar Sadat and Menachem Begin
24 John Stonehouse
25 Anthony Eden

Famous Europeans
1 Sergio Garcia
2 Helmut Kohl
3 François Mitterrand
4 Berlusconi
5 Jean-Marie Le Pen
6 Didier Deschamps
7 Cervantes
8 ETA
9 Napoleon
10 Roberto Benigni
11 Luc Besson
12 Gérard Depardieu
13 Sophia Loren
14 *Das Boot*
15 Jürgen Klinsmann
16 Sergei Eisenstein
17 Serge Diaghilev
18 Martin Luther
19 Aimée Jacquet
20 Peter the Great
21 Edith Cresson
22 Juan Carlos
23 Puccini
24 Camus
25 Benjamin Disraeli

Michael Caine
1 Maurice Micklewhite
2 *Without a Clue*
3 *The Wrong Arm of the Law*
4 Christopher Reeve
5 *The Ipcress File*
6 *Hannah and her Sisters*
7 Terence Stamp
8 He was executive producer
9 After his favourite movie, *The Caine Mutiny*
10 1983
11 *The Cider House Rules*
12 Steve Martin
13 Maggie Smith
14 Shelley Winters
15 He was knighted
16 *Little Voice*
17 Bob Hoskins
18 *Dressed to Kill*
19 *Get Carter*
20 *Zulu*
21 Lawrence Olivier
22 Ken Russell
23 *The Man Who Would be King*
24 Jack Nicholson
25 'Not a lot of people know that'

Peter Sellers
1 Stanley Kubrick
2 The US president, Dr Strangelove and Group Captain Mandrake, an RAF officer
3 Sophia Loren
4 A diamond
5 *Only Two Can Play*
6 *Murder By Death*
7 *Being There*
8 *A Shot in the Dark*
9 *I'm All Right, Jack*
10 Britt Ekland
11 Major Kong, the bomber pilot
12 Goldie Hawn
13 *The Ladykillers*
14 Stan Laurel
15 Herbert Lom
16 *The Fiendish Plot of Dr Fu Manchu*
17 *Lolita*
18 Rex Harrison in *My Fair Lady*
19 Cato
20 *The Party*
21 'Goodness Gracious Me'
22 *The Magic Christian*
23 The March Hare
24 *The Mouse That Roared*
25 Peter Ustinov

London
1 The Royal Albert Hall
2 The lions in Trafalgar Square
3 Isambard Kingdom Brunel
4 The Houses of Parliament/House of Commons
5 Horace Walpole
6 Thomas Carlyle who, one day in 1841, waited two hours for a book at the British Library
7 'Lyn Dun': the fortified town on the lake
8 William the Conqueror in 1066
9 'So-ho!', a hunting cry
10 The Norwegian brown rat
11 The Clash
12 Clarence House
13 Claridge's
14 Pudding Lane
15 The Theatre
16 Pall Mall
17 The Millennium Bridge
18 Geoffrey Chaucer
19 The Bow Street Runners
20 The 7th Earl of Shaftesbury
21 At Tyburn, now Marble Arch, in 1571
22 William Shakespeare
23 Highgate cemetery
24 Sir Robert Peel
25 It was London's first suspension bridge

Parks
1 The Maidan in Calcutta, India
2 Bruce Springsteen
3 Antonio Gaudí
4 Central Park, New York
5 Martin Cruz Smith
6 The Boboli Gardens
7 The Villa Borghese
8 Copenhagen
9 Prospect Park
10 Madrid's Retiro Gardens
11 The Montjuic
12 Death Valley
13 The Great Barrier Reef National Park
14 Small Faces
15 Blur
16 Olmstead and Vaux
17 Two million
18 Tanzania
19 Acadia National Park, Maine
20 The Hetch Hetchy Dam
21 Yellowstone
22 Jim Corbett, after whom the first national park, Corbett, was named
23 Mount Teide National Park, Tenerife
24 The Phoenix Park, Dublin
25 The Tiergarten

Punk Rock
1 *Horses*
2 Iggy Pop
3 Beneath The Plastic Palm Trees
4 The New York Dolls
5 Poly Styrene
6 CBGBs
7 Glen Matlock
8 Richard Hell
9 John Lydon
10 Jonathan Richman and the Modern Lovers
11 Stiff Little Fingers
12 Blondie
13 The Ramones
14 John Cale
15 Rat Scabies
16 Vivienne Westwood
17 EMI
18 The Stranglers
19 Joe Strummer
20 Howard Devoto
21 Elvis Costello
22 Levi's
23 Devo
24 Blondie
25 The Heartbreakers

Record Labels
1 Motown
2 Sun
3 Elton John
4 Arista
5 A&M, EMI, Virgin
6 True
7 HMV
8 Atlantic Records
9 Phil Spector
10 a) 1938
11 Capitol
12 Apple Records
13 Maverick
14 The Beach Boys
15 Stiff
16 Frank Sinatra
17 Virgin
18 Island
19 MGM
20 Radio Corporation of America
21 Chess
22 Decca
23 Straight or Bizarre
24 Factory
25 Creation

Transport
1 Dudley, East Midlands, 1712
2 1869
3 Trans-Siberian Railway
4 The *Rocket*
5 KLM (started a London to Amsterdam service in 1920)
6 Scottish (Kirkpatrick Macmillan, in 1840)
7 Northern France
8 Fort Meyer, Virginia

9 Ferdinand Porsche
10 Sir Alexander Issigonis
11 Paraffin
12 Sir Christopher Cockerell
13 Cat's eye reflector lights in the road
14 Bucephalus
15 Elephants
16 Sir Marc Isambard Brunel (father of Isambard Kingdom Brunel)
17 The financier George Hudson, who controlled more than 1,000 miles of railway
18 The *Victoria*, Magellan's ship
19 Rozinante
20 Dr Beeching
21 Daedalus's
22 London
23 The Grand Canal in China stretches 1,000 miles from Beijing to Hang-Chou
24 The Pan-American Highway
25 Stockton and Darlington

French Revolution

1 26 million
2 David
3 Seven
4 'Liberty, Equality, Fraternity'
5 The guillotine
6 'Let them eat cake'
7 To drag the king and queen back to Paris
8 *A Tale of Two Cities*
9 The Scarlet Pimpernel
10 Literally, the 'without-breeches'. They were ordinary people who refused to wear traditional clothes and, instead, wore trousers
11 The tumbrel
12 Danton
13 Louis XVI
14 Ten
15 The 83 départements were created
16 The metric system was invented
17 The Légion d'Honneur
18 Napoleon Bonaparte
19 An alliance of other European governments trying to fight the ideas of Revolutionary France
20 'La Marseillaise'
21 The War of American Independence
22 The Palace of Versailles
23 The Conciergerie
24 Fouquier-Tinville
25 Place de la Concorde, Paris

Athletics Records

1 Oxford
2 46 days
3 Mary Decker
4 Javier Sotomayor, Cuba
5 Al Oerter
6 Ralph Boston, USA
7 She broke it again
8 Sebastian Coe, Steve Ovett and Steve Cram
9 Michael Johnson, USA
10 Pole vault (he was also first over 18 feet)
11 Stuttgart, 1983
12 He broke the eight-minute barrier
13 Jonathan Edwards, GB
14 Irena Szewinska
15 The specification of the javelin was altered
16 Canadian Ben Johnson's
17 Taiwanese
18 Los Angeles, 1984
19 New York
20 Lasse Viren
21 Denmark
22 Sergey Bubka
23 Jackie Joyner-Kersee, USA
24 Fourteen
25 Soweto

Commentators

1 Kenneth Wolstenholme
2 Barry Davies
3 Snooker
4 Darts commentator
5 Bill McLaren
6 Nigel Starmer-Smith
7 Alan Green
8 John Inverdale
9 John Motson
10 Brian Moore
11 David Coleman
12 Clive Tyldesley
13 David Icke
14 Ron Pickering
15 Steve Cram
16 Roger Black
17 Norway
18 John Snagge
19 Richie Benaud
20 Brian Johnston
21 Jonathan Agnew
22 Henry Blofeld
23 Christopher Martin Jenkins
24 St John's Wood
25 Murray Walker

Artists

1 Gauguin
2 The Pharmacy
3 Camille Pissarro
4 William Blake
5 Pierre Bonnard
6 Hieronymus Bosch
7 Georges Braque
8 Lucas Cranach the Elder
9 Alberto Giacometti
10 Diego Velázquez
11 Leo and Gertrude Stein
12 Mexico City
13 Frida Kahlo
14 Albrecht Dürer
15 Michelangelo da Caravaggio
16 *Un Chien Andalou*
17 *The Last Judgement*
18 Paris
19 David Hockney
20 *A Rake's Progress*
21 Giovanni Tiepolo
22 Rembrandt van Rijn
23 Venus de Milo
24 *The Lady on the Swing*
25 *An Experiment on a Bird in the Air Pump*, 1768

Dickens

1 *Boz*
2 Oliver Twist
3 Miss Havisham's
4 Marshalsea Debtor's Prison
5 Labelled bottles in a factory at Hungerford Market
6 Scrooge
7 *Bleak House*
8 David Lean
9 *Pickwick Papers*
10 *Our Mutual Friend*
11 Mrs General in *Little Dorrit*
12 *Martin Chuzzlewit*
13 Little Nell
14 *Barnaby Rudge*
15 Mr Micawber in *David Copperfield*
16 The French Revolution – opening lines of *A Tale of Two Cities*
17 Jarndyce and Jarndyce
18 Pip in *Great Expectations*
19 *Edwin Drood* (1870)
20 *Nicholas Nickleby*
21 *The Morning Chronicle*
22 Jonas Chuzzlewit
23 *Bentley's Miscellany*
24 Mr Wackford Squeers's Academy, in *Nicholas Nickleby*
25 Westminster Abbey

Words & Names

1 From the French 'bis' (twice) and 'cuit' (cooked)
2 Kaleidoscope (kalos, eidos, scopeo)
3 Franz Mesmer
4 Viking
5 Vermicelli
6 Checkmate
7 Ricochet, or reduplicated words
8 Bumfreezer
9 Nocent
10 Homburg
11 Yacht
12 Sherry
13 A blend of gigantic and enormous
14 Sinn Fein
15 Jeep (GP – general purpose)
16 George Bernard Shaw
17 Gobbledegook
18 Pianoforte
19 Motown
20 Salary
21 My teacher
22 Queer Street
23 Punctual
24 Mesopotamia
25 Gaffer

Debuts

1 *The Rachel Papers*
2 It was the first film to be directed by a black African director – Paulin Vieyra in 1925
3 They were the first professional actors to perform in a film, 1886
4 Prince Charles
5 His daughter, Geraldine
6 Henry Fielding
7 *The Charge of the Light Brigade*
8 W H Auden (*The Dance of Death*, 1935)
9 *The Pathfinder* (Norway, 1987)
10 Günter Grass (*The Tin Drum*)
11 All 19 featured players making their screen debuts
12 Graham Greene
13 Sir John Gielgud
14 *Things Are Looking Up*, in 1934
15 R K Narayan
16 Judi Dench
17 Bugs Bunny
18 *Steamboat Willie* (1928)
19 Marie Lloyd
20 *Cornbread, Earl and Me*
21 Vikram Seth
22 *The Dubliners*
23 Alan Bennett's (*Forty Years On*, 1968)
24 Alain-Fournier (1913)
25 Guy Ritchie

THE ULTIMATE BOOK
OF TRIVIA

QUIZ

1 Who is the narrator of *Moby Dick*?

2 What nationality was James Bond's mother?

3 What was Sidney Carton's profession in *A Tale of Two Cities*?

4 'Scud' East was the eponymous hero's friend in which famous 19th-century novel?

5 Who was the central character in Oscar Wilde's only novel?

6 What were the Christian names of Dr Jekyll and Mr Hyde?

7 Who did Sherlock Holmes call *the* woman?

8 Which surname is common to the central characters of *Kim* and *Gone With the Wind*?

9 What is the Christian name of P G Wodehouse's famous gentleman's gentleman?

10 How are Marco and Giuseppe Palmieri better known?

11 Who created Sam Spade?

12 Who was known as Trusty Scout to his constant companion?

13 How is Jack Dawkins better known in a Dickens novel?

14 Which famous novel features the Starkadder family?

15 In the world of TV soap operas what was the claim to fame of Kristin Shephard?

16 What is the name of the one-legged sea cook in *Treasure Island*?

17 In which famous novel does the character Major Major Major appear?

18 Lara Antipova is a central character in which famous novel and movie?

19 Who created the detective Lew Archer?

20 Vlad V of Wallachia (Vlad the Impaler) was the inspiration for which notorious character?

21 In which children's book would you encounter the Oompa Loompas?

22 Virgil Tibbs was the central character of which famous movie?

23 Who created Brer Rabbit?

24 In which Shakespearean comedy does Malvolio appear?

25 Who was the gypsy girl loved by Quasimodo

1 In the early 1970s, Barry Manilow acted as musical director for which famous comedienne?

2 Who was Jennifer Aniston's godfather?

3 What was the name of the character played by Lucille Ball in *I Love Lucy*?

4 Who played the title role in *I Dream of Jeannie*?

5 Who went on from *The Dick Van Dyke Show* to star in her own show about a Minneapolis girl-about-town?

6 Which spoof sitcom featured Katherine Helmond as Jessica Tate?

7 Who won a Cannes best actress award for *Nil by Mouth*?

8 Who played Mindy in *Mork & Mindy*?

9 Which US comedienne is best known for husbands, facelifts and jewellery?

10 Who played Elaine in *Seinfeld*?

11 Who is Ellen's ex?

12 Who played the barmaid Carla in *Cheers*?

13 Shelley Long left *Cheers* in 1987. What reason was given in the script for her character Diane's departure?

14 Which UK comedienne gave an acclaimed performance as a ballet teacher in *Billy Elliot*?

15 Which US comedienne did Mariel Hemingway share a controversial small-screen kiss with?

16 Which 'Friend' was the sometime screen love interest of Richard Burke, played by Tom Selleck?

17 Which US character counts Paige, 'Coffee' Joe, Adam and Audrey among her friends?

18 Julie Kavner is the voice of Marge in which cartoon series?

19 ... and who played Rhoda herself?

20 In which US comedy does Peri Gilpin star?

21 Which TV series gave Goldie Hawn her first big break?

22 Who announced 'Yep, I'm gay!' on the cover of *Time* magazine in 1997?

23 Which 1980s TV characters were played by Susan Saint James and Jane Curtin?

24 Who wrote *Fawlty Towers* with John Cleese?

25 What nationality is acerbic Lily Tomlin?

1 In which musical would you hear the song 'Edelweiss'?

2 Which musical won the best picture Oscar in 1968?

3 Who wrote the lyrics to the songs in *West Side Story*?

4 For which film was director Bob Fosse awarded an Oscar in 1972?

5 In which musical was there a dance routine set at a barn raising?

6 In which musical did Donald O'Connor perform the breathtaking 'Make 'em Laugh' routine?

7 Which of the Gold Diggers movies contains the song 'We're in the Money'?

8 Where was the setting for *On the Town*?

9 On which Shakespeare play was *Kiss Me Kate* based?

10 Who directed *A Chorus Line*?

11 In which film did Doris Day sing the Oscar-winning song 'Secret Love'?

12 Who played the lead role in the screen adaptation of Dennis Potter's *Pennies from Heaven*?

13 In which film did Fred Astaire and Ginger Rogers first team up?

14 In the song 'Oh, What a Beautiful Mornin'' from *Oklahoma*, how high does the corn grow?

15 Why does Gene Kelly suddenly stop in the 'Singin' in the Rain' routine?

16 Which big-voiced singer is usually associated with the Irving Berlin song 'There's No Business like Show Business'?

17 In which musical does the song 'Old Man River' feature?

18 Who played Anna in the 1956 film *The King and I*?

19 In which musical did Clint Eastwood perform 'I Talk to the Trees'?

20 The soundtrack to which musical topped the UK album charts for 70 consecutive weeks between 1958 and 1960?

21 Which 60s model starred in Ken Russell's film of the musical *The Boyfriend*?

22 Who won an Oscar for his portrayal of Broadway legend George M Cohan in *Yankee Doodle Dandy*?

23 In addition to co-directing *West Side Story* with Robert Wise, what was Jerome Robbins's other contribution to the film?

24 Who starred as Cole Porter in the 1945 film *Night and Day*?

25 What was the title of the 1956 musical remake of *The Philadelphia Story*?

1 Which James Stewart film is based on the story *The Greatest Gift*, by Philip Van Doren?

2 In which 1956 film does he star alongside Doris Day?

3 For which film did Stewart receive his best actor Oscar in 1940?

4 In which film does Stewart play the leader of a chain of boys' clubs known as the Boy Rangers, who, as a junior senator, is exposed to government corruption?

5 In which film does he rescue Kim Novak from beneath the Golden Gate Bridge?

6 Who plays the prosecuting counsel opposite James Stewart in the courtroom scenes in *Anatomy of a Murder*?

7 Which aviator was played by Stewart in *The Spirit of St Louis*?

8 In which Hitchcock film does he co-star with Grace Kelly?

9 In 1955 Stewart made the film *Strategic Air Command*. What rank did he actually attain in the US Air Force Reserve?

10 What is the significance of the name Maitland?

11 What was the first all-colour film made by Alfred Hitchcock in 1948, starring James Stewart?

12 Which band leader is portrayed by Stewart in a 1954 film biography?

13 In *The Cheyenne Social Club*, starring Stewart and Henry Fonda, what kind of establishment has Stewart's character inherited?

14 In 1976 he appeared in *The Shootist*. Who was the star, whose last film it was?

15 In which of the 70s disaster movies does Stewart appear?

16 Which Western character does he play in the 1964 film *Cheyenne Autumn*?

17 Which Western starring James Stewart takes its title from the name of a gun?

18 What type of circus entertainer does Stewart play in the 1952 film *The Greatest Show on Earth*?

19 Who is Harvey, in the 1951 film of that name?

20 In *It's a Wonderful Life*, who plays hard-hearted Mr Potter?

21 In 1951 Stewart starred with Marlene Dietrich in *No Highway in the Sky*. In which 1939 Western did they first appear together?

22 Throughout which film is Stewart confined to a wheelchair?

23 Which earlier Stewart film has a title which differs from *It's a Wonderful Life* by one word?

24 In which 1965 Western does he play a widower with six sons and a daughter?

25 What was James Stewart's favourite among his own films?

1 The two stars to the right of the Plough, in the constellation of Ursa Major, are called the Pointers. To what do they point?

2 Sharing its name with an Arnold Schwarzenegger film, what name is given to the line dividing the light and dark portions of the moon?

3 On which planet are the Herschel and Newton craters?

4 Approximately how long does it take the sun's light to reach Earth?

5 Why is Pluto not in Gustav Holst's music suite *The Planets*?

6 What is the name of the largest moon in the solar system?

7 In which year was Comet Hale-Bopp last visible?

8 In 1995 the star 51 Pegasi was the first star to be confirmed as having what?

9 Which planet was discovered in 1781 by amateur astronomer William Herschel, working at his home in Bath, England?

10 How many years does it take for Neptune to orbit the sun?

11 Who made the discovery that the sun spins?

12 Which constellation has three stars that appear to be in a straight line, and that are referred to as a belt?

13 On which body are the Sea of Waves and the Sea of Vapours?

14 Which is the only star in our solar system?

15 The northern lights are called the *aurora borealis*. What are the southern lights known as?

16 Io is the most volcanically active body in the solar system. Which planet does it orbit?

17 By what nickname is the star Sirius known?

18 What was discovered by Clyde Tombaugh from the Lowell Observatory, Arizona, in 1930?

19 How many moons are there in our solar system: a) 43 b) 53 or c) 63?

20 Which planet spins on a near-horizontal axis, as opposed to vertical or near-vertical?

21 In which constellation are the stars Castor and Pollux?

22 During which event can you witness a phenomenon nicknamed the 'diamond ring'?

23 Why is Neptune sometimes the farthest planet from the sun?

24 Are sunspots the hottest or coolest regions of the sun's surface?

25 Which planet in the solar system is nearest in size to Earth?

1 Which group of islands lies approximately 300 miles southwest of India?

2 Which is the largest of the Balearic Islands?

3 Which Pacific Island, famous for its giant sculptures of heads, is also known as Rapa Nui?

4 Which island lies off the west coast of mainland Canada, just over the border from the United States?

5 Of which large island in the Indian Ocean is Antananarivo the capital?

6 Between which two islands does the Denmark Strait flow?

7 Which island is larger, Trinidad or Tobago?

8 On which of the Hawaiian islands is the capital, Honolulu?

9 Which two countries make up the Caribbean island of Hispaniola?

10 In which ocean are the Micronesia and Melanesia islands?

11 Of which country is Shikoku one of the four main islands?

12 In which lake would you find the Isle Royale National Park?

13 On which island is the volcanic Mount Etna?

14 Lying off England's northeast coast, by what name is Holy Island also known?

15 From which of the United States of America do the Aleutian Islands stretch into the Pacific Ocean?

16 Which island's features include Blue Mountain Peak, Portland Point and Montego Bay?

17 Under which country's administration are the islands of New Caledonia in the Coral Sea?

18 By what name do we know the islands that Spanish-speaking nations call the Islas Malvinas?

19 On which island are the New York boroughs of Brooklyn and Queens?

20 On which of the Channel Islands are cars not permitted?

21 Which Mediterranean island has Iraklion as its capital?

22 Which Indonesian island lies off the east coast of Java?

23 The scene of one of the Pacific battles during the Second World War, in which group of islands is Guadalcanal?

24 In which ocean is Christmas Island?

25 Where in Canada would you find Elk Island and Reindeer Island?

1 What is Madonna's surname?

2 Which instrument did she play in the band the Breakfast Club?

3 When is Madonna's birthday?

4 To which record label did Madonna first sign?

5 What was Madonna's first UK number one single?

6 In which film did Madonna play her first significant role?

7 Which other actress also starred in that film?

8 What is the name of Madonna's second child?

9 Madonna first met Sean Penn in 1985 during the shooting of which single's video?

10 What is Madonna's nickname for her daughter Lourdes Maria?

11 Who directed Madonna in the 1996 film *Evita*?

12 What was the location for Madonna and Sean Penn's wedding in 1985?

13 Which track from the *True Blue* album was used in Sean Penn's film *At Close Range*?

14 Who starred opposite Madonna in the film *Dick Tracy*?

15 Which outrageous fashion designer was responsible for Madonna's pointed brassières?

16 In which film did Madonna and Sean Penn star together?

17 What is the name of Madonna's own record label?

18 Who is Lourdes's father?

19 In which film was Madonna less than complimentary about Kevin Costner?

20 With which company did Madonna sign a $60 million deal in 1992?

21 Who played Che Guevara opposite Madonna in the film *Evita*?

22 From which album was the single 'Papa Don't Preach' taken?

23 What is Madonna's shoe size?

24 Which British comic character appeared in the video for Madonna's single 'Music'?

25 Who produced the singles 'Holiday' and 'Crazy For You'?

1 Who was Pink Floyd's 'Crazy Diamond'?

2 In which year was the Summer of Love?

3 What kind of pillow did Jefferson Airplane promote?

4 Who released an album titled *Forever Changes*?

5 They started out as the Warlocks. By what name did they become world famous?

6 Who designed the 'banana cover' of the Velvet Underground's debut album?

7 Name the legendary fourteen-hour show that was held at London's Alexandra Palace in 1967.

8 Who had an album titled *Incense and Peppermints*?

9 Name the British prime minister linked with a Cream LP.

10 Which Rolling Stones album featured a 3-D cover?

11 Which Californian festival brought Jimi Hendrix fame in the US?

12 Name the group led by violinist David La Flamme.

13 Who led The Crazy World?

14 From which Aldous Huxley book did the Doors take the inspiration for their name?

15 Which Beatles song links tangerine trees and marmalade skies?

16 Which ex-Animal was Jimi Hendrix's manager?

17 Which legendary Beach Boys album was never completed?

18 Name the film that featured a spaced-out George Harrison soundtrack.

19 Which artist produced the Velvet Underground's debut album?

20 How many miles high were The Byrds on their fifth single?

21 Before she joined Jefferson Airplane, for which group did Grace Slick sing?

22 Which Donovan hit was inspired by the rumour that you could get high by smoking dried bananas?

23 By what name is Don Van Vliet better known?

24 Who was the lead singer of Big Brother and the Holding Company?

25 Which Small Faces album originally came in a circular sleeve and, later, in a round tin?

1 What came to an end in the United States in December 1933?

2 Of which country did Robert Menzies become prime minister in April 1939?

3 Which great ocean liner was launched in 1934?

4 Which London building was gutted by fire in November 1936?

5 Which woman flew from England to Australia in 1930?

6 Which novel, published in 1932, was a vision of the future as a sanitised society?

7 To what position was John Masefield appointed in May 1930?

8 In 1939 which pub game was banned in Glasgow for being 'too dangerous'?

9 Which great American inventor died in October 1931?

10 Which Australian cricketer, playing for New South Wales against Queensland, scored a then world record first-class innings of 452 not out?

11 Which two European leaders signed a non-aggression pact on 23 August 1939?

12 What was the name of the vehicle in which Sir Malcolm Campbell broke the 300 mph barrier in 1935?

13 Which vehicle, designed by Ferdinand Porsche, went into mass production in 1936?

14 Which type of vegetable went on sale in frozen form in Massachusetts in June 1930?

15 What was the name of the man who pioneered the above method of freezing food?

16 Which American gangster was shot dead outside a Chicago cinema in July 1934?

17 Which black athlete's successes at the 1936 Berlin Olympics caused Hitler to storm out of the stadium?

18 What was the maiden name of Wallis Simpson, for whom Edward VIII abdicated in 1936?

19 On 1 May 1931 the world's then tallest building was opened in New York City. Which building was it?

20 Which Margaret Mitchell novel, later a successful film, won the 1937 Pulitzer Prize?

21 Which former Labour MP formed the New Party in 1931?

22 Whose radio production of *War of the Worlds* caused panic in America in 1938?

23 Which corporation opened its new headquarters in Portland Place, London, in May 1932?

24 What type of natural disaster hit the American Midwest in 1935?

25 Composer George Gershwin died in 1937 at the age of 38. How did he die?

1 What material was invented by Belgian-born US chemist Leo Baekeland in 1905?

2 In 1905, Albert Einstein wrote that $E = mc^2$. What theory is commonly associated with this equation?

3 In the 1940s George Gamow developed a theory that a giant explosion, 10–20,000 million years ago, began the expansion of the universe. What is the name given to this theory?

4 A common sight in most high streets, what was invented in 1967 by Englishman John Shepherd-Barron?

5 Which metal was invented by British metallurgist Harold Brearley in 1912?

6 What nationality is Erno Rubik, inventor of the 80s craze the Rubik's Cube?

7 In which decade was the Breathalyzer invented?

8 First marketed in 1958 by the Kodak company as 'Eastman 910', by what name is their cyanoacrylate adhesive better known?

9 Which company introduced the first 'instamatic' camera in 1963?

10 Who discovered penicillin in 1928?

11 Which German aircraft company invented the ejector seat in 1942?

12 What did British engineer Christopher Cokerell invent in 1953?

13 In 1967 an American engineer invented a noise reduction system to which he gave his name. What is it called?

14 What fastening device, common on clothing, was invented by George Abraham in 1901?

15 What did Englishman Percy Shaw contribute to road safety in 1934?

16 What familiar roadside item, in which money is placed, was invented in 1935 by American journalist Carlton Magee?

17 In 1953 US surgeon Evarts Graham discovered the link between tobacco tar and what?

18 What nationality was inventor Léon Gaumont, who introduced a type of colour motion picture film in 1912?

19 Who invented the bouncing bomb in the Second World War?

20 In 1955 Dane Ole Christiansen invented a children's construction toy. Still in use today, and with theme parks of its own, what is it called?

21 Which drink machine was produced in 1946 by Italian inventor Achille Gaggia?

22 In which decade did German chemist Albert Hoffman discover Lyserg-Saure-Diathylamid, or lysergic acid diethylamide (LSD)?

23 Which hormone was discovered by Canadian and Scottish physiologists in 1912?

24 In 1901 which Italian inventor developed the first transatlantic telegraphy system?

25 Which water transport aid was invented by Norwegian-born engineer Ole Evinrude in 1906?

1 What are the four Grand Slam events?

2 Which player won her last Grand Slam tournament in Paris in 1999?

3 Who was the first Russian player to win a Grand Slam event when he won the French title in 1996?

4 Which player was stabbed in the back at a tournament in Hamburg in 1993?

5 Although she represents Switzerland, in which country was Martina Hingis born?

6 Which event was won by Miroslav Mecir in 1988, Marc Rosset in 1992, Andre Agassi in 1996 and Yevgeny Kafelnikov in 2000?

7 Between the years 1978 and 1984 which two men dominated the US Open singles title?

8 When Billie-Jean King won the first open Wimbledon in 1968, what was her prize money?

9 Who was the beaten finalist in the Wimbledon men's singles in 1992, 1994 and 1998?

10 What was unusual about the 1986 Australian Open?

11 Which American woman was never beaten at Wimbledon, winning three consecutive titles in the 1950s before retiring after a riding accident?

12 Before Venus Williams won at Wimbledon in 2000, which of the Grand Slam tournaments had her younger sister Serena won?

13 Who won the US Open men's title in 1990 at the age of nineteen?

14 Who won her first Wimbledon title, the women's doubles with Helena Sukova, in 1996 at the age of 15?

15 What is the only score at which a player can serve from the right-hand side of the court to win a game?

16 The new main court for the US Open, opened in 1997, is named in memory of which American player?

17 Which British TV presenter won the women's singles title at the 1976 French Open?

18 Which player topped the women's rankings for a record 377 weeks, including a run of 186 weeks between 1987 and 1991?

19 Between 1974 and 1981, which man won six French titles, five Wimbledons, and was runner-up four times in the US?

20 How often are the balls changed in tennis tournaments?

21 Which woman won the US singles title in 1968, the Australian in 1972, and Wimbledon in 1977?

22 In which year did Greg Rusedski opt to play for Great Britain instead of Canada?

23 Which Dutch player beat Pete Sampras at Wimbledon in 1996?

24 In Grand Slam events, what do these numbers mean: winner 520; runner-up 364; semifinalist 234; quarterfinalist 130?

25 Which Australian woman won all four Grand Slam titles in 1970?

1 Which Australian was the first to score 60 tries in international rugby?

2 Who was the first English player to play in 50 internationals?

3 In which part of London did The Broncos start out?

4 Which colours do Bath play in?

5 Who played the opening match at Wales's Millennium Stadium?

6 Which Welsh Union player was a regular captain on *A Question of Sport*?

7 Which television channel sponsored a floodlit Rugby League trophy?

8 What were Bradford before they were Bulls?

9 Who was Wigan's leading try-scorer in the 1994–5 season?

10 Where would you watch Rhinos play rugby?

11 Which Harlequins hooker was called 'Pitbull'?

12 Where was the 2000 League World Cup held?

13 Who is the current England Union coach?

14 Who was the youngest Englishman to score 30 points in a match?

15 Which international side has the shortest name?

16 Who was the leading try-scorer in the 1995 World Cup?

17 Which Union team are known as the Shoguns?

18 Who was the first non-white Springbok?

19 In which decade was Rugby Union last played in the Olympics?

20 Who played 69 times for England at fly half?

21 In 1980, who led England to their first Grand Slam in 23 years?

22 Where is the annual Varsity match played?

23 Who did Offiah play for in his first years as a League player?

24 Which England player was exposed by the *News of the World* as a drug-taker?

25 Which League team play at Headingley?

1 Which legendary band made its US TV debut on the Ed Sullivan Show?

2 Which US TV presenter starred in *The Color Purple*?

3 Which famous British broadcaster, who died in 1965, has two broadcasting sons called Jonathan and David?

4 Which disc jockey played himself in George Lucas's film *American Graffiti*?

5 Which American newsman broke the news of President Kennedy's death to the nation?

6 Which famous rock 'n' roll disc jockey fell from grace during the Payola scandal of the late 1950s?

7 Which London-born presenter, a familiar face to US and UK television audiences, was once mayor of Cincinnati?

8 Which celebrated broadcaster presents 'Letter from America' on BBC Radio 4 every week?

9 Which presenter/actress has her own production company called Harpo?

10 In which field are Connie Chung and Tom Brockaw known in the US?

11 Which fashion designer once co-hosted *Eurotrash* with Antoine de Caunes?

12 Which American show is hosted by Jay Leno?

13 Which US disc jockey was nicknamed 'The Fifth Beatle'?

14 Which film director appeared in a series in the 50s and 60s in which he introduced tales of suspense?

15 Which American comedian hosts the talk show *Politically Incorrect*?

16 Arnold Schwarzenegger, Michael J Fox and Tom Hanks have all served as presenters on which Sky mystery anthology?

17 Which actress-turned-chat-show-host made her name in the film *Hairspray*?

18 Which US comedy series is based around a talk show and stars Garry Shandling in the title role?

19 Which TV series featured the radio DJs Dr Johnny Fever and Venus Flytrap?

20 What were Rowan and Martin's first names?

21 Which American talk show presenter features top ten lists on his show?

22 Vic Perrin regularly intoned 'There is nothing wrong with your television set' at the start of which 1960s sci-fi series?

23 Which Australian presenter has made travel documentaries in various foreign locations, the programmes being called *A Postcard from ...*?

24 Which controversial radio presenter starred as himself in the film *Private Parts*?

25 Who was the resident DJ on KBHR radio in *Northern Exposure*?

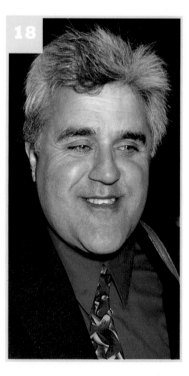
18

1 Which American series of the 1960s starred Richard Chamberlain as the eponymous hero?

2 What was the name of the hospital given the nickname St Elsewhere in the show of the same name?

3 What is the title of the New Zealand soap set in and around a hospital?

4 What branch of medicine did *ER*'s Dr Douglas Ross, aka George Clooney, specialise in?

5 In which American series does actress Christine Lahti don the white coat?

6 Which famous big-screen actor played Dr Philip Chandler in *St Elsewhere*?

7 What do the initials M*A*S*H stand for?

8 Which hospital show featured a pathologist who had a penchant for making love in the morgue?

9 How did Lucy Knight make her exit from *ER*?

10 Which two members of the Ally McBeal team, one in front of camera, one behind, once worked on *Chicago Hope*?

11 Blair General Hospital was the setting for which hospital show?

12 In the final show of which series was the hospital in which it was set revealed to be a model inside a toy snowstorm?

13 Before gaining worldwide fame in *ER*, George Clooney appeared in an 80s hospital comedy with Elliott Gould. What was it called?

14 Between 1961 and 1966 Vince Edwards played the title role in which American series?

15 Which characters in *M*A*S*H* were engaged in an affair?

16 Who directed the 1970 movie *M*A*S*H* that inspired the TV series?

17 Which *ER* actress appeared as Laura Kelly in *NYPD Blue*?

18 What is the name of the character played by Alex Kingston in *ER*?

19 Which hospital show starred Mandy Pantinkin?

20 In which US city was *St Elsewhere* set?

21 What is the name of the chief consultant in *Holby City*, played by George Irving?

22 Which Canadian-born stand-up comedian played Dr Wayne Fiscus in *St Elsewhere*?

23 Which Australian hospital show was set in the outback town of Cooper's Crossing?

24 Which 1960s hospital series opened with the line 'Man, woman, birth, death, infinity'?

25 The final episode of which show was titled 'Goodbye, Farewell and Amen'?

1 Who was the androgyne offspring of Hermes and Aphrodite?

2 Which giant was made to carry the heavens on his shoulders as punishment for having fought against Zeus?

3 In which country's mythology is Yi the divine order?

4 Which huge, ferocious monster of Phoenician mythology is referred to in the Book of Isaiah as the 'crooked serpent'?

5 Who is the Egyptian god of the moon?

6 What name is given to the immense hall for the glorious dead in Norse mythology?

7 By what other names is the god Odin known?

8 Which creature had the head of a bull and the body of a man?

9 By which collective name are Clio, Euterpe, Thalia, Melpomene, Terpsichore, Erato, Polyhymnia, Urania and Calliope known?

10 What is the Roman equivalent of the Greek god Poseidon?

11 Which serpent haunted the caves of Parnassus, whose name lives on in one of the world's largest snakes?

12 To which place was the mortally wounded Arthur ferried by three mysterious women in a black boat?

13 Which band of warriors was responsible for the safety of the High King of Ireland?

14 With Vishnu and Brahma, who is the third god of the Hindu Trimurti?

15 Who is the Egyptian sun god?

16 Who was the half-sister of King Arthur?

17 Who went into Hades to bring back his wife Eurydice?

18 What is the name given to Vishnu's incarnations on earth?

19 Who possessed a hammer called Mjollnir?

20 In which country was Zoroaster, or Zarathustra, a great religious reformer?

21 Who was the only knight of the round table to see the entire Grail?

22 What is the name given to an 'enlightened being' destined to become a buddha?

23 In Chinese mythology, which creature symbolises the male, yang element?

24 Which animal's form does the Egyptian goddess Bastet take?

25 Who sapped Merlin's power and bound him in stone?

ANSWERS TO QUIZ 5

Fictional Characters
1 Ishmael
2 Swiss
3 Barrister
4 *Tom Brown's Schooldays*
5 Dorian Gray
6 Henry (Jekyll), Edward (Hyde)
7 Irene Adler
8 O'Hara (Kimball and Scarlett)
9 Reginald (Jeeves)
10 The Gondoliers
11 Dashiell Hammett
12 The Lone Ranger (Kemo Sabe)
13 The Artful Dodger
14 *Cold Comfort Farm*
15 She shot J R Ewing
16 Long John Silver
17 *Catch-22*
18 *Dr Zhivago*
19 Ross Macdonald
20 Count Dracula
21 *Charlie and the Chocolate Factory*
22 *In the Heat of the Night*
23 Joel Chandler Harris
24 *Twelfth Night*
25 Esmeralda

Comediennes
1 Bette Midler
2 Telly Savalas
3 Lucy Ricardo
4 Barbara Eden
5 Mary Tyler Moore
6 *Soap*
7 Kathy Burke
8 Pam Dawber
9 Joan Rivers
10 Julia-Louis Dreyfuss
11 Anne Heche
12 Rhea Perlman
13 She left to write a novel
14 Julie Walters
15 Roseanne Barr
16 Monica
17 Ellen
18 Julie Kavner, who appeared as Brenda in *Rhoda* and provides the voice of Marge in *The Simpsons*
19 Valerie Harper
20 *Frasier*
21 *Rowan and Martin's Laugh-In*
22 Nathalie Walter
23 Kate and Allie
24 Connie Booth
25 American

Musicals
1 *The Sound of Music*
2 *Oliver!*
3 Stephen Sondheim
4 *Cabaret*
5 *Seven Brides for Seven Brothers*
6 *Singin' in the Rain*
7 *Gold Diggers of 1933*
8 New York
9 *The Taming of the Shrew*
10 Richard Attenborough
11 *Calamity Jane*
12 Steve Martin
13 *Flying Down to Rio*
14 As high as an elephant's eye
15 He notices the policeman
16 Ethel Merman
17 *Showboat*
18 Deborah Kerr
19 *Paint Your Wagon*
20 *South Pacific*
21 Twiggy
22 James Cagney
23 Choreography
24 Cary Grant
25 *High Society*

James Stewart
1 *It's a Wonderful Life*
2 *The Man Who Knew Too Much*
3 *The Philadelphia Story*
4 *Mr Smith Goes to Washington*
5 *Vertigo*
6 George C Scott
7 Charles Lindbergh
8 *Rear Window*
9 Brigadier General
10 It was James Stewart's middle name
11 *Rope*
12 Glenn Miller
13 A brothel
14 John Wayne
15 *Airport '77*
16 Wyatt Earp
17 *Winchester .73*
18 A clown
19 An invisible rabbit
20 Lionel Barrymore
21 *Destry Rides Again*
22 *Rear Window*
23 *It's a Wonderful World*
24 *Shenandoah*
25 *It's a Wonderful Life*

The Night Sky
1 Polaris, the Pole Star

2 The terminator
3 Mars
4 Eight minutes
5 The piece was written before Pluto's discovery
6 Ganymede
7 1997
8 An orbiting planet
9 Uranus
10 165
11 Galileo
12 Orion
13 On the moon
14 The sun
15 *Aurora australis*
16 Jupiter
17 The Dog Star
18 Pluto
19 c) 63
20 Uranus
21 Gemini
22 A solar eclipse
23 Because Pluto's orbit is elliptical, so it sometimes cuts inside the orbital path of Neptune
24 Coolest
25 Venus

Islands
1 The Maldives
2 Majorca
3 Easter Island
4 Vancouver Island
5 Madagascar
6 Greenland and Iceland
7 Trinidad
8 Oahu
9 Haiti and the Dominican Republic
10 Pacific
11 Japan
12 Lake Superior
13 Sicily
14 Lindisfarne
15 Alaska
16 Jamaica
17 France
18 The Falkland Islands
19 Long Island
20 Sark
21 Crete
22 Bali
23 The Solomon Islands
24 Indian
25 Lake Winnipeg

Madonna
1 Ciccone
2 Drums
3 16 August

4 Sire
5 'Into the Groove'
6 *Desperately Seeking Susan*
7 Roseanna Arquette
8 Rocco
9 'Material Girl'
10 Lola
11 Alan Parker
12 A cliffside in Malibu
13 'Live to Tell'
14 Warren Beatty
15 Jean-Paul Gaultier
16 *Shanghai Surprise*
17 Maverick
18 Carlos Leon
19 *In Bed with Madonna*
20 Time Warner
21 Antonio Banderas
22 *True Blue*
23 Five
24 Ali G
25 John 'Jellybean' Benitez

Psychedelia
1 Syd Barrett
2 1967
3 Surrealistic
4 Love
5 The Grateful Dead
6 Andy Warhol
7 'The 14-Hour Technicolour Dream'
8 Strawberry Alarm Clock
9 Disraeli (*Disraeli's Gears*)
10 *Their Satanic Majesties Request*
11 Monterey
12 It's a Beautiful Day
13 Arthur Brown
14 *The Doors of Perception*
15 'Lucy in the Sky with Diamonds'
16 Chas Chandler
17 *Smile*
18 *Wonderwall*
19 Andy Warhol
20 Eight
21 The Great Society
22 'Mellow Yellow'
23 Captain Beefheart
24 Janis Joplin
25 *Ogden's Nut Gone Flake*

The 1930s
1 Prohibition
2 Australia
3 The *Queen Mary*
4 The Crystal Palace
5 Amy Johnson
6 *Brave New World*
7 Poet Laureate

8 Darts
9 Thomas Edison
10 Donald Bradman
11 Hitler and Stalin
12 *Bluebird*
13 The Volkswagen
14 Peas
15 Clarence Birdseye
16 John Dillinger
17 Jesse Owens
18 Warfield
19 Empire State Building
20 *Gone With the Wind*
21 Sir Oswald Mosley
22 Orson Welles
23 The BBC
24 Dust storms
25 Brain tumour

Inventions & Discoveries

1 Bakelite
2 The theory of relativity
3 The Big Bang theory
4 The cash dispenser
5 Stainless steel
6 Hungarian
7 1930s
8 Superglue
9 Kodak
10 Alexander Fleming
11 Heinkel
12 The hovercraft
13 Dolby
14 The press-stud
15 He invented cats'-eyes
16 The parking meter
17 Cancer
18 French
19 Barnes Wallis
20 Lego
21 Espresso coffee machine
22 1940s
23 Insulin
24 Guglielmo Marconi
25 The outboard motor

Tennis

1 Australian Open, French Open, Wimbledon, US Open
2 Steffi Graf
3 Yevgeny Kafelnikov
4 Monica Seles
5 Czechoslovakia
6 The men's Olympic singles title
7 Jimmy Connors and John McEnroe
8 £750
9 Goran Ivanisevic
10 There wasn't one – the 1985 championship was the

last one to be held in December, switching to January in 1987
11 Maureen Connolly
12 The US Open, 1999
13 Pete Sampras
14 Martina Hingis
15 40-15
16 Arthur Ashe
17 Sue Barker
18 Steffi Graf
19 Bjorn Borg
20 After the first seven games, then after every nine games
21 Virginia Wade
22 1995
23 Richard Krajicek, 1996
24 Ranking points
25 Margaret Court

Rugby

1 David Campese
2 Rory Underwood
3 Fulham
4 Blue, black and white
5 Wales and Argentina
6 Gareth Edwards
7 BBC2
8 Northern
9 Martin Offiah
10 Leeds
11 Brian Moore
12 England
13 Clive Woodward
14 Johnny Wilkinson
15 Fiji
16 Jonah Lomu
17 Bristol
18 Errol Tobias
19 1920s
20 Rob Andrew
21 Bill Beaumont
22 Twickenham
23 Widnes
24 Laurence Dallaglio
25 Leeds

Presenters

1 The Beatles
2 Oprah Winfrey
3 Richard Dimbleby
4 Wolfman Jack
5 Walter Kronkite
6 Alan Freed
7 Jerry Springer
8 Alistair Cooke
9 Oprah Winfrey
10 TV news
11 Jean-Paul Gaultier
12 *The Tonight Show*
13 Murray the K

14 Alfred Hitchcock
15 Bill Maher
16 *Tales From the Crypt*
17 Ricki Lake
18 *The Larry Sanders Show*
19 *WRKP in Cincinnati*
20 Dan Rowan and Dick Martin
21 David Letterman
22 *The Outer Limits*
23 Clive James
24 Howard Stern
25 Chris Stevens, played by John Corbett

Hospital Shows

1 *Dr Kildare*
2 St Eligius
3 *Shortland Street*
4 Paediatrics
5 *Chicago Hope*
6 Denzel Washington
7 Mobile Army Surgical Hospital
8 *St Elsewhere*
9 She was stabbed to death
10 Writer/producer David E Kelley and actor Peter MacNicol
11 *Dr Kildare*
12 *St Elsewhere*
13 Coincidentally, it was called *E/R*
14 *Ben Casey*
15 Margaret 'Hot Lips' Hoolihan and Frank Burns
16 Robert Altman
17 Sherry Stringfield
18 Dr Elizabeth Corday
19 *Chicago Hope*
20 Boston
21 Anton Meyer
22 Howie Mandel
23 *The Flying Doctors*
24 *Ben Casey*
25 *M*A*S*H*

Mythology

1 Hermaphroditus
2 Atlas
3 China
4 Leviathan
5 Thoth
6 Valhalla
7 Woden or Wotan
8 The Minotaur
9 The Muses
10 Neptune
11 Python
12 Avalon
13 The Fianna or Fenians
14 Shiva

15 Ra
16 Morgan Le Fay
17 Orpheus
18 Avatars
19 Thor
20 Ancient Persia
21 Sir Galahad
22 Bodhisattva
23 The dragon
24 A cat
25 The Lady of the Lake

THE ULTIMATE BOOK OF TRIVIA

QUIZ 6

1 What is the real name of the American rap star Eminem?

2 Who is the youngest man to win the Wimbledon tennis singles title?

3 Who directed the 1946 Oscar-winning film *The Best Years of our Lives*?

4 Which cartoon character has a pet named Dino?

5 Who scored twice for France in the 1998 World Cup final?

6 *The Misfits* marked the last film appearance of two Hollywood legends. Clark Gable was one, who was the other?

7 By what name do we better know Doris von Kappelhoff?

8 Who assassinated Robert Kennedy?

9 Who takes it upon himself to teach Eliza Doolittle to speak properly?

10 Who plays the part of Richard Fish in *Ally McBeal*?

11 Who completed the tennis Grand Slam when he won the 1999 French title?

12 Who starred alongside Cary Grant in the film *His Girl Friday*?

13 Who was the 40th president of the United States?

14 Which American golfer shares his surname with a style of music?

15 Who won the 1967 Eurovision Song Contest?

16 Who was the first black heavyweight boxing champion of the world?

17 What is the full name of the central character in Dickens's *Great Expectations*?

18 Which French actress has devoted most of her life to animal causes since her career ended?

19 Whose works include a painting inspired by the bombing of a town called Guernica in the Spanish Civil War?

20 Who was the star of the film *Mrs Miniver*?

21 Who is lead guitarist with The Kinks?

22 Under what name did the Police drummer have the solo hit 'Don't Care' in 1978?

23 Who directed the films *Ordinary People* and *A River Runs Through it*?

24 Which British boxer has won an Olympic gold medal for Canada?

25 Which character was played by Shelley Duvall opposite Robin Williams in a film of the adventures of a popular cartoon character?

1 Which Sergei Eisenstein film was released in 1925?

2 In which of Rudolph Valentino's films did he play a bullfighter?

3 What was 'Fatty' Arbuckle's Christian name?

4 Which actress began her career in silent movies, went on to make several films with director Cecil B de Mille, and later played a fading movie star in the 1950 film *Sunset Boulevard*?

5 Which two stars of the silent screen married each other in 1920?

6 In which of his films does Charles Chaplin help a blind flower girl?

7 What was the title of the adventure serial starring Pearl White, which ran in conjunction with a weekly newspaper version?

8 On whom was the character of Susan Alexander based in Orson Welles's *Citizen Kane*?

9 Who directed *The Birth of a Nation*?

10 Whom did Mack Sennett sign at the end of 1913 for $150 per week?

11 Who was the star of the 1925 film *The Phantom of the Opera*?

12 By what nickname was actress Clara Bow known?

13 Who played Rudolph Valentino in Ken Russell's 1977 biopic of the silent star?

14 Which actress starred in such films as *The Birth of a Nation*, *Orphans of the Storm* and *The Wind*, and received a special Oscar in 1970?

15 What was the title of Robert Flaherty's 1922 documentary about Eskimo life?

16 Sharing its name with a famous British crime of the 1960s, which eleven-minute Western of 1903 is one of the first story films ever made?

17 Which two stars were brought together by producer Hal Roach in 1926?

18 Who directed, co-wrote and starred in the 1927 film *The General*?

19 Which two words were used to promote Greta Garbo's 1930 film *Anna Christie*?

20 What was striking about comedy actor Ben Turpin's appearance?

21 In the 1923 film *Safety Last*, who is seen dangling from a clock face?

22 Jackie Coogan appeared in Chaplin's *The Kid* when he was six. Over 40 years later he appeared on TV as a member of which family?

23 A huge hit in 1939 as a musical, which story by L Frank Baum was first filmed in 1910, and again in 1924?

24 Which group of uniformed actors made several slapstick comedies between 1912 and 1920?

25 What did four brothers called Harry, Sam, Albert and Jack start in 1923?

1 What was the first full-length cartoon, released in 1937?

2 Who provides the voice of the genie in the 1992 film *Aladdin*?

3 Which British-born director, whose attitude to actors is well known, said, 'Disney has the best casting. If he doesn't like an actor he just tears him up'?

4 In which American city was Walt Disney born?

5 What was the first Disney live-action feature, released in 1950?

6 Which 1991 cartoon was nominated for a best picture Oscar?

7 Who provided Mickey Mouse's voice for the final time in the 1940 film *Fantasia*?

8 Which cartoon has a lead character who never speaks and whose mother only speaks to him through the song 'Baby Mine'?

9 Which film concerns the fate of a princess called Ariel?

10 Who plays the father in the 1960 film *Swiss Family Robinson*?

11 Which 1995 film was given a special Academy Award for its pioneering use of computer wizardry?

12 What connects Mafusa in *The Lion King* with Darth Vader in *Star Wars*?

13 President of Disney film production from 1985 to 1994, Jeffrey Katzenberg left to form which company with Steven Spielberg and David Geffen?

14 What is the significance of the 1932 short animation *Flowers and Trees*?

15 In which film do we see Thomas O'Malley?

16 Which 1964 film won Oscars for best actress, visual effects, editing, song and original score?

17 Walt Disney died in December 1966 before the completion of which film?

18 Who did Geppetto create in his workshop?

19 What is the name of Simba's jealous uncle in *The Lion King*?

20 Which famous artist worked at the Disney studios for a few months in 1946 on a project that was eventually abandoned?

21 Whose are the voices of Prince John, the cowardly lion, and the snake, Sir Hiss, in the 1973 film *Robin Hood*?

22 In which live-action film is the star a dog whose real name was Spike?

23 What type of birds encourage Dumbo to fly?

24 Who plays Captain Nemo in the 1954 film *20,000 Leagues Under the Sea*?

25 Which 1996 film featured the voices of Tom Hulce, Demi Moore and Kevin Kline?

1 What is the currency of Ireland?

2 What is the Irish word for the police?

3 When is St Patrick's Day?

4 Whose memoir of growing up in Ireland in the 1930s won the Pulitzer Prize for Nonfiction in 1997?

5 What is a 'dubh linn' (as in Dublin)?

6 When was the Easter Rising and where was its symbolic centre?

7 Which Irish hotel employed Aloys Hitler, Adolf's half-brother, as a wine-waiter?

8 Where is the Northern Ireland Assembly held?

9 James Joyce's *Ulysses* is set in Dublin over the course of a single day. Which day?

10 When did Cromwell invade Ireland?

11 How is 'the village of Avoca' better known?

12 How was Lady Elgee (1826–96) better known?

13 Which port city in Ireland is most famous for its crystal factory?

14 What is the Irish word for 'welcome'?

15 Which limestone outcrop was the seat of the Munster kings from the 4th to the 12th centuries?

16 What does the word 'Cork' mean?

17 Who was the only woman ever to be initiated into the Irish Masons?

18 What is the origin of the word 'blarney'?

19 Where did the *Titanic* pay its last call before sinking in 1912?

20 Which town was captured by the Spaniards but retaken by the English in 1601?

21 Which town was the target of an Algerian raiding party in 1631, when a hundred locals were captured and sold for the white slave trade?

22 Which Irish word, meaning 'chief', is used for the Irish prime minister?

23 What is Ireland's only native toad?

24 Which Dublin building was founded by Queen Elizabeth I and houses the Book of Kells?

25 Of which Church of Ireland cathedral was Jonathan Swift dean?

1 How many hotels are there on the island of Mustique?

2 Which tourist attraction is the only living structure visible from outer space?

3 Which holiday destination became the capital of the Portuguese Empire in the East?

4 Which glamorous but small independent state is ruled by the Grimaldi family?

5 Which city contains the Rialto district?

6 In which classical resort did D H Lawrence choose to live from 1920 to 1923?

7 Which Canary Island's main resort town is called Playa de Las Americas?

8 Which Mediterranean island's two main beaches are called Ses Salines and Es Cavellet?

9 What is the capital of Mallorca?

10 Where is Sidi Bou Said?

11 Where would you be if you were throwing a lucky coin into the Trevi Fountain?

12 Which desert resort was the shooting location for much of *Star Wars*?

13 Which is Thailand's largest island?

14 Where were the final scenes of *Indiana Jones and the Last Crusade* filmed?

15 Which city was destroyed by a volcanic eruption in AD 79 but still remains one of southern Italy's major tourist attractions?

16 Which Mediterranean island became the home of Gracie Fields?

17 What are the Doldrums?

18 In which country are the Angel Falls?

19 Which city claims Table Mountain as its backdrop?

20 And which city claims the Sugar Loaf Mountain as its main backdrop?

21 Where are the Eastern and Western Ghats?

22 In which country are the ruins of Lalibela?

23 Where is the original geyser?

24 What is Euskadi?

25 What is the oldest known walled town?

1 What name connects Gary Numan and Cliff Richard?

2 Which band connects Robert Palmer's 'Addicted to Love' and David Bowie's 'Let's Dance'?

3 Although poles apart musically, what connects Foreigner with The Clash?

4 What do Shirley Bassey, Sheena Easton and Duran Duran have in common?

5 What name connects the third symphony by Vaughan Williams to Beethoven's sixth?

6 What connects Frankie Goes to Hollywood, Jennifer Rush, and Huey Lewis and the News?

7 In terms of Grammy Awards, what connects Louis Armstrong, Mahalia Jackson and Charlie Parker?

8 Which musician links The Rolling Stones, The Jeff Beck Group and The Faces?

9 In addition to being UK number one singles, what connects Norman Greenbaum's 'Spirit in the Sky' to Fleetwood Mac's 'Albatross'?

10 What honour is shared by Irene Cara's hits 'Fame' and 'Flashdance...What a Feeling'?

11 With whom did Queen, Bing Crosby and Mick Jagger all record singles?

12 What connects the artists who recorded 'Say What You Want', 'Yummy Yummy Yummy', and 'The Ballad of Davy Crockett'?

13 In terms of UK charts, what connects Jim Reeves' 'Distant Drums', and Elvis Presley's 'Way Down'?

14 What is the connection between Peter Gabriel's first four albums?

15 What is the connection between Stevie Wonder's 'Happy Birthday' and U2's 'Pride (In the Name of Love)'?

16 What do Van Halen, The Bachelors and Spandau Ballet have in common?

17 What is the connection between Richard, who sang 'Tutti Frutti' in 1957 and Eva, who sang 'The Loco-Motion' in 1962?

18 Which song was recorded by Bing Crosby and Grace Kelly, and also by Elton John and Kiki Dee?

19 What connects UK chart-toppers 'I Feel for You' by Chaka Khan and 'Nothing Compares 2 U' by Sinead O'Connor?

20 What do Abba have in common with Buddy Holly?

21 By what common nickname were jazz pianist Waller and rock 'n' roll pianist Domino known?

22 Who recorded duets with Mary Wells, Kim Weston, Tammi Terrell and Diana Ross?

23 What connects Elvis Costello, Declan MacManus, Napoleon Dynamite and The Impostor?

24 The title of which Sam Cooke song, when inserted in the gap shown, completes a Louis Armstrong song title, and forms the first half of the title of a Jimmy Cliff hit: What a .... Beautiful People?

25 What song links Badfinger, Harry Nilsson and Mariah Carey?

1 Who had a 1976 hit with 'Young Hearts Run Free'?

2 From which film did the Bee Gees' 'Stayin' Alive' originally stem?

3 The Tramps came from which US city?

4 Name The Andrea True Connection's only top ten hit.

5 'Le Freak' and 'Good Times' were hits for which New York group?

6 Name Disco Tex's group.

7 Who introduced a Disco Duck?

8 Who sang 'Never Can Say Goodbye' in 1974?

9 In Village People, there was an American Indian, a cowboy, a construction worker, a biker and who else?

10 Which label released Donna Summer's 'Love To Love You Baby'?

11 Silver Convention was a studio-created group. In which country was the studio situated?

12 What was the real name of Kool, of Kool and the Gang fame?

13 Whose 1976 debut hit was 'You to Me Are Everything'?

14 Name Dan Hartman's first hit.

15 Who did Earth, Wind and Fire link with for 'Boogie Wonderland'?

16 KC and the Sunshine Band stemmed from which US state?

17 A Taste of Honey's 'Boogie Oogie Oogie' was a major hit in which year?

18 'Don't Leave Me This Way' was a 1976 success for both Harold Melvin and the Blue Notes and Thelma Houston. But who scored with a cover version in 1986?

19 On which label did all Sylvester's 1970s hits appear?

20 Name the 40-piece orchestra led by Barry White.

21 In which film did Donna Summer make her debut as an aspiring disco singer?

22 Which LA group charted with 'Rock the Boat'?

23 Name the Bee Gees' ill-fated young brother who charted with 'Shadow Dancing'.

24 What was the name of Van McCoy's orchestra on his 'The Hustle' instrumental?

25 Who brought fame to a Disco Lady in 1976?

1 The Middle Ages traditionally began with the fall of which empire?

2 Which event in 1453 marked the end of the Middle Ages?

3 Which historical period, marked by achievement, followed the Middle Ages?

4 In the feudal system, what did a lord (or suzerain) grant to his subject (or vassal)?

5 And what did the vassal owe to the suzerain in return?

6 Allegiance to a suzerain was sworn over either a Bible or what?

7 Which event introduced this feudal system to England?

8 What was the name of Chaucer's chronicle of life in the Middle Ages?

9 Which region of France became an English possession by the marriage of Eleanor to Henry II in 1152?

10 Who was crowned emperor in Rome in 800?

11 Who did William the Conqueror marry?

12 According to tradition, what did she supervise?

13 What is the Book of Kells?

14 By what name are the biblical plays of the Middle Ages known?

15 Which Archbishop of Canterbury was murdered in 1170?

16 Which medieval cathedral has the widest nave of all French cathedrals?

17 In 1348, 28 per cent of the entire English population died. Why?

18 Henry IV of France's marriage to whom started the Thirty Years War?

19 Between which two countries was the Thirty Years War fought?

20 Who was Richard the Lionheart's famous opponent during the Third Crusade?

21 When he returned to Europe after the Third Crusade, where was Richard the Lionheart held prisoner?

22 Henry V of England defeated the French at which famous battle?

23 Which city did Joan of Arc deliver from the English to the French in 1429?

24 Between which two groups were the Wars of the Roses fought?

25 How did Henry VII put an end to the Wars of the Roses in 1485?

1 Which Steven Spielberg film won Oscars for its portrayal of the Normandy landings?

2 Having been stormed by the French and the Germans in 1741, which city was then besieged by the Austrians the following year?

3 When did Constantinople fall to the Turks?

4 Where was the first investiture of the Victoria Cross held on 26 June 1857?

5 When Vasco da Gama landed in India in 1498, which technological advantage gave his fleet victory over the locals?

6 Where did the Boer War take place?

7 With how many soldiers did Francisco Pizarro overcome the Incas in 1531?

8 Which island was awarded the George Cross in 1942?

9 What was the name of the Aztec leader whom Cortés defeated in battle?

10 Which war led the Chinese to cede Hong Kong to the British in 1842?

11 Who fought against Russia in the Livonian War of 1558–83?

12 What kind of war did Hitler plan to use against Britain in 1940?

13 Where and when was gunpowder first discovered?

14 Which country was defeated by the British and the French in the Crimean War?

15 Which 16th-century German artist published a treatise on fortification despite never having been in a war?

16 Where was Custer's Last Stand?

17 Which famous slave led the revolt on San Domingo which began in 1791?

18 During which famous 'suicide mission' were British troops utterly defeated by the Russians in 1854?

19 Which country invaded and took control of Ethiopia in 1895?

20 Whose New Model Army was the first English army to conquer Scotland?

21 Over how many American 'colonies' had Britain lost control by 1776?

22 What was the only major sea battle in the First World War?

23 Which 1746 battle marked the end of the Jacobite Rebellions?

24 What was the name given to the sudden-strike German bombing campaigns of 1939 and 1940?

25 After the Chinese Civil War of 1946–9, the Nationalists remained in control of only one island. Which one?

1 Which were the only three teams to beat Manchester United in the 1999/2000 season?

2 Which team plays at the Boleyn Ground?

3 Who has played in local derbies in Manchester and Liverpool and, most recently, Glasgow in the Scottish Premiership?

4 Which club did Nigerian international Daniel Amokachi join after the 1994 World Cup?

5 At the time of writing, which two players hold the record for most goals in a single Premiership season, and also the most goals in a premiership match?

6 Which Czech Republic player joined Manchester United after Euro '96?

7 Who did Harry Redknapp replace as manager of West Ham United in 1994?

8 Who scored a wonderful individual goal for Derby County on his debut in their 3-2 win at Old Trafford in 1997?

9 Which team finished second in the Premiership in 1996 and 1997?

10 Which Blackburn Rovers strike partnership of the mid-90s was known as SAS?

11 Which player joined Sheffield Wednesday from Inter Milan in 1996?

12 Which team did the Premier League and FA Cup double in 1997/98?

13 Which team rejoined the Premiership in 2000 after a four-year absence, during which time they spent one season in the Second Division?

14 Which award was won by Liverpool's Robbie Fowler in 1995 and 1996?

15 Which was the last season that the Premiership was contested over 42 games?

16 Who was Arsenal's caretaker manager prior to the arrival of Arsène Wenger in November 1996?

17 Which Premiership team used to play at the Baseball Ground?

18 At which club's school of excellence did Ryan Giggs train until he was fourteen?

19 Who has been manager at Liverpool, Blackburn Rovers and Newcastle United?

20 Who was voted Carling Player of the Year for the 1999/2000 season?

21 Who were the last champions of the old First Division in 1992, prior to the formation of the Premier League?

22 About whom did George Best say, 'He can't head the ball, tackle or kick with his left foot and he doesn't score enough goals'?

23 Which three teams were relegated at the end of the 1999/2000 season?

24 Which club was deducted three points in 1996 for failing to fulfil a fixture at Blackburn?

25 Which Premiership club was formed in 1905 by a group of fourteen- and fifteen-year-olds living in streets by the Thames?

1 How many gold medals did Ian Thorpe win in Sydney?

2 What size are Thorpe's feet?

3 Where is Eric the Eel from?

4 Who won the Olympic 50 metres in both 1992 and 1996?

5 Which country has won most gold medals in the 4x100 metres?

6 When were the first world championships?

7 Which Irish swimmer won four Atlanta golds but was banned two years later for failing a drug test?

8 How many Olympic golds has Steve Redgrave won with Matthew Pinsent?

9 Who won the rowing eights gold in Sydney?

10 What is the nickname for the Aussie rowing four?

11 When was the first Olympic rowing competition?

12 Who won the Boat Race in 2000?

13 Which famous football ground does the Boat Race pass?

14 Where is the Royal Regatta?

15 How many sailing golds did Great Britain win in Sydney?

16 In what class does Ben Ainslie compete?

17 Who holds the Americas Cup?

18 When was yachting first included in the Olympics?

19 Where is Britain's biggest regatta?

20 What is the longest yacht race?

21 When was canoeing introduced to the Olympics?

22 Who is Germany's best canoeist?

23 Which water sport was introduced to the Olympics at Sydney 2000?

24 Who has won the most diving medals?

25 What was Prince William's favourite sport at school?

1 Who offered his kingdom in exchange for a horse?

2 What did Shakespeare's father do for a living?

3 Who asked Kate to kiss him?

4 What was Shakespeare's first performed play?

5 Who set *A Midsummer Night's Dream* to music and called his version the *M N Dream*?

6 What were Shakespeare's own twins called?

7 Which was the first Shakespeare play to receive a professional performance in America?

8 Who swears 'A plague o' both your houses'?

9 Which two characters were ill met by moonlight?

10 Which play did Catherine the Great translate into Russian under the title 'What it is Like to have Linen in a Basket'?

11 What was the name of Shakespeare's theatre company?

12 Which play introduced the character of Falstaff?

13 After their first playhouse was dismantled, which new theatre did the Chamberlain's Men then build?

14 Who was the first director of the Royal Shakespeare Company in 1961?

15 Who asks 'If you prick us, do we not bleed?'?

16 Orson Welles starred in and directed two film adaptations of Shakespeare's tragedies. One was *Othello*. Which was the other?

17 Who asks his friends, Romans and countrymen to 'lend me your ears'?

18 Whose film version of *Romeo and Juliet* shot Leonardo di Caprio to stardom?

19 What does Hamlet call Frailty?

20 Who took over from Shakespeare as the Chamberlain's Men's chief dramatist?

21 What name was given to the first edition of Shakespeare's collected works?

22 What is the name of the play that Hamlet and the Players perform for the King and Queen?

23 Which was Shakespeare's last play?

24 In Max Reinhardt's film version of *A Midsummer Night's Dream,* who played Bottom?

25 Who considers that this is 'a brave new world That hath such people in't!'?

1 What do the initials MG stand for?

2 Who first used electric ignition by battery and coil in 1886?

3 Which Lotus car came on the market in 1963 and featured in *The Avengers*?

4 Predating the Model T Ford, which was the world's first car to be made in large quantities, 19,000 being sold between 1902 and 1906?

5 What is represented by the blue and white quartered circle of the BMW logo?

6 The E-type Jaguar was introduced in fixed-head coupé form at the 1961 Geneva Motor Show. To the nearest hundred pounds, what was its original selling price?

7 What type of car did Michael Caine drive in the film *Get Carter*?

8 What was the significance of the number 40 in relation to the Ford GT40?

9 Which British sports car company was founded in 1962 by Jem Marsh and Frank Costin, whose names inspired the more continental-sounding company name?

10 What make of car did Don McLean drive to the levee in 'American Pie'?

11 Which car was first patented in 1909?

12 What do the initials DB stand for in conjunction with Aston Martin?

13 Which British car company's first car was the two-seater Oxford in 1913?

14 Which British car was driven by Paddy Hopkirk to win the 1964 Monte Carlo rally, and also featured in the film *The Italian Job*?

15 Why was the Jaguar XJ220 so named?

16 Which now-standard fittings were first featured on a car in 1916?

17 Which Italian company's emblem features a raging bull?

18 In which country is the Daewoo company based?

19 Which model Ferrari has a name which means 'redhead'?

20 Why did Henry Ford say that people could have a Model T in any colour so long as it was black?

21 Which company began manufacturing the Jeep in 1943?

22 What do the initials SLK mean in relation to the Mercedes car of that name?

23 Which American car of the 1940s had a third central headlight that swivelled with the front wheels?

24 In which year did the Volkswagen Beetle make its first appearance?

25 The world's first motorway opened in 1924. In which country?

16 Outside which London station did Buster Edwards, the former Great Train Robber, have a flower stall?

17 Where is the oldest Stock Exchange?

18 Who directed *L'argent*, a film about a forged 500-franc note changing hands, in 1983?

19 What, because of its location, is the New York Stock Exchange commonly called?

1 Where is British currency coined?

2 Which band first recorded 'Money's Too Tight to Mention'?

3 What is the Paris Stock Exchange called?

4 Who said, 'Time is money'?

5 What is 'The Old Lady of Threadneedle Street'?

6 Name the moneylender in *The Merchant of Venice*.

7 Who recorded the original version of 'Money' with Bern Elliott in 1963?

8 Who first advocated monetarism?

9 Which Peter Sellers film is quoted in the lyrics of Pink Floyd's 'Money'?

10 In which state is Fort Knox?

11 Who invented coinage?

12 How did the Owl and the Pussycat carry their 'honey and plenty of money'?

13 By what name is the European Currency Unit better known?

14 Which American humourist once commented, 'The two most beautiful words in the English language are "cheque enclosed"'?

15 What took place in the London Stock Exchange on 27 October 1986?

20 Where is it written that 'the love of money is the root of all evil'?

21 How did Lord Thomson of Fleet describe a stake in commercial TV?

22 Which 1976 Truffaut film begins with a group of children arriving for school?

23 Who starred as an ex-con in the 2000 film *Where the Money Is*?

24 Who composed the *Cabaret* song 'Money (makes the world go round)'?

25 In his 1969 debut as his own director, who wanted to *Take the Money and Run*?

ANSWERS TO QUIZ 6

Double Initials

1 Marshall Mathers
2 Boris Becker
3 William Wyler
4 Fred Flintstone
5 Zinedine Zidane
6 Marilyn Monroe
7 Doris Day
8 Sirhan Sirhan
9 Henry Higgins
10 Greg Germann
11 Andre Agassi
12 Rosalind Russell
13 Ronald Reagan
14 Fred Funk
15 Sandie Shaw
16 Jack Johnson
17 Philip Pirrip
18 Brigitte Bardot
19 Pablo Picasso
20 Greer Garson
21 Dave Davies
22 Klark Kent
23 Robert Redford
24 Lennox Lewis
25 Olive Oyl

The Silent Era

1 *Battleship Potemkin*
2 *Blood and Sand*
3 Roscoe
4 Gloria Swanson
5 Douglas Fairbanks and Mary Pickford
6 *City Lights*
7 *The Perils of Pauline*
8 Marion Davies
9 D W Griffith
10 Charles Chaplin
11 Lon Chaney (Senior)
12 The 'It' Girl
13 Rudolf Nureyev
14 Lillian Gish
15 *Nanook of the North*
16 *The Great Train Robbery*
17 Stan Laurel and Oliver Hardy
18 Buster Keaton
19 Garbo talks
20 He was cross-eyed
21 Harold Lloyd
22 The Addams family – Uncle Fester
23 *The Wizard of Oz*
24 The Keystone Kops
25 Warner Brothers Pictures Inc

Disney Films

1 *Snow White and the Seven Dwarfs*
2 Robin Williams
3 Alfred Hitchcock
4 Chicago
5 *Treasure Island*
6 *Beauty and the Beast*
7 Walt Disney
8 *Dumbo*
9 *The Little Mermaid*
10 John Mills
11 *Toy Story*
12 The voice of James Earl Jones
13 Dreamworks
14 It was the first to be made in full colour
15 *The Aristocats*
16 *Mary Poppins*
17 *The Jungle Book*
18 Pinocchio
19 Scar
20 Salvador Dali
21 Peter Ustinov and Terry-Thomas
22 *Old Yeller*
23 Crows
24 James Mason
25 *The Hunchback of Notre Dame*

Ireland

1 The euro
2 Gardai
3 17 March
4 Frank McCourt's (*Angela's Ashes*)
5 A black pool
6 1916; the proclamation of the Irish Republic was made from the Dublin general Post Office
7 The Shelbourne Hotel, Dublin
8 Stormont Castle, Belfast
9 16 June 1904
10 August 1649
11 It is the real village setting for the television series *Ballykissangel*
12 As Lady Wilde, Oscar's mother
13 Waterford
14 Failte
15 The Rock of Cashel
16 The Gaelic for Cork, 'Corcaigh', means marshy
17 Elizabeth Aldworthy
18 Cormac MacCarthy, the Gaelic lord of Blarney, was so successful at inventing excuses for not complying with the demands of Queen Elizabeth I that she dismissed his blather as 'blarney'
19 Cobh harbour, County Cork
20 Kinsale
21 Baltimore, County Cork
22 The Taoiseach
23 The natterjack
24 Trinity College, Dublin
25 St Patrick's Cathedral

Holiday Destinations

1 One
2 The Great Barrier Reef
3 Goa
4 Monaco
5 Venice
6 Taormina, Sicily
7 Tenerife
8 Ibiza
9 Palma
10 Tunisia
11 Rome
12 Matmata, Tunisia
13 Phuket
14 Petra, Jordan
15 Pompeii
16 Capri
17 Calm regions of water near the equator
18 Venezuela
19 Cape Town, South Africa
20 Rio de Janeiro, Brazil
21 In India: they are mountain ranges
22 Ethiopia
23 In Iceland: 'geysir' is the Icelandic for 'to rush forth'
24 It is the Basque word for the Basque country
25 Jericho

Connections

1 Both were born with the surname Webb
2 Chic: Bernard Edwards and Nile Rodgers produced respectively
3 Both had members called Mick Jones
4 They all recorded James Bond themes
5 They are both known as 'Pastoral' symphonies
6 They all released singles called 'The Power of Love'
7 They all received the Lifetime Achievement Award posthumously
8 Ron Wood
9 Fleetwood Mac guitarist Peter Green was born Peter Greenbaum
10 They are both Oscar-winning songs
11 David Bowie
12 American states – Texas, Ohio Express and Tennessee Ernie Ford
13 They were posthumous number ones
14 They were all called *Peter Gabriel*
15 They are both about Martin Luther King, Jr
16 They all have two brothers in the group
17 They were both known as 'Little'
18 'True Love'
19 They were both written by Prince
20 They have both inspired stage musicals
21 Fats
22 Marvin Gaye
23 They are the same person
24 'Wonderful World'
25 'Without You'

Disco

1 Candi Staton
2 *Saturday Night Fever*
3 Philadelphia
4 'More, More, More'
5 Chic
6 The Sex-O-Lettes
7 Rick Dees and His Band of Idiots
8 Gloria Gaynor
9 A policeman
10 Casablanca
11 Germany
12 Robert Bell
13 The Real Thing
14 'Instant Replay'
15 The Emotions
16 Florida
17 1978
18 The Communards
19 Fantasy
20 Love Unlimited Orchestra
21 *Thank God It's Friday*
22 The Hues Corporation
23 Andy Gibb
24 Soul City Symphony
25 Johnnie Taylor

The Middle Ages

1 The Roman Empire
2 The Fall of Constantinople to the Turks
3 The Renaissance
4 A fief or protection
5 Total 'homage' or personal services
6 The relics of a saint
7 The Norman Conquest in 1066

8 *The Canterbury Tales*
9 Aquitaine
10 Charlemagne
11 Queen Matilda
12 The weaving of the Bayeux Tapestry
13 The Irish masterpiece of illumination
14 The mystery plays/miracle plays
15 Thomas Becket
16 Chartres
17 They died of plague – the 'Black Death'
18 Eleanor of Aquitaine
19 England and France
20 Saladin
21 Austria
22 The Battle of Agincourt
23 Orléans
24 Lancastrians and Yorkists
25 He married Elizabeth of York after defeating Richard III at the Battle of Bosworth Field

Military History
1 *Saving Private Ryan*
2 Prague
3 1453
4 Hyde Park, London
5 The cannon
6 South Africa
7 168, but they also had horses
8 Malta
9 Montezuma
10 The Opium Wars of 1839–41
11 Sweden and Poland
12 Blitzkrieg
13 China in the ninth century
14 Russia
15 Albrecht Dürer
16 Little Big Horn in 1876
17 Toussaint L'Ouverture
18 The Charge of the Light Brigade at Balaclava
19 Italy
20 Oliver Cromwell
21 All thirteen
22 The Battle of Jutland
23 Culloden
24 Operation Sealion
25 Taiwan

The Premiership
1 Chelsea, Newcastle United and Tottenham Hotspur
2 West Ham United (Boleyn Ground, Green Street, Upton Park)
3 Andrei Kanchelskis
4 Everton

5 Andy Cole and Alan Shearer, both with 34 and 5
6 Karel Poborsky
7 Billy Bonds
8 Paulo Wanchope
9 Newcastle United
10 Alan Shearer and Chris Sutton
11 Benito Carbone
12 Arsenal
13 Manchester City
14 PFA Young Player of the Year
15 1994/95
16 Stewart Houston
17 Derby County
18 Manchester City
19 Kenny Dalglish
20 Kevin Phillips
21 Leeds United
22 David Beckham
23 Wimbledon, Sheffield Wednesday and Watford
24 Middlesbrough
25 Charlton Athletic

Water Sports
1 Four
2 Seventeen
3 Equatorial Guinea
4 Popov
5 USA
6 1973
7 Michelle Smith (Bruin)
8 Three
9 Great Britain
10 Awesome Foursome
11 1900
12 Oxford
13 Craven Cottage (Fulham)
14 Henley
15 Three
16 Laser
17 USA
18 1900
19 Cowes
20 Whitbread
21 1936
22 Brigitte Fisher
23 Water polo
24 China
25 Water polo

Shakespeare
1 Richard III
2 He was a glover
3 Petruchio in *The Taming of the Shrew*
4 *Henry IV, Part One*
5 Benjamin Britten
6 Hamnet and Judith
7 *Richard III* – New York, 1750
8 Mercutio in *Romeo and Juliet*

9 Oberon and Titania
10 *The Merry Wives of Windsor*
11 The Chamberlain's Men
12 *Henry IV, Part One*
13 The Globe
14 Sir Peter Hall
15 Shylock in *The Merchant of Venice*
16 *Macbeth*
17 Antony in *Julius Caesar*
18 Baz Luhrmann
19 'Frailty, thy name is woman'
20 John Fletcher
21 The First Folio
22 The Mousetrap
23 *The Tempest*
24 James Cagney
25 Miranda in *The Tempest*

Cars
1 Morris Garages
2 Karl Benz
3 The Elan
4 The Curved Dash Oldsmobile
5 A spinning propeller
6 £1,550
7 Jaguar Mk II 3.4
8 It stood 40 inches tall
9 Marcos
10 Chevy (Chevrolet)
11 Model T Ford
12 David Brown (one-time owner of the company)
13 Morris
14 Mini Cooper
15 Its top speed was 220 mph
16 Automatic windscreen wipers
17 Lamborghini
18 Korea
19 Testarossa
20 Japan black enamel was the only colour that would dry quickly enough to keep up with the assembly line
21 Willys
22 *Sportlich, Licht, Kompact* (Sporty, Light, Compact)
23 Tucker Torpedo
24 1945
25 Italy

Money
1 The Royal Mint
2 The Valentine Brothers in 1983
3 La Bourse
4 Benjamin Franklin
5 The Bank of England
6 Shylock

7 The Fenmen
8 Milton Friedman
9 *I'm All Right, Jack*
10 Kentucky
11 The Chinese in the 2nd millennium BC
12 Wrapped up in a £5 note
13 The euro
14 Dorothy Parker
15 The 'Big Bang'
16 Waterloo
17 Antwerp (1460)
18 Robert Bresson
19 Wall Street
20 The Bible (Timothy 6:10)
21 'A licence to print money'
22 *L'argent de Poche*
23 Paul Newman
24 John Kander
25 Woody Allen

THE ULTIMATE BOOK
OF TRIVIA

QUIZ

7

1 Whose baby was Bruno Hauptmann accused of kidnapping and killing in 1932?

2 Hanged at Wandsworth prison in 1949 for killing six people, by what pseudonym was John George Haigh known?

3 Who was electrocuted in January 1989 after murdering between nineteen and 40 people between 1974 and 1977?

4 What is the better known nickname of the unidentified murderer known as the 'Whitechapel Murderer'?

5 Who was the subject of a film starring Richard Attenborough, and lived at 10 Rillington Place, London?

6 Who became Surveyor of the Queen's Pictures in 1972, despite confessing to being a Soviet spy twelve years earlier?

7 John Dillinger was shot by FBI agents outside a cinema in which city?

8 Why were the death sentences of the Manson family commuted to life imprisonment in 1972?

9 Who was responsible for the deaths of seventeen young men in Wisconsin and Ohio and was murdered by a fellow prisoner?

10 Which pair of 19th-century killers sold their victims' bodies to the medical profession?

11 Who claimed thirteen victims in the north of England between 1975 and 1980?

12 According to legend, who 'took an axe and gave her mother forty whacks'?

13 Who hanged himself in his prison cell on New Year's Day 1995, before being tried for the crimes he committed?

14 Although involved in various murders, including the 'St Valentine's Day Massacre', for what was Al Capone eventually imprisoned?

15 Which two sons of millionaires, themselves only teenagers, killed a fourteen-year-old boy in 1924 for kicks?

16 Who, in 1986, admitted to the murders of Pauline Reade and Keith Bennett more than two decades before?

17 By what nickname was mobster Benjamin Siegel better known?

18 Who was the last woman to be hanged in Britain, on 13 July 1955?

19 The *Montrose* was one of the first ships equipped with Marconi's radio telegraph. Which passenger did this invention help bring to justice for his wife's murder in 1910?

20 On 23 May 1934, a Miss Parker and a Mr Barrow were killed in a hail of police gunfire. What were the first names of these two, who had killed 13 people?

21 By which name was 30s New York gangster Arthur Flegenheimer better known?

22 In which year were Ronald and Reginald Kray sentenced to life imprisonment for the murders of George Cornell and Jack 'The Hat' McVitie?

23 Which gang boss, who took over Al Capone's old Chicago territory, was shot dead by intruders at his home in 1975?

24 By what name was Albert De Salvo better known?

25 By what name was Salvatore Luciana better known?

2

1 Which US president was a distant relative?

2 What was her official title?

3 Who was her chauffeur on her final journey?

4 Who co-wrote *A Princess in Love* with Anna Pasternak?

5 Who survived the car crash?

6 For which organization did Diana take an advisory role?

7 Who was older, her mother or stepmother?

8 Who interviewed her on *Panorama*?

9 Who designed her dress when she danced with John Travolta?

10 How many Princesses of Wales were there before her?

11 What was her nickname for Camilla Parker Bowles?

12 Who did her make-up on her wedding day?

13 With which sportsman was she linked?

14 What did she describe as a shameful friend?

15 Of which ballet company was she patron?

16 What is her brother's title?

17 Which year saw the divorce between Diana and Prince Charles?

18 At which London hospital did Diana give birth to both of her sons?

19 What was sewn into the hem of her dress for luck?

20 What was her occupation prior to her marriage?

21 What name is shared by the Duchess of York's sister and one of Diana's sisters?

22 Who wrote the book that exposed her bulimia?

23 Who took over from her as the Red Cross's spokesperson on landmines?

24 What was Diana's second name?

25 Who designed her wedding dress?

1 Which actress won an Oscar for her role as a bimbo in *Mighty Aphrodite*?

2 In which film does an actor step out of the cinema screen to confront a woman sitting in the stalls?

3 In which 1975 film did Woody Allen star as a restaurant cashier and small-time bookie who is hired to lend his name to TV scripts written by blacklisted writers?

4 In which film do a pair of burglars answer the telephone and become random contestants in a phone-in quiz show?

5 What was Allen's first film as director?

6 Which character did Allen play in *Casino Royale*?

7 Which of Allen's films is about a comedy director in mid-life and career crisis?

8 In which film is Allen's character resuscitated in the 22nd century?

9 Who played Hannah in *Hannah and her Sisters*?

10 Which composer's music was used extensively in *Manhattan*?

11 Which film is about a playwright having his play backed by a mobster, whose girlfriend has to be given a starring role?

12 Which film has Allen as a Russian countryman at the time of the Napoleonic wars?

13 In which film did Allen and Diane Keaton first star together?

14 Who played Allen's smug TV producer brother-in-law in *Crimes and Misdemeanors*?

15 Which two directors, along with Woody Allen, were responsible for the 1989 movie *New York Stories*?

16 In 1979 Allen directed and co-narrated a short film entitled *My Favorite Comedian*. Who was the film's subject?

17 In which film does Allen star as a small-time variety agent?

18 For which film did Allen receive Oscars for direction and original screenplay?

19 In which film does Allen's character become involved in politics, eventually becoming president of San Marcos?

20 Which film's central character is described as a 'human chameleon'?

21 In which film did Allen make his acting debut?

22 Which instrument does Allen play in his New Orleans-style jazz band?

23 Which film's release coincided, ironically, with Allen's break-up with Mia Farrow?

24 Who was Allen's co-star in *Scenes from a Mall*?

25 The original script ideas for *Annie Hall* became the basis of which later movie, again co-starring Diane Keaton?

1 In which film did Gary Cooper win an Oscar in 1941?

2 Which 1978 film starred Robert De Niro, Christopher Walken and John Savage?

3 Who plays the part of Napoleon in the 1971 film *Waterloo*?

4 Which conflict is the setting for Brian De Palma's 1989 movie *Casualties of War*?

5 The music of which composer was used during Lieutenant-Colonel Kilgore's helicopter operation against the enemy in *Apocalypse Now*?

6 Which 1915 film was based on Thomas Dixon's novel *The Clansman*?

7 During the making of which 1936 film is director Michael Curtiz supposed to have issued the command, 'Bring on the empty horses'?

8 Who played the title role in *Saving Private Ryan*?

9 For which film did Oliver Stone win an Oscar for direction in 1986?

10 What is the subject of the 1962 film *The Longest Day*?

11 In which 1957 film did Alec Guinness win an Oscar for his portrayal of a dogged British colonel?

12 What distinction is held by the 1927 First World War film *Wings*?

13 Who played General Omar Bradley opposite George C Scott in *Patton*?

14 Who played Oskar Schindler in *Schindler's List*?

15 Who was the star of the 1981 film *Gallipoli*?

16 In which American Civil War movie did Denzel Washington win a best supporting actor Oscar in 1989?

17 Of which 1930 film did the *Variety* review suggest that the League of Nations 'reproduce it in every language to be shown to every nation every year until the word "war" is taken out of the dictionaries'?

18 What is the title of Noel Coward's 1942 film based on the experiences of Lord Louis Mountbatten and his ship HMS *Kelly*?

19 Which film features the famous beach scene with Burt Lancaster and Deborah Kerr?

20 Who starred in and directed the 1968 film *The Green Berets*?

21 Which offbeat 1970 film features the theft of some gold bullion from a German officer, and stars Clint Eastwood, Telly Savalas and Donald Sutherland?

22 Twenty years after his previous film, *Days of Heaven*, what was the title of Terrence Malick's 1998 film of the Guadalcanal conflict?

23 Who directed the 1957 First World War film *Paths of Glory*?

24 Which 1993 American Civil War film stars, among others (and amongst a lot of fake facial hair), Jeff Daniels, Martin Sheen, Tom Berenger and Sam Elliott?

25 Who directed the 1977 movie *A Bridge Too Far*?

1 Butterflies and moths are in the insect group Lepidoptera. Which group contains ants, bees and wasps?

2 Which insect is popular with gardeners because it feeds on aphids?

3 What type of insects are hawkers, clubtails, biddies, emeralds, darts and skimmers?

4 What are the three divisions of an insect's body?

5 Female honeybees that receive royal jelly throughout their larval stage develop into what?

6 Which aptly-named spider devours its partner after mating?

7 Why is the mole cricket so called?

8 What name is given to the study of insects?

9 From which material do wasps build their nests?

10 Which insect transmits African sleeping sickness?

11 What is an ovipositor?

12 Which stage of an insect's life cycle comes between egg and pupa?

13 Does the male or female horsefly feed on blood?

14 What is the common name for the crane fly?

15 What are insects' chewing jaws called?

16 Do butterflies usually rest with their wings together or open?

17 How long can a stag beetle spend as a larva?

18 Found on plants, what is the protective bubbly section of the nymphs of the spittle bug commonly called?

19 There are four classes of myriapods, two of which are pauropoda and symphyla. What are the two better known classes called?

20 Which insect can infect humans with malaria?

21 What type of insect is a weevil?

22 Which insect has a pair of prominent pincers at the tip of its abdomen?

23 Which is the largest species of beetle?

24 Which shiny insect feeds on such materials as wallpaper paste and bookbindings?

25 What is an exoskeleton?

1 Which National Park includes the Black Mountains and Usk Valley?

2 What is the most famous landmark on the second-largest of the Orkney Islands?

3 Which Irish river, the site of a famous battle, rises in the Bog of Allen, County Kildare and enters the Irish Sea just south of Drogheda?

4 Which river forms most of the boundary between the English counties of Essex and Suffolk?

5 Lying at the southern edge of the Highlands, which is the largest lake in Scotland?

6 What are McGillycuddy's Reeks?

7 Featured in the TV series *The Prisoner*, what is the name of the Italianate Welsh village designed by architect Clough Williams-Ellis?

8 Where is Alum Bay, which is famous for its many-coloured sandstone cliffs?

9 Which part of south Staffordshire was originally a royal preserve and hunting forest and includes large areas of forestry?

10 Which range of hills forms a 30-mile stretch of the border between England and Scotland?

11 Which island in the English Channel was known as 'Sarnia' to the Romans?

12 Which island in the Irish Sea is roughly equidistant from the coasts of England, Ireland and Scotland?

13 In which national park would you find the peaks Skiddaw, Helvellyn and Great Gable?

14 What is the northernmost point of the British mainland?

15 Ynys Mon is the largest island in England and Wales. By what name is it known in English?

16 On which river is the High Force waterfall?

17 Wookey Hole is part of which range of hills?

18 Which feature of the east of England was caused by the flooding of medieval peat diggings?

19 Ripon is the tourist centre for which National Park?

20 Until about 5000 BC it was a river valley, now the French call it the Pas de Calais. How is it known in English?

21 Among others, Fuggles and Goldings are grown widely in Kent and Worcestershire. What are they?

22 The town of Rothesay is on which Scottish isle?

23 Which is the most westerly of London's boroughs?

24 Which river, famed for its salmon, rises in the Cairngorm Mountains and flows east to the North Sea at Aberdeen?

25 What name is given to the famous prehistoric route between the English Channel and the centre of ancient Wessex that survives as minor roads or bridle paths?

1 In which US city was Motown records founded?

2 Which group was originally called The Primettes?

3 Who founded the Motown label?

4 Which vocal group, formed in 1954 as The Four Aims, gave the Motown label its first UK number one single in 1966?

5 Which white Motown singer/songwriter had hits with 'Indiana Wants Me' and 'There's a Ghost in My House'?

6 Which singer began his career in The Moonglows, with Motown boss Berry Gordy's brother-in-law Harvey Fuqua?

7 Which Motown singer/songwriter was once described by Bob Dylan as America's greatest living poet?

8 What was the first top twenty hit in the UK for Stevie Wonder?

9 Which artist, along with his All Stars, had a hit with '(I'm a) Road Runner'?

10 What was Diana Ross's last hit with The Supremes?

11 Who had a hit in 1967 with 'When You're Young and In Love'?

12 To which city did Motown move its headquarters in 1971?

13 What was the name on the front of the first Motown office and studio building in Detroit?

14 Which two Motown artists recorded duets with Paul McCartney?

15 Which of Marvin Gaye's singing partners died of a brain tumour in 1970?

16 What was Stevie Wonder's first album on gaining artistic control of his own output in 1972?

17 How old was Smokey Robinson when the Miracles released, 'Got a Job'?

18 Which two groups combined on the 1969 hit 'I'm Gonna Make You Love Me'?

19 Which group was the label's biggest selling act of the 1990s?

20 Why did The Jackson Five change their name to The Jacksons when they left Motown?

21 Which instruments were played by Motown session men James Jamerson and Benny Benjamin respectively?

22 Who sang lead on the hits 'Jimmy Mack' and 'Nowhere to Run'?

23 With which group do you associate David Ruffin and Eddie Kendricks?

24 An untypical Motown record, which single gave singer Charlene a UK number one in 1982?

25 When The Supremes hit the number one spot in the UK in 1964 with 'Baby Love' it was not released on Motown, but on which other label?

1 From which film did Duran Duran take their name?

2 Who recorded the original version of Soft Cell's 'Tainted Love'?

3 Susanne Sulley and Joanne Catherall sang with which band?

4 Name Culture Club's debut number one.

5 With which European city is Ultravox linked, songwise?

6 Gary Webb had a top ten hit on both sides of the Atlantic with 'Cars'. By what name is he better known?

7 Which New Romantic star was once voted the most beautiful man in the world?

8 What was singer Chris Hamill's stage name?

9 By what name is George O'Dowd better known?

10 Name A Flock of Seagulls' top ten US hit.

11 Who was lead singer with Spandau Ballet?

12 What single gave the Human League a transatlantic number one?

13 Their debut album was titled *Lexicon of Love*. Who was the band?

14 Name the 'Fade to Grey' band fronted by Steve Strange.

15 The Lover Speaks's only chart entry was later covered by Annie Lennox. What was it called?

16 'Planet Earth' was Duran Duran's first hit. But what was their first top ten entry?

17 Rusty Egan and Steve Strange worked as DJs at a legendary club. What was it called?

18 Name the film in which Spandau Ballet's Kemp brothers later starred.

19 Which band did Peter Murphy of Bauhaus and Mick Karn of Japan form?

20 With which famous disco producer did Phil Oakey collaborate on the soundtrack for the film *Electric Dreams*?

21 Name Kajagoogoo's debut single.

22 In which year was Culture Club's 'Karma Chameleon' a hit?

23 Which James Bond film did Duran Duran provide the theme music for?

24 Which ex-Rich Kid played with Visage and Ultravox?

25 Whose breakthrough single came with 'Messages'?

15

1 Who wrote *The Naked and the Dead*?

2 Which conflict provided the setting for Ernest Hemingway's *For Whom the Bell Tolls*?

3 Which author inspired the names of bands Steely Dan and Soft Machine?

4 What was the title of beat writer Jack Kerouac's story of a journey across America by car?

5 Who wrote *The Witches of Eastwick*?

6 Who is the most famous creation of Edgar Rice Burroughs?

7 Which American poet and writer was married to poet Ted Hughes?

8 Which Tom Wolfe story was made into a film by Brian de Palma, starring Tom Hanks and Bruce Willis?

9 Whose books include *The World According to Garp*, *The Hotel New Hampshire* and *The Cider House Rules*?

10 Which author took a bus full of 'Merry Pranksters' on a three-year bus trip around America, filming the country and its people?

11 Who created the character Jack Ryan, hero of such stories as *Patriot Games*, *Clear and Present Danger* and *The Hunt for Red October*?

12 What was Erica Jong's first novel, published in 1973?

13 Whose last book was *The Last Tycoon*?

14 Which crime writer's work includes *The Big Sleep*, *The Lady in The Lake* and *The Long Goodbye*?

15 Who has written under the name Richard Bachman?

16 Whose book *Rosinante to the Road Again* is set in Spain after the first World War?

17 Which poet's work includes *Just Give Me a Cool Drink of Water 'fore I Die*?

18 Who wrote *The Maltese Falcon*?

19 Whose book *The Right Stuff* deals with the early years of the American space programme?

20 Whose thrillers include *The Ostermen Weekend*, *The Bourne Identity* and *The Prometheus Deception*?

21 Who wrote the Pulitzer Prize-winning novel *To Kill a Mockingbird*?

22 Made into a film, who wrote the book *American Psycho*?

23 For which particular genre is Zane Grey best known?

24 Which writer moved to England in 1977 and whose work includes *Mother Tongue*, *The Lost Continent* and *Made in America*?

25 Which short story writer, humorist and illustrator wrote, among others, *My World – and Welcome to It*?

1 What happened on 22 January 1901?

2 Who is the first female in line to the throne at present?

3 What relation was Kaiser Wilhelm II to King Edward VII?

4 Who was appointed chancellor of the University of London on the resignation of the Queen Mother in 1981?

5 How did seventeen-year-old Marcus Sergeant make the news in June 1981?

6 Who was created Chief Morning Star by Canada's Stormy Creek Indians in 1919?

7 Why was Edward VII's coronation put back from June to August in 1902?

8 Who owned Anmer, the horse under which suffragette Emily Davison threw herself at the 1913 Derby?

9 Lambert Simnel and Perkin Warbeck were pretenders to the throne of which king?

10 Which monarch had to wear leg splints as a child to combat knock-knees?

11 Aged fourteen and ten respectively, who spoke to the nation on the BBC's *Children's Hour* on 13 October 1940?

12 According to her wishes, in what colour was Queen Victoria dressed for her funeral?

13 Where did the royal version of the TV programme *It's a Knockout* take place?

14 Who served on board the HMS *Invincible* during the Falklands war?

15 What are Prince William's three middle names?

16 Which member of the royal family opened the 1956 Olympic Games in Melbourne?

17 Who was granted a *decree nisi* in Ipswich on 27 October 1936?

18 Who broke into Buckingham Palace and spent ten minutes in the Queen's bedroom in July 1982?

19 Who was the first monarch to visit Russia?

20 Under which monarch did the family change its name to Windsor?

21 Where did Diana visit on her first overseas tour as Princess of Wales in 1983?

22 Of which school was Prince Charles made head boy in January 1967?

23 Where did Princess Margaret marry photographer Antony Armstrong-Jones in May 1960?

24 Which member of the royal family participated in the 1926 Wimbledon men's doubles?

25 By which of his seven Christian names was Edward VIII usually called by his family?

1 When was the first World Cup held?

2 Where did it take place?

3 Where did the 1987 World Cup take place?

4 Who were the first winners?

5 How many finals have England reached?

6 Who won the World Cup in 1999?

7 What is the highest innings score?

8 What is the lowest score?

9 Who has the highest individual score?

10 Who has the best bowling figures?

11 Who has the only hat trick?

12 Who has scored the most runs in the competition?

13 Who is the highest scoring Englishman?

14 Who has taken the most wickets?

15 Who is the highest English wicket-taker?

16 Who is the most successful Kiwi?

17 What is Lara's World Cup batting average?

18 Who is the most successful Indian?

19 Who is the most successful Australian?

20 Where was the 1987 final played?

21 Where do Scotland usually play their home games?

22 Who did Sri Lanka beat to win in 1996?

23 Who did Australia beat in Calcutta?

24 Who has won the most times?

25 Who is known as the Mighty Springbok?

1 Which two stars of a current US sitcom have formed their own production company called Bristol Cities?

2 Which dame of British theatre is James Bond's latest boss and stars in a TV series playing opposite Geoffrey Palmer?

3 Who plays Alicia Witt and Deedee Pfeiffer's screen mother in her own US sitcom?

4 Who played the only female cab driver in *Taxi*?

5 Who replaced Farrah Fawcett-Majors in *Charlie's Angels*?

6 Who played Ross's British wife in *Friends*?

7 Who played Samantha, the nose-twitching witch, in *Bewitched*?

8 Who connects 1970s sitcom *Rhoda* with *The Simpsons*?

9 Who formed a production company called Desilu with her husband Desi Arnaz?

10 Who did Kirstie Alley replace in *Cheers*?

11 Which star of *Absolutely Fabulous* once played a crime-fighter alongside Patrick Macnee and Gareth Hunt?

12 Which British actress, famous for her role as Elizabeth I in a 1970s TV series, became a Labour MP in 1992?

13 Who replaced Barbara Bel Geddes in the role of Miss Ellie Ewing for a short time on *Dallas*?

14 Who played Mrs Bennett in the BBC's 1995 production of *Pride and Prejudice*?

15 Which ex-Benny Hill girl is part of a multi-Emmy-winning comedy show?

16 Which actress appears in both *Ally McBeal* and *ER*?

17 Now a star in Hollywood, who came to TV screens in a homely 1991 series based on novels by H E Bates?

18 Who appeared dishevelled as a prisoner of war in *Tenko* and as glamorous as it gets in *Dynasty*?

19 Which actress/comedienne has starred with two different surnames and with no surname at all?

20 Which family's mother was played by Miss Michael Learned?

21 How were veteran actresses Helen Hayes and Mildred Natwick known in a lighthearted detective series in the 1970s?

22 Which former model and child star is the central character in *Suddenly Susan*?

23 Sarah Michelle Gellar plays Buffy the Vampire Slayer in the TV series of the same name, but who played the part in the 1992 film?

24 Which actress co-starred in *The Dick Van Dyke Show* and went on to have her own series, which itself spawned a couple of spin-offs?

25 Which established star of a US sitcom was originally due to play the part of Roz Doyle in *Frasier*?

1 Who was the star of the show *Ray's a Laugh*?

2 First broadcast in 1951, what did *Crazy People* go on to become?

3 Who were the two original stars of the show *Bandwagon*?

4 What did the initials stand for in the show *ITMA*?

5 Who was the subject of that show's title?

6 What was the ventriloquist's name in the 1950s series *Educating Archie*?

7 Which actor/comedian starred in *Variety Bandbox* as a spiv?

8 What was the name of Christopher Morris's radio news spoof which begat the TV series *The Day Today*?

9 What was the full name of the occupant of 23 Railway Cuttings, East Cheam?

10 Which former members of *The Mary Whitehouse Experience* star in *The Now Show*?

11 What was Mrs Mopp's best-known catchphrase on the *ITMA* shows?

12 Which section of BBC radio started on 29 July 1945?

13 At which mythical RAF base were Richard Murdoch and Kenneth Horne teamed?

14 Which comedy duo, renowned for their later TV appearances, starred in *Laughter Incorporated* in 1958?

15 Which 'antidote to panel games' is hosted by Humphrey Lyttelton?

16 Who was the regular female member of the *Round the Horne* team?

17 Which show ran for thirteen series between 1959 and 1977, featuring among its cast Leslie Phillips, Jon Pertwee, Michael Bates and Ronnie Barker?

18 Who came to prominence as Archie Andrews' teacher, with the catchphrase 'Flippin' kids'?

19 Which show had episodes entitled 'The Nadger Plague', 'Who is Pink Oboe?' and 'The Toothpaste Expedition'?

20 Who was scriptwriter on *Educating Archie*, later to write and star in his own TV series?

21 Who is the host of *Just a Minute*?

22 Who played the camp duo Julian and Sandy in *Round the Horne*?

23 Which Australian and South African performers played regular supporting roles in *Hancock's Half Hour*?

24 Which family were introduced to the nation in the early 1950s on the show *Take It From Here*?

25 Which TV spoof chat show host started life as a spoof radio sports correspondent?

1 Which company started as the Pacific Aero Products Company in 1916, was given its present name in 1917, and is today the largest aviation company in the world?

2 What do the initials IATA stand for?

3 Which term is used for electronic instruments for use in aviation?

4 Which acronym is used for the long-range radar surveillance and control centre for air defence developed originally in the USA?

5 Which engine powered both the Spitfire and Hurricane fighters of World War II?

6 Who was the first woman to fly solo across the Atlantic Ocean?

7 In 1997 there was a mid-air collision between a Saudi Boeing 747 and a Kazak airliner that claimed the lives of all 349 on board. Near which city did it occur?

8 Which aviation company produces the DC series of aircraft?

9 What is Charles E 'Chuck' Yeager's claim to fame in aviation?

10 In which country did Charles Lindbergh land after the first solo transatlantic flight in 1927?

11 What was the name of the Java-born Dutch aircraft manufacturer who, during World War I, produced more than 40 types of airplanes for the German High Command?

12 Which aircraft manufacturer produced the Spitfire?

13 What was the family name of the French brothers who were pioneer developers of the hot-air balloon and who conducted the first untethered flights?

14 Who was chief of aeronautical research and development at the British Aircraft Corporation 1945 to 1971, having previously designed the Wellington bomber of World War II?

15 Which company produced the world's first commercial jet airliner?

16 Who made the world's first over-the-ocean flight in a heavier-than-air craft?

17 What name was given to the Boeing B-52 heavy bomber that first flew in 1952?

18 What is the name of the Russian-born US pioneer in aircraft design who is best known for his successful development of the helicopter?

19 Who was dubbed 'Queen of the Air' by the British press in the 1930s after her solo flight from England to Australia?

20 Sydney's main airport is named after which great Australian aviator?

21 Lester B Pearson International Airport is in which Canadian city?

22 How was the Mitsubishi A6M fighter aircraft better known?

23 The Lockheed F-117 Nighthawk was the first of which type of aircraft?

24 Which famous series of aircraft was designed by Artem Mikoyan and Mikhail Gurevich?

25 Which famous aircraft of World War II had a frame of wood and a skin of plywood, and was glued and screwed together in England, Canada and Australia?

1 Who played the Mad Hatter in Jonathan Miller's television version of his party in 1966?

2 Which grasping, lecherous cleric is Molière's star creation?

3 Where was the Tea Party that marked the beginning of the American revolt against British rule?

4 Which Venetian painter's nickname derives from his father's occupation as a dyer?

5 Which band had hits with 'Ride a White Swan' and 'Telegram Sam'?

6 What was Talking Heads' first hit single?

7 Under the Hafsids, which city became the Arab world's leading metropolis?

8 Which example of New British Cinema, adapted from a stage play, is said to have led to a change in the law with its depiction of a pregnant girl's plight?

9 Which band had a number one hit with 'Pray'?

10 In which film did Jodie Foster get her first starring role, playing a teenage prostitute?

11 Jim Henson's Creature Shop manufactured these man-sized amphibians. Who are they?

12 When did the Isle of Man first stage its TT race?

13 In 1975, which band wasn't in love?

14 Mel Smith's directorial debut featured what kind of guy?

15 At the utterance of which phrase did Carole Lombard get raunchy every evening in Ernst Lubitsch's 1942 film?

16 Which town is Sicily's best-known resort?

17 Who ain't gonna bump no more with no big fat woman?

18 What is Yasujiro Ozu's best-known film?

19 During the filming of which Martinique classic did Humphrey Bogart and Lauren Bacall fall in love?

20 Who sure played a mean pinball?

21 Which Swiss sculptor's 'junk sculpture' work satirizes modern technology?

22 To which Irish town is it a long way, according to the song?

23 According to myth, which people owe their existence to the union of an ogress and a monkey on Mt Gangpo Ri?

24 Which art gallery was named after the millionaire inventor of the sugar cube?

25 Which band won both best band and best album awards at the Brit Awards 2000?

ANSWERS TO QUIZ 7

Criminals
1 Aviator Charles Lindbergh
2 The Acid Bath Murderer
3 Ted Bundy
4 Jack the Ripper
5 John Christie
6 Anthony Blunt
7 Chicago
8 California abolished the death penalty
9 Jeffrey Dahmer
10 Burke and Hare
11 Peter Sutcliffe, the Yorkshire Ripper
12 Lizzie Borden
13 Fred West
14 Tax evasion
15 Leopold and Loeb
16 Myra Hindley
17 Bugsy
18 Ruth Ellis
19 Dr Crippen
20 Bonnie and Clyde
21 Dutch Schultz
22 1969
23 Sam Giancana
24 The Boston Strangler
25 'Lucky' Luciano

Diana
1 Ronald Reagan
2 Diana, Princess of Wales
3 Henri Paul
4 James Hewitt
5 Trevor Rees-Jones
6 International Red Cross
7 Stepmother
8 Martin Bashir
9 Victor Edelstein
10 Eight
11 Rottweiler
12 Barbara Daly
13 Will Carling
14 Bulimia
15 English National Ballet
16 Earl Spencer
17 1996
18 St Mary's, Paddington
19 A diamond stud
20 Kindergarten assistant
21 Jane
22 Andrew Morton
23 David Ginola
24 Frances
25 David and Elizabeth Emanuel

Woody Allen
1 Mira Sorvino
2 *The Purple Rose of Cairo*
3 *The Front*
4 *Radio Days*
5 *Take the Money and Run*
6 Jimmy Bond
7 *Stardust Memories*
8 *Sleeper*
9 Mia Farrow
10 George Gershwin
11 *Bullets Over Broadway*
12 *Love and Death*
13 *Play It Again, Sam*
14 Alan Alda
15 Martin Scorsese and Francis Coppola
16 Bob Hope
17 *Broadway Danny Rose*
18 *Annie Hall*
19 *Bananas*
20 *Zelig*
21 *What's New, Pussycat?*
22 Clarinet
23 *Husbands and Wives*
24 Bette Midler
25 *Manhattan Murder Mystery*

War Films
1 *Sergeant York*
2 *The Deer Hunter*
3 Rod Steiger
4 The war in Vietnam
5 Richard Wagner
6 *The Birth of a Nation*
7 *The Charge of the Light Brigade*
8 Matt Damon
9 *Platoon*
10 The Normandy landings, 6 June 1944
11 *The Bridge on the River Kwai*
12 It was voted best film at the first Academy Awards
13 Karl Malden
14 Liam Neeson
15 Mel Gibson
16 *Glory*
17 *All Quiet on the Western Front*
18 *In Which We Serve*
19 *From Here to Eternity*
20 John Wayne
21 *Kelly's Heroes*
22 *The Thin Red Line*
23 Stanley Kubrick
24 *Gettysburg*
25 Richard Attenborough

Insects & Spiders
1 Hymenoptera
2 The ladybird
3 Dragonflies
4 Head, thorax and abdomen
5 Queens
6 The Black Widow
7 It spends most of its time underground
8 Entomology
9 Wood fibre
10 The tsetse fly
11 It is an appendage through which a female insect lays her eggs
12 Larva
13 The female
14 Daddy-longlegs
15 Mandibles
16 Together
17 Up to three years
18 Cuckoo spit
19 Centipedes and millipedes
20 The mosquito
21 A beetle
22 The earwig
23 The Goliath beetle
24 The silverfish
25 An insect's external skeleton

The British Isles
1 Brecon Beacons National Park
2 The Old Man of Hoy
3 Boyne
4 Stour
5 Loch Lomond
6 A mountain range in Ireland
7 Portmeirion
8 Isle of Wight
9 Cannock Chase
10 Cheviot Hills
11 Guernsey
12 Isle of Man
13 Inner Hebrides
14 Cape Wrath
15 Anglesey
16 Tees
17 Mendips
18 The Broads
19 Yorkshire Dales
20 Straits of Dover
21 Hops
22 Bute
23 Hillingdon
24 River Dee
25 Pilgrim's Way

Motown
1 Detroit
2 The Supremes
3 Berry Gordy, Jr
4 The Four Tops
5 R Dean Taylor
6 Marvin Gaye
7 Smokey Robinson
8 'Uptight (Everything's Alright)'
9 Junior Walker
10 'Someday We'll Be Together'
11 The Marvelettes
12 Los Angeles
13 Hitsville USA
14 Stevie Wonder and Michael Jackson
15 Tammi Terrell
16 *Music of My Mind*
17 It was released on his eighteenth birthday
18 Diana Ross and The Supremes and The Temptations
19 Boyz II Men
20 Motown owned the name 'Jackson Five'
21 Bass and drums
22 Martha Reeves
23 The Temptations
24 'I've Never Been to Me'
25 Stateside

New Romantics
1 *Barbarella*
2 Gloria Jones
3 The Human League
4 'Do You Really Want to Hurt Me?'
5 Vienna
6 Gary Numan
7 David Sylvian of the group Japan
8 Limahl
9 Boy George
10 'I Ran (So Far Away)'
11 Tony Hadley
12 'Don't You Want Me'
13 ABC
14 Visage
15 'No More I Love Yous'
16 'Girls On Film'
17 Blitz
18 *The Krays*
19 Dali's Car
20 Giorgio Moroder
21 'Too Shy'
22 1983
23 *A View to a Kill*
24 Midge Ure
25 Orchestral Manoeuvres in the Dark

American Writers
1 Norman Mailer
2 Spanish Civil War
3 William Burroughs
4 *On the Road*
5 John Updike
6 Tarzan

7 Sylvia Plath
8 *The Bonfire of the Vanities*
9 John Irving
10 Ken Kesey
11 Tom Clancy
12 *Fear of Flying*
13 F Scott Fitzgerald
14 Raymond Chandler
15 Stephen King
16 John Dos Passos
17 Maya Angelou
18 Dashiell Hammett
19 Tom Wolfe
20 Robert Ludlum
21 Harper Lee
22 Bret Easton Ellis
23 The Western
24 Bill Bryson
25 James Thurber

The Royal Family
1 Queen Victoria died
2 Princess Beatrice, 5th in line
3 Nephew
4 Princess Anne
5 He fired six blanks at the Queen during the Trooping the Colour parade
6 The Prince of Wales, later Edward VIII
7 He had emergency surgery for appendicitis
8 King George V
9 Henry VII
10 George VI
11 Princesses Elizabeth and Margaret
12 White
13 Alton Towers theme park
14 Prince Andrew
15 Arthur Philip Louis
16 Prince Philip
17 Wallis Simpson
18 Michael Fagen
19 Edward VII, 1908
20 George V, 1917
21 Australia and New Zealand
22 Gordonstoun
23 Westminster Abbey
24 The Duke of York, later George VI
25 David

Cricket World Cup
1 1975
2 England
3 India and Pakistan
4 West Indies
5 Three
6 Australia

7 398–5
8 45
9 Viv Richards
10 Winston Davies
11 Chetan Sharma
12 Javed Miandad
13 Graham Gooch
14 Imran Khan
15 Ian Botham
16 Martin Crowe
17 50
18 Sachem Tendulkar
19 Steve Waugh
20 Calcutta
21 Edinburgh
22 Australia
23 England
24 West Indies
25 Lance Klusener

Female Stars
1 Jane Leeves and Peri Gilpin (Daphne and Roz in *Frasier*)
2 Judi Dench
3 Cybill Shepherd
4 Marilu Henner
5 Cheryl Ladd
6 Helen Baxendale
7 Elizabeth Montgomery
8 *The Simpsons*
9 Lucille Ball
10 Shelley Long (but not as the same character)
11 Joanna Lumley
12 Glenda Jackson
13 Donna Reed
14 Alison Steadman
15 Jane Leeves
16 Lisa Nicole Carson
17 Catherine Zeta Jones
18 Stephanie Beacham
19 Roseanne
20 The Waltons
21 The Snoop Sisters
22 Brooke Shields
23 Kristy Swanson
24 Mary Tyler Moore
25 Lisa Kudrow (Phoebe in *Friends*)

Radio Comedy
1 Ted Ray
2 *The Goon Show*
3 Arthur Askey and Richard Murdoch
4 *It's That Man Again*
5 Adolf Hitler
6 Peter Brough
7 Arthur English
8 *On the Hour*
9 Anthony Aloysius St John Hancock

10 Hugh Dennis and Steve Punt
11 'Can I do you now, Sir?'
12 The Light Programme
13 *Much Binding in the Marsh*
14 Morecambe and Wise
15 *I'm Sorry I Haven't a Clue*
16 Betty Marsden
17 *The Navy Lark*
18 Tony Hancock
19 *The Goon Show*
20 Eric Sykes
21 Nicholas Parsons
22 Hugh Paddick and Kenneth Williams
23 Bill Kerr and Sid James
24 The Glums
25 Alan Partridge

Aviation
1 Boeing
2 International Air Transport Association
3 Avionics
4 AWACS
5 Rolls-Royce Merlin
6 Beryl Markham
7 New Delhi
8 McDonnell-Douglas
9 First man to fly faster than the speed of sound
10 France
11 Anthony Fokker
12 Supermarine
13 Montgolfier
14 Barnes Wallis
15 De Havilland (the Comet)
16 Louis Bleriot
17 Stratofortress
18 Igor Sikorsky
19 Amy Johnson
20 Sir Charles Kingsford-Smith
21 Toronto
22 Zero
23 Stealth
24 MiG
25 De Havilland Mosquito

The Letter T
1 Peter Cook
2 Tartuffe
3 Boston
4 Tintoretto ('*tintore*', 'to dye' in Italian)
5 T-Rex
6 'Once in a Lifetime' (1981)
7 Tunis
8 *A Taste of Honey*
9 Take That
10 *Taxi Driver*

11 Teenage Mutant Ninja Turtles
12 1907
13 10 CC
14 *The Tall Guy*
15 'To be or not to be'
16 Taormina
17 Joe Tex
18 *Tokyo Story*
19 *To Have and Have Not*
20 Tommy
21 Jean Tinguely
22 Tipperary
23 The Tibetans
24 Tate Gallery (Sir Henry Tate)
25 Travis

THE ULTIMATE BOOK
OF TRIVIA

QUIZ 8

1 Which Rugby Union player created a world record by playing in 53 consecutive matches for Wales between 1967 and 1978?

2 Who left to his wife his 'second-best bed'?

3 Who weighed nearly 53 stone (742 lb, 337 kg) at his death in 1809?

4 Which very famous lady was christened with the name of the city in which she was born?

5 Which footballer made 106 appearances for England, scoring 49 international goals?

6 What are the Christian names of Torvill and Dean?

7 Which bestselling author wrote *The Cruel Sea*?

8 In terms of their names, what do Paul McCartney and Harold Wilson have in common?

9 Which character actor made his name in the 1978 TV serial *Pennies from Heaven*?

10 Who was born in 1758 at Burnham Thorpe, Norfolk and died at the age of 47?

11 Which Prime Minister won the Nobel Prize for Literature?

12 In which year did Sharron Davies first compete in an Olympic Games?

13 What was the surname of the artist whose forenames were Joseph Mallord William?

14 How is Emma Bunton better known?

15 Who first became well known writing radio scripts with Frank Muir?

16 Which Rugby player was known as 'The King'?

17 Which jockey rode Aldaniti to victory in the 1981 Grand National, having spent the previous two years winning a battle with cancer?

18 Which famous soldier was drowned when HMS *Hampshire* sank after striking a mine in 1916?

19 Which British actor had to change his name because there was already a very famous James Stewart?

20 Which actor was married to actresses Vivien Leigh and Joan Plowright (at different times, of course!)?

21 Who won the women's singles championship at Wimbledon in 1961?

22 Who was the original question master on *University Challenge*?

23 Which impresario, who shares a name with an item of clothing, is famous for staging hit musicals such as *Cats*, *Miss Saigon* and *Les Misérables*?

24 What was the name of the 24-year-old RAF bomber pilot who led the Dam Busters raid?

25 Who is the only Briton to have won the Formula One world motor racing championship three times?

1 Which bookie did Vince Pinner work for?

2 Who had a black home help?

3 In which series did George and Kramer appear?

4 What was Reg Varney's character called in *On the Buses*?

5 Where was Elaine Nardo the only female cabbie?

6 Who played Roger's wife in *Outside Edge*?

7 Who was the barman at the Nag's Head?

8 Who is the main character in *One Foot in the Grave*?

9 What was Lovejoy's profession?

10 What was Phil Silvers's rank?

11 Who played Terry in *Terry and June*?

12 Which Eric played with Hattie Jacques?

13 Where did Mork come from?

14 Who was the main character in *All Creatures Great and Small*?

15 Who played Frank Spencer?

16 Who played Columbo?

17 What was Fitz's full name in *Cracker*?

18 Which detective did Stacy Keach play?

19 What was the name of Edina's PA in *Absolutely Fabulous*?

20 In *The Good Life*, who was Lenin?

21 Who was Blackadder's servant?

22 What is the Vicar of Dibley's name?

23 What was Dorien's surname in *Birds of a Feather*?

24 Who played Uncle Albert?

25 Who was Stan's nagging wife in the Street?

1 With 26 appearances, who was in the most *Carry On* films?

2 Before returning to star in the 1992 *Carry On Columbus*, who last appeared in the 1969 film *Carry On Again, Doctor*?

3 In which film does Barbara Windsor's bra fly off while she is exercising?

4 What was Sid James's final *Carry On* film?

5 Which part of Britain was used for the location shooting of *Carry On Up the Khyber*?

6 Which star of previous *Carry On* films died days before shooting started on *Carry On Columbus*?

7 Who made her *Carry On* debut in *Carry On Spying* in 1964?

8 Who played the title role in *Carry On Cleo*?

9 Who respectively produced and directed the *Carry On* series?

10 Which member of hospital staff was portrayed by Hattie Jacques in all four of the medical *Carry Ons*?

11 Which film starred Phil Silvers, of *Bilko* fame?

12 What was significant about the 1962 film, *Carry On Cruising*?

13 What was the first film in the series?

14 In *Carry On Nurse*, with what does Wilfrid Hyde-White have his 'temperature' taken, in place of a thermometer?

15 Which star of radio played the headmaster in the 1959 film *Carry On Teacher*?

16 In which 1960 film did Sid James make his *Carry On* debut?

17 Which Hammer horror spoof starred Harry H Corbett as a policeman with the 'fitting name' of Bung?

18 What was Jim Dale's suggestively named medic in *Carry On Again, Doctor*?

19 Which film was retitled *Carry On Round the Bend* for some foreign releases?

20 Which period from history provided the setting for *Carry On, Don't Lose Your Head*?

21 In which film does the Miss Fircombe beauty contest take place?

22 Who play the rival taxi-firm bosses in *Carry On Cabby*?

23 Who plays the vamp in *Carry On Screaming*?

24 Which two members of the *Dad's Army* cast feature in the 1970 film *Carry On Loving*?

25 Who plays saloon owner Belle in *Carry On Cowboy*?

1 Who was the first European to set eyes on Manhattan?

2 Which Indian tribe were the original inhabitants of Manhattan?

3 What was the name of the city's original defensive moat?

4 In which building was the world's first working elevator installed in 1857?

5 Which symbol of freedom, designed by Frédéric-Auguste Bartholdi, was a gift to the city from the French?

6 Which mayor of New York City was awarded an honorary knighthood in 2001?

7 Which of New York City's five boroughs was formerly called Richmond?

8 Who wrote the poem that begins 'Give me your tired, your poor, your huddled masses', as inscribed on the Statue of Liberty?

9 What does the name SoHo stand for?

10 Which famous local resident owns the TriBeCa Grill?

11 Why is No. 33 Union Square famous?

12 Which building appeared in the finale of the film *King Kong*?

13 Why was Times Square so called?

14 How long did it take the Chrysler building to lose its title of 'world's tallest building'?

15 Who purchased the site for the new UN headquarters?

16 Approximately how many works of art are there in the Museum of Modern Art?

17 What was the first complex in the world to integrate offices with shops and entertainment?

18 Which building turned down Madonna's application for residency as 'unsuitable'?

19 Outside which building was John Lennon shot?

20 Who designed the Solomon R Guggenheim museum?

21 What was transported complete from Egypt in 1960 in order to become an exhibit at the Metropolitan Museum?

22 During the 1930s, what was the most famous club in Harlem?

23 How did the Bronx get its name?

24 In the gay spa of which hotel was Bette Midler discovered?

25 In which hotel did Sid Vicious die?

1 Which castle served as the European headquarters of the Nasrid dynasty for over 250 years?

2 Which castle holds an annual service for the knights of the Order of the Garter?

3 Which 19th-century castle was designed by a Munich scene painter called Christina Jank?

4 Whose private castle, known as San Simeon, was the inspiration for Orson Welles's film *Citizen Kane*?

5 Which park's central attraction is Cinderella's Castle?

6 Which castle's first tenant was General Eisenhower?

7 Which 'castle' sells tickets for the ferry to the Statue of Liberty?

8 From which castle did Perkin Warbeck start his rebellion in 1497?

9 In which castle did King Arthur live with Queen Guinevere?

10 Which castle was constructed by the owner of the Home and Colonial Tea Stores?

11 In which castle was King Edward the Martyr stabbed to death in 978?

12 Which castle did Sir Walter Raleigh persuade Queen Elizabeth to lease to him for £260?

13 In which castle did Judge Jeffreys hold his Bloody Assizes?

14 Which castle is generally held to be the site of the legendary Camelot?

15 How much did Queen Victoria pay for Balmoral Castle in 1852?

16 Which castle in Ireland was built for the Marquis of Donegal?

17 Which castle's records office did Michael Collins break into?

18 Which castle is reputed to be the most haunted house in Ireland?

19 Which castle contains the Great Telescope which, in 1845, was the largest in the world?

20 Which castle was the home of John of Gaunt?

21 Which French castle was the birthplace of the English King Stephen?

22 On a lintel in which castle did Charles VIII of France knock his head, causing his own death?

23 Which castle was the French marital home of Mary, Queen of Scots?

24 Which castle was finally surrendered by the Crusaders to Sultan Baibars in 1271?

25 In which Scottish county is Glamis Castle?

1 Elton's first singles and albums were on the DJM label. What do the initials stand for?

2 With whom did Elton duet on the 1996 single 'Live Like Horses'?

3 Which 1974 single features members of The Beach Boys on backing vocals?

4 For which song did Elton and Tim Rice win the 1994 Academy Award?

5 What was Elton's first UK single release on his own Rocket label?

6 Who are the only two artists to have spent more weeks in the UK singles charts than Elton John?

7 Which other song was released on the single 'Candle in the Wind '97'?

8 Which album did Elton première at Wembley Stadium in June 1975?

9 What was Elton's first US number one single?

10 Which of Elton's albums was the biggest-selling album in the UK in 1973?

11 Which of Elton's singles was a tribute to a despatch rider killed in an accident?

12 Which American city did Elton sing about in a 1974 single?

13 On which album did the original recording of 'Candle in the Wind' first appear?

14 In the song 'Rocket Man', what time is 'zero hour'?

15 Who were the other three major artists featured on the 1985 charity single 'That's What Friends are For'?

16 With whom did Elton duet on 'Don't Go Breaking My Heart' in 1994?

17 Which 1982 single was written as a tribute to John Lennon?

18 On what occasion did Elton sing the hymn 'Abide with Me' at Wembley Stadium?

19 Which album features Elton's real name in its title?

20 Which song did Elton sing in the Ken Russell film of The Who's *Tommy*?

21 Which singer, later to release a live duet with Elton, featured uncredited on Elton's 1985 single 'Wrap Her Up'?

22 What type of venues did Elton play on his 2000 summer tour of Britain?

23 What was the title of Elton's 1973 Christmas single?

24 On which John Lennon single did Elton guest on piano and backing vocals?

25 What was Elton's first solo UK number one single?

1 What is Cliff Richard's real name?

2 In which year did Cliff perform an impromptu hit medley at Wimbledon's Lawn Tennis Championship?

3 Name the original reverse side of 'Move It'.

4 In which Indian city was Cliff born?

5 Name the character played by Cliff in *Serious Charge*.

6 Which role did he play in a 1966 London Palladium production of *Cinderella*?

7 What was the title of Cliff's 1987 Euro-tour?

8 Who played all the instruments on Cliff's 1985 single 'She's So Beautiful'?

9 Who recorded a new hit version of 'Living Doll' with Cliff in 1986?

10 What was Cliff's 100th single?

11 On which label was 'The Millennium Prayer' released?

12 What was the title of Cliff's first chart album?

13 In which film was Cliff cast as Bongo Herbert?

14 What was the name of the Dave Clark musical in which Cliff starred in 1986–7?

15 Name Cliff's hit duet with Phil Everly.

16 In which film did Cliff sing 'Bachelor Boy'?

17 Who wrote the 1966 hit 'Blue Turns to Grey'?

18 Which song beat 'Congratulations' in the 1968 Eurovision Song Contest?

19 During 1976, which music paper did Cliff refuse to have in his house?

20 What were The Shadows formerly called?

21 With whom did Cliff perform at the Royal Albert Hall in 1979 as part of the venue's 75th birthday appeal?

22 In which film did Cliff attempt to sell 'Brumburgers', a form of hamburger stemming from the Midlands?

23 Who had the original hit with 'Daddy's Home'?

24 Cliff's mother married an East End undertaker. True or false?

25 Name Cliff's biggest-selling single worldwide.

1 Which island served as the United States principal immigration depot from 1892 to 1943?

2 Who was the first European to set foot in North America?

3 Where did Christopher Columbus first land in America in 1492?

4 Who sailed into San Francisco Bay in 1579 and claimed it for Queen Elizabeth I?

5 Who devised the first draft of the Declaration of Independence?

6 In 1847, who led a group of Latter-day Saints to Utah to save them from persecution and which city did he found there?

7 Which president dedicated the Statue of Liberty on 28 October 1886?

8 For which British newspaper did the broadcaster Alistair Cooke write in the 1960s?

9 Who assassinated Abraham Lincoln?

10 Into the face of which mountain were the faces of four presidents carved in 1939?

11 Which gangster was behind the creation of Las Vegas as a gambling heaven?

12 Which arch commemorates the role of St Louis as 'The Gateway to the West'?

13 Who founded New Orleans?

14 Whose autobiography was called *How to Talk Dirty and Influence People*?

15 When did the Stars and Stripes become the official flag?

16 When did Prohibition start and end?

17 What was JFK Airport originally called?

18 Who was John F Kennedy's vice-president?

19 Which two journalists first revealed details of Watergate in the *Washington Post*?

20 Which American wrote the classic native tale *The Legend of Sleepy Hollow*?

21 Which is the nation's oldest chartered city?

22 Which platform did the Chatanooga Choo Choo leave from?

23 Which was the biggest city in America until 1775?

24 Where is Arlington National Cemetery?

25 In which city is the Liberty Bell, which rang out for each patriot victory and was later an anti-slavery symbol?

1 Who was the first Yorkist king of England?

2 Who ordered the bombing of Dresden during the Second World War?

3 What was the name of Oliver Cromwell's army?

4 Who told the British people, 'You've never had it so good'?

5 Who is traditionally regarded as the first British prime minister?

6 Who was the first English king to have held the title Prince of Wales?

7 What did Winston Churchill win in 1953?

8 Who was the first sovereign to live at Buckingham Palace?

9 Who was the first woman to be elected Speaker of the House of Commons?

10 Who was the last British prime minister to have led government from the House of Lords?

11 Who summoned the Model Parliament?

12 Who was the king of the Scots from 1040 to 1057?

13 Who was the mother of James I of England?

14 In which year was VAT introduced in Britain?

15 Which prime minister took Britain into the EEC?

16 Who was prime minister at the time of the General Strike?

17 Who was the first woman to take her seat as an MP?

18 Who was the last Liberal to be prime minister of Britain?

19 When did Henry VIII begin to dissolve the monasteries?

20 Which city contains the largest number of standing medieval churches of any city in Europe?

21 Which document, signed by King John and a group of barons in 1215, led to the creation of the House of Lords?

22 Which was England's first designated National Park?

23 Which Scottish king defeated the English in 1314 in a decisive battle to retain independence?

24 What was the name of the women's rights movement led by Emmeline Pankhurst?

25 Where did the Great Fire of London start?

1 Who was the first long jumper to exceed 29 feet?

2 What event occurred at Chamonix, at the foot of Mont Blanc, in 1924?

3 Who was the first British footballer to be transferred for £1 million?

4 Who was the first snooker player to score a maximum 147 break in the world championships?

5 Which British racing driver was the first man to win the Indianapolis 500 at the first attempt in 1966?

6 What was significant about the 1968 Olympic men's 100 metres final?

7 Cuban high jumper Javier Sotomayor was the first to better which key height in the event?

8 Who, in 1964, became the first Manchester United player to be voted European Footballer of the Year?

9 Who was the first unseeded player to win the men's singles title at Wimbledon?

10 Who was the first woman to officiate at a Football League fixture?

11 Which two teams contested the first Wembley FA Cup final?

12 Who were the first winners of the Rugby Union World Cup in 1987?

13 In the 1996 Atlanta games 400-metre hurdler Deon Hemmings became the first woman from which country to win an Olympic gold medal?

14 Who was the first man to run the 5,000 metres in under thirteen minutes?

15 In 1967 Keith Peacock of Charlton Athletic became the first Football League player to do what?

16 In which sporting event was Oxford student Sue Brown the first of her sex to participate in 1981?

17 At which women's event was Moroccan Nawal el Moutawakel the first Olympic champion in 1984?

18 In which year was the European Cup-Winners Cup first contested?

19 When Jonathan Edwards broke the world triple jump record in 1995 he did so twice in successive jumps. The first took him over the 18-metre mark; what 'milestone' was achieved with the second?

20 What was American Gertrude Ederle's achievement in 1926, bettering any previous performance by a man?

21 In which season did Manchester United first achieve the double?

22 Which American football team won the first Superbowl in 1967?

23 Who was the first black footballer to play in a senior international for Sweden?

24 Who was the first man to pole vault over 19 feet?

25 In 1780 jockey Sam Arnull rode Diomed to victory in the first running of which horse race?

1 Which football league club did George Best play for on leaving Manchester United?

2 Who scored Ipswich Town's FA Cup winner?

3 Who was Leicester's playboy?

4 Who was England manager during the 1970s?

5 Who lifted the cup for Ipswich?

6 Which non-British nationalities did Robson sign for Ipswich?

7 Who did Geoff Astall play for?

8 Which hammer now pundits?

9 Which West Ham player of the 1960s and 1970s died of cancer?

10 Who was England's and Liverpool's goalkeeper?

11 Where did Rodney Marsh achieve fame?

12 Who did Clough manage before moving to Leeds?

13 Who won the 1978 World Cup?

14 What was ITV's football highlights show called?

15 Who presented *Match of the Day*?

16 Who scored the goal of the season in 1977?

17 Who managed Manchester United for the second half of the 1970s?

18 Who did Duncan McKenzie play for?

19 Who was Leeds's Scottish hard man and Captain?

20 Who did Alan Hunter play for?

21 For which club did Talbot leave Ipswich?

22 Who did Stuart Pearson play for?

23 Who played the cup final with a broken neck?

24 Who did Dennis Law play for before his move to Manchester City?

25 Which 1970s player went on to manage Birmingham City and Crystal Palace?

1 Name the type of Italian improvised comedy popular from the 16th to the 18th century.

2 With which company did Sir John Gielgud make his first stage appearance?

3 Which English playwright died of injuries when his coach overturned en route to Bath?

4 Sarah Bernhardt's career survived the amputation of which limb in 1915?

5 Of which company did the Barbican Theatre become the London home in 1982?

6 Traditionally, the phrase 'the Scottish play' is used in the theatre to refer to a work that it is supposed to be bad luck for actors to refer to by its real title. What is the play?

7 Which Greek dramatist lived in a cave on the island of Salamis?

8 In the original stage production of Alan Bennett's *A Question of Attribution*, who played Anthony Blunt?

9 Which actor had to stop playing Hamlet on the London stage because the experience caused him to have visions of his own dead father while performing?

10 With which London theatre is Sam Mendes most closely associated?

11 Which company, formerly Molière's, was founded in 1680 by Louis XIV?

12 Which Japanese theatre form, performed by a male cast, combines singing, dancing and acting?

13 Eduardo, Peppino and Titina opened their own playhouse – the Umoristico – in Naples in 1932. What was their surname?

14 Which American theatrical dynasty was founded when Louisa Lane married her third husband?

15 For which festival were T S Eliot's last three plays commissioned?

16 What was Tom Stoppard's first play?

17 Who ran the Actors' Studio in New York, where he tutored Marilyn Monroe and Marlon Brando among others?

18 Which French dramatist scored a world hit with *Cyrano de Bergerac*?

19 Yukio Ninagawa directed the first commercial production of Shakespeare in Japan. What was the play?

20 Which famous playwright worked as a music critic under the pseudonym 'Corno di Bassetto'?

21 What is the Green Room?

22 Whose theatrical version of the *Mahabharata* lasted nine hours?

23 From 1660 until 1968, to whom did every play in Britain have to be submitted for scrutiny with reference to indecency and seditious matter?

24 Who founded the Berliner Ensemble?

25 In which play does Serge buy a blank white canvas from a fashionable painter, much to the amusement of his friends?

1 Where was Thomas Hardy born?

2 Who 'was moderately truthful towards men, but to women lied like a Cretan'?

3 In what profession was Hardy employed when he moved to London?

4 What was his first published novel?

5 Whom did Julie Christie play in Schlesinger's film version of *Far from the Madding Crowd*?

6 In which novel do the 'Mellstock Quire' feature?

7 Which editor at Chapman Hall begged Hardy not to publish his first novel since it was 'too socialistic'?

8 In which novel's preface does it state that 'A novel is an impression, not an argument'?

9 Who played the Mayor of Casterbridge in the BBC series?

10 In Michael Winterbottom's film *Jude*, who played Jude's cousin, Sue?

11 The success of which novel enabled him to give up architecture and marry Emma Gifford?

12 Who was the best-known photographer of Hardy's landscapes?

13 In which fictional English county is most of his work set?

14 His second wife, Florence Dugdale, ostensibly wrote his biography. Who dictated the text?

15 Which university did Jude fail to get into?

16 Who evocatively photographed Dorset for the John Schlesinger film?

17 Roman Polanski's version of *Tess* was filmed in Britain and which other country?

18 Who starred in the film as Tess?

19 Where does the final dramatic scene of the novel take place?

20 In *The Mayor of Casterbridge*, who does Michael Henchard sell for five guineas?

21 In the ruins of which castle was Michael Henchard standing when he saw his daughter returning to Casterbridge?

22 Hardy wrote a novel about a pair of which coloured eyes?

23 From where was the title *Under the Greenwood Tree* taken?

24 For which town was 'Casterbridge' Hardy's pseudonym?

25 Fancy Day in *Under the Greenwood Tree* and Sue Bridehead in *Jude the Obscure* both did the same job. What was it?

1 In which century was Alfred the Great king of the West Saxons?

2 What relation was George III to George II?

3 Which king of England was killed while hunting in the New Forest in 1100?

4 Whose death warrant was signed by Elizabeth I at Greenwich on 1 February 1587?

5 Who was monarch at the time of Archbishop of Canterbury Thomas à Becket's murder?

6 How old was Henry III when he came to the throne in 1216?

7 What was the family name of Robert I of Scotland?

8 Who became king in 1422 at less than nine months old?

9 At whose coronation was Handel's anthem 'Zadok the Priest' first performed in 1727?

10 What was Macbeth from 1040 to 1057?

11 Who was the last Tudor monarch of England?

12 Which of Henry VIII's wives was the mother of Queen Mary I?

13 When James VI of Scotland became James I of England in 1603, for how long had he occupied the Scottish throne?

14 Which monarch died from smallpox in 1694, at the age of 32?

15 Which king suffered from the illness porphyria?

16 Who was the longest-reigning British monarch?

17 Which family of monarchs reigned after the Normans and before the House of Lancaster?

18 Who was on the throne at the time of the Great Fire of London?

19 Which king of England seized Normandy from his brother, Robert, in 1106 and imprisoned him for life?

20 Between 1340 and 1360, and again from 1369 to 1377, which monarch asserted his claim to the French throne?

21 Which two of Henry VIII's wives outlived him?

22 What is the relationship of princes William and Harry to Queen Victoria?

23 Where in July 1969 was Prince Charles invested as Prince of Wales?

24 Mary I and Elizabeth I were half-sisters. Who were the only sisters to be queens of England?

25 Who deposed his twelve-year-old nephew Edward V to become king in 1483?

1 What is the name of my black hen who lays eggs for gentlemen?

2 What did the old woman who lived in a shoe give her children to eat?

3 Who was the black sheep's second bag of wool for?

4 What will poor Robin do when the north wind blows?

5 With what did Jack mend his head?

6 Who stole the tarts that the Queen made?

7 What did Grandfa' Grig have?

8 How much money did Simple Simon have?

9 How many blackbirds were in the king's pie?

10 Where did Mary's lamb follow her?

11 Why did the boy let the fish go again?

12 After the cow jumped over the moon, who laughed?

13 By which time should the cobbler mend my shoe?

14 Why did Doctor Foster never return to Gloucester?

15 With which letter should the baker mark the cake?

16 What did Little Miss Muffett eat?

17 What grows in Mary, Mary's garden?

18 Where did Peter, Peter put his wife?

19 If one's for sorrow, what is five for?

20 What is Tuesday's child?

21 What did Jack Horner pull out of the pie?

22 Who put Pussy in the well?

23 Which one of Ladybird's children hasn't gone?

24 How many miles to Babylon?

25 What happened to Solomon Grundy on Thursday?

ANSWERS TO QUIZ 8

Famous Britons
1 Gareth Edwards
2 William Shakespeare
3 Daniel Lambert
4 Florence Nightingale
5 Bobby Charlton
6 Jayne and Christopher
7 Nicholas Monsarrat
8 Their first name is James
9 Bob Hoskins
10 Horatio Nelson
11 Winston Churchill
12 1976
13 Turner
14 Baby Spice
15 Denis Norden
16 Barry John
17 Bob Champion
18 Lord Kitchener
19 Stewart Granger
20 Laurence Olivier
21 Angela Mortimer
22 Bamber Gascoigne
23 Cameron Mackintosh
24 Guy Gibson
25 Jackie Stewart

TV Characters
1 Eddie Brains
2 Alf Garnett
3 *Seinfeld*
4 Stan Butler
5 The Sunshine Cab co.
6 Brenda Blethyn
7 Mike
8 Victor Meldrew
9 Antique dealer
10 Sergeant
11 Terry Scott
12 Sykes
13 Ork
14 James Herriot
15 Michael Crawford
16 Peter Falk
17 Eddie Fitzgerald
18 Mike Hammer
19 Bubble
20 A cockerel
21 Baldrick
22 Geraldine Granger
23 Green
24 Buster Merryfield
25 Hilda Ogden

Carry On
1 Kenneth Williams
2 Jim Dale
3 *Carry On Camping*
4 *Carry On Dick*, 1974
5 Snowdonia
6 Frankie Howerd
7 Barbara Windsor
8 Amanda Barrie
9 Peter Rogers and Gerald Thomas
10 Matron
11 *Follow that Camel*
12 It was the first one to be shot in colour
13 *Carry On Sergeant*
14 A daffodil
15 Ted Ray
16 *Carry On Constable*
17 *Carry On Screaming*
18 Dr Nookey
19 *Carry On at Your Convenience*
20 The French Revolution
21 *Carry On Girls*
22 Sid James and Hattie Jacques
23 Fenella Fielding
24 James Beck and Bill Pertwee
25 Joan Sims

New York
1 Giovanni da Verrazano
2 The Algonquin Indians
3 Wall Street
4 The Haughwout Building
5 The Statue of Liberty
6 Rudi Giuliani
7 Staten Island borough
8 Emma Lazarus
9 South of Houston Street
10 Robert de Niro
11 It was the site of Andy Warhol's home and film studio, The Factory
12 The Empire State Building
13 In honour of the *New York Times*, which moved its office there in 1904
14 Two months
15 John D Rockefeller, in 1946
16 100,000
17 The Rockefeller Center
18 145 Central Park West
19 The Dakota
20 Frank Lloyd Wright
21 The first-century Temple of Dendur
22 The Cotton Club
23 From Jonas Bronck's purchase of 500 acres of local land from the Dutch West India Company in 1641
24 The Ansonia
25 The Chelsea

Castles
1 The Alhambra, Granada
2 Windsor Castle
3 Neuschwanstein Castle, Bavaria
4 Randolph Hearst's Castle, California
5 Walt Disney World, Florida
6 Culzean Castle, Scotland
7 Castle Clinton, a former immigration station on the southern tip of Manhattan
8 St Michael's Mount
9 Tintagel
10 Castle Drogo, Devon
11 Corfe Castle, Dorset
12 Sherborne Castle, Dorset
13 Taunton Castle
14 Cadbury Castle, Somerset
15 £31,000
16 Belfast Castle
17 Dublin Castle
18 Leap Castle
19 Birr Castle Demesne, County Offaly
20 Kenilworth Castle
21 Blois
22 Amboise
23 Château de Chenonceau
24 Crac des Chevaliers, Syria
25 Angus

Elton John
1 Dick James Music
2 Luciano Pavarotti
3 'Don't Let the Sun Go Down on Me'
4 'Can You Feel the Love Tonight'
5 'Don't Go Breaking My Heart', duet with Kiki Dee
6 Elvis Presley and Cliff Richard
7 'Something About the Way You Look Tonight'
8 *Captain Fantastic and the Brown Dirt Cowboy*
9 'Crocodile Rock', 1973
10 *Don't Shoot Me, I'm Only the Piano Player*
11 'Song for Guy'
12 Philadelphia
13 *Goodbye Yellow Brick Road*
14 9 am
15 Dionne Warwick, Gladys Knight and Stevie Wonder
16 RuPaul
17 'Empty Garden'
18 Before the 1984 FA Cup final (along with everyone else)
19 *Reg Strikes Back*, 1988
20 'Pinball Wizard'
21 George Michael
22 Stately homes

23 'Step Into Christmas'
24 'Whatever Gets You Through the Night'
25 'Sacrifice/Healing Hands'

Cliff Richard
1 Harry Webb
2 1996
3 'Schoolboy Crush', which was originally intended as the A-side
4 Lucknow
5 Curly Thompson. He had to have his hair curled with hot tongs for the part
6 Buttons
7 The 'Always Guaranteed' tour
8 Stevie Wonder
9 The Young Ones
10 'The Best of Me', a hit in 1989
11 Papillon
12 *Cliff*
13 *Expresso Bongo*
14 *Time*
15 'She Means Nothing to Me'
16 *Summer Holiday*
17 Mick Jagger and Keith Richard
18 'La La La', performed by Spain's Massiel
19 *New Musical Express*, because of its high swear-word content
20 The Drifters
21 He appeared with Kate Bush and the London Symphony Orchestra
22 *Take Me High*
23 Shep and the Limeliters, in 1961
24 True. She married under-taker Derek Bodkin in 1966
25 'We Don't Talk Anymore', which has sold over five million copies

American History
1 Ellis Island
2 Leif Erikson, a Norseman
3 The Bahamas
4 Sir Francis Drake
5 Thomas Jefferson, third president
6 Brigham Young, who founded of Salt Lake City as a Mormon centre
7 President Grover Cleveland
8 *The Guardian*
9 John Wilkes Booth
10 Mount Rushmore

11 Bugsy Siegel
12 Gateway Arch
13 Sieur de Bienville, a Frenchman who founded a settlement on the site in 1718
14 Lenny Bruce
15 1777
16 It started in 1919 and ended in 1933
17 Idlewild
18 Lyndon Johnson
19 Bob Woodward and Carl Bernstein
20 Washington Irving
21 Albany, New York
22 Track 29
23 Boston
24 Washington, DC
25 Philadelphia

British History
1 Edward IV
2 Sir Arthur 'Bomber' Harris
3 New Model Army
4 Harold Macmillan
5 Robert Walpole
6 Edward II
7 Nobel Prize for Literature
8 Queen Victoria
9 Betty Boothroyd
10 The Marquess of Salisbury
11 Edward I in 1295
12 Macbeth
13 Mary, Queen of Scots
14 1973
15 Sir Edward Heath
16 Stanley Baldwin
17 Nancy Astor
18 Lloyd George
19 1536
20 Norwich
21 Magna Carta
22 The Peak District
23 Robert the Bruce
24 The suffragette movement (strictly speaking, the Women's Franchise League and the Women's Social and Political Union)
25 In Farriner's baking house in Pudding Lane

Sporting Firsts
1 Bob Beamon
2 The first Winter Olympic Games
3 Trevor Francis
4 Cliff Thorburn
5 Graham Hill
6 It was the first all-black Olympic sprint final
7 Eight feet

8 Denis Law
9 Boris Becker
10 Wendy Toms
11 Bolton Wanderers and West Ham United
12 New Zealand
13 Jamaica
14 Said Aouita
15 Substitute another player
16 The University Boat Race
17 400-metre hurdles
18 1960
19 The first jump over 60 feet
20 She was the first woman to swim the English Channel
21 1993/94
22 Green Bay Packers
23 Martin Dahlin
24 Sergey Bubka
25 The Derby

70s Football
1 Fulham
2 Osborne
3 Worthington
4 Don Revie
5 Mick Mills
6 Dutch
7 West Brom
8 Trevor Brooking
9 Bobby Moore
10 Ray Clemence
11 QPR
12 Derby
13 Argentina
14 *The Big Match*
15 Jimmy Hill
16 Keith Weller
17 Tommy Docherty
18 Leeds
19 Billy Bremner
20 Ipswich
21 Arsenal
22 Manchester United/West Ham
23 Bert Trautman
24 Manchester United
25 Trevor Francis

World of Theatre
1 Commedia dell'arte
2 The Old Vic
3 William Congreve
4 Her leg
5 The Royal Shakespeare Company
6 *Macbeth*
7 Euripides
8 Alan Bennett
9 Daniel Day Lewis
10 The Donmar Warehouse
11 The Comédie Française

12 Kabuki
13 De Filippo
14 The Barrymores
15 The Edinburgh Festival
16 *Rosencrantz and Guildenstern are Dead*
17 Lee Strasberg
18 Edmond Rostand (1898)
19 *Romeo and Juliet*
20 George Bernard Shaw
21 A room behind the stage where actors gather before the performance to relax
22 Peter Brook
23 The Lord Chamberlain
24 Bertolt Brecht
25 *Art*

Thomas Hardy
1 Higher Brockhampton, near Dorchester
2 Sergeant Troy in *Far From the Madding Crowd*
3 Architecture
4 *Desperate Remedies* (1871)
5 Bathsheba
6 *Under the Greenwood Tree*
7 George Meredith
8 *Tess of the D'Urbervilles*
9 Alan Bates
10 Kate Winslet
11 *Far From the Madding Crowd* (1874)
12 Hermann Lea
13 Wessex
14 Thomas Hardy
15 Christminster (Oxford)
16 Nicolas Roeg
17 France
18 Nastassja Kinski
19 At Stonehenge
20 His wife, Susan
21 Maiden Castle, the largest prehistoric earthwork in south England
22 *A Pair of Blue Eyes* (1873)
23 A song in *As You Like It*
24 Dorchester
25 Certified teacher

British Monarchs
1 The ninth
2 Grandson
3 William II (Rufus)
4 Mary, Queen of Scots
5 Henry II
6 Nine
7 Bruce
8 Henry VI
9 George II
10 King of the Scots
11 Elizabeth I

12 Catherine of Aragon
13 Almost thirty-six years
14 Mary II
15 George III
16 Victoria (June 1837 to January 1901)
17 The Plantagenets
18 Charles II
19 Henry I
20 Edward III
21 Anne of Cleves and Catherine Parr
22 Great-great-great-great-grandsons
23 Caernarfon Castle
24 Mary II and Anne
25 Richard III

Nursery Rhymes
1 Hickety Pickety
2 Some broth without any bread
3 The dame
4 He'll sit in a barn and keep himself warm and hide his head under his wing
5 Vinegar and brown paper
6 The Knave of Hearts
7 A pig
8 None
9 Four and twenty
10 To school
11 Because it bit his finger so
12 The dog
13 Half past two
14 Because he stepped in a puddle right up to his middle
15 B
16 Her curds and whey
17 Silver belles and cockle shells
18 In a pumpkin shell
19 Silver
20 Full of grace
21 A plum
22 Little Johnny Green
23 Little Ann
24 Threescore and ten
25 He took ill

THE ULTIMATE BOOK OF TRIVIA

QUIZ 9

1 Which famous silver screen act made their debut in 1929's *The Cocoanuts*?

2 Which American president married his cousin?

3 What was the Christian name of the brother of writers Edith and Sacheverell Sitwell?

4 What name connects the actors Henry, Peter, Jane and Bridget?

5 Pope Alexander VI, who died in 1503, was a member of which family?

6 Which American athlete, himself an Olympic gold medallist at the 1984 games, was the husband of one 1988 gold medallist and brother of another?

7 Kristin shot JR in *Dallas*. The actress who played her had a famous singer as a father. Who was he?

8 What was the surname of French brothers Etienne and Joseph, who pioneered hot-air balloon flight in 1783?

9 Who was the actress sister of Olivia de Havilland?

10 What are the Christian names of Australian cricketers the Waugh twins?

11 Which musical family rose to fame on Andy Williams' TV shows and had ten UK hits between 1972 and 1976?

12 Which family were grand dukes of Tuscany from 1569 to 1737?

13 How many brothers did the Brontë sisters have?

14 Which French father and son were, respectively, a painter and film director?

15 In which field are brothers Ridley and Tony Scott famous?

16 Which Barrymore is the odd one out from these: John, Ethel, Lionel, Drew and Michael?

17 Which American TV family was based on the *'Til Death Us Do Part* Garnett family, and featured Carrol O'Connor as Archie?

18 With which sport do you associate Fred Stolle and his son Sandon?

19 What is the surname of the actors Beau and Jeff and their late father, Lloyd?

20 From what did the royal family change its name to Windsor?

21 Which TV series launched the career of David Cassidy?

22 Which families are central to the story of Romeo and Juliet?

23 What is the name of the Viennese family associated with the waltz?

24 What was the family connection between singer Marvin Gaye and Motown boss Berry Gordy?

25 What were the Christian names of the parents of President John F Kennedy?

1 What part does Moose play in *Frasier*?

2 In the TV series that ran from 1962 to 1965, what was the name of the palamino horse that could talk?

3 What is the name of the premier dog show?

4 What was the name of Clint Eastwood's orangutan buddy in *Every Which Way But Loose* and *Any Which Way You Can*?

5 In what sport did Princess Anne compete?

6 Who were Lassie's young human co-stars in 1943's *Lassie Come Home*?

7 What breed was the sled-dog in Jack London's *Call of the Wild*?

8 Which subsequently famous world leader appeared alongside a chimpanzee in *Bedtime For Bonzo*?

9 Which magician has pet tigers?

10 Which two countries continue whaling?

11 What happens in Pamplona every year?

12 What happens in Siena annually?

13 The kidnapping of two small children was thwarted by a small dog in a 1974 hit film. The dog's real name was Higgins. What was his stage name?

14 Which naturalist was portrayed by Sigourney Weaver in *Gorillas in the Mist*?

15 What is the name of the imaginary feline used to explain the indeterminacy of the wave function in quantum theory?

16 Which naturalist wrote *Born Free* about raising a lion cub as a pet in Kenya?

17 Which doctor talked to the animals?

18 Which film star, once married to Roger Vadim, opened an animal sanctuary?

19 What is the name of the cat that appears in a David Hockney painting of the fashion designer Ossie Clark and his wife?

20 Which Beatles song was an ode to Paul McCartney's old English sheepdog pet?

21 Which Egyptian deity was the cat goddess?

22 Which vegetarian activist and photographer died of cancer in the 1990s?

23 Which dogs are favoured by the Queen?

24 Which fictional character famously rode elephants?

25 What's the name of Michael Jackson's chimpanzee?

1 Which of the stars of *Easy Rider* also directed the movie?

2 What is the setting for Tod Browning's 1932 film *Freaks*?

3 Where does the finale of the final confrontation in *Enter the Dragon* take place?

4 Which statuesque actress walks through Rome's Trevi Fountain in Fellini's *La Dolce Vita*?

5 What did director Ridley Scott do with Harrison Ford's narration in *Blade Runner – The Director's Cut*?

6 Who played Hannibal Lecter in the 1986 film *Manhunter*, four years before *The Silence of the Lambs*?

7 In which Ken Russell film did Oliver Reed play the Jesuit-educated Father Grandier and Vanessa Redgrave a hunchbacked Mother Superior?

8 Which real-life comedian/actor is the kidnap victim in Martin Scorsese's *King of Comedy*?

9 Which flamboyant fashion designer was responsible for the costumes in Peter Greenaway's *The Cook, The Thief, His Wife and Her Lover*?

10 Terrence Malick's directorial debut in 1973 starred Martin Sheen and Sissy Spacek, on the run from the law. What was the film?

11 Which actor won an Academy Award for his role in *The Usual Suspects*?

12 Who played the title role in the 1963 film *The Servant*?

13 Which Mel Brooks film featured the 'Springtime for Hitler' routine?

14 In which film did Steve Martin recite the 'Pointy Birds' poem?

15 In which film does Edward Woodward star as a police sergeant investigating the disappearance of a twelve-year-old girl on a Scottish island?

16 Which Orson Welles film starts with a three-and-a-half-minute continuous shot of a bomb being planted in a car, and the car's subsequent fate?

17 In which 1961 film did Paul Newman play Fast Eddie Felson?

18 Which film features an eighteen-inch-high model of Stonehenge, Elvis Presley's grave, and an amplifier that 'goes up to eleven'?

19 Which 1974 film introduced a character called Leatherface?

20 Which film's action takes place in a warehouse after a bungled diamond robbery?

21 In which film were Brad Pitt and Morgan Freeman teamed as detectives on the trail of a serial killer?

22 Which 1986 film starred Richard E Grant and Paul McGann as a couple of out-of-work actors needing to get away from London to 'rejuvenate'?

23 Who wrote *The Rocky Horror Show*, from which came *The Rocky Horror Picture Show*?

24 Who played the title role in *Betty Blue*?

25 Which 1971 Stanley Kubrick film was given a new cinema and video release only after the death of the director?

1 What is the name of the spaceship on which the cast of *Alien* are travelling?

2 What was the title of the Disney studios' big-budget response to *Star Wars* in 1979?

3 In which 1968 film did Roger Vadim direct his then wife, Jane Fonda?

4 Who wrote the book on which the 1959 movie *Journey to the Center of the Earth* was based?

5 In which Tim Burton SF comedy does Jack Nicholson play the president of the United States?

6 Which big-budget update of *The War of the Worlds* won an Academy Award in 1996 for visual effects?

7 Which 1976 film is about an alien in search of water for his dying planet who becomes an alcoholic in the process?

8 Who directed the 1926 film *Metropolis*?

9 Which band provided the theme song to the 1980 film *Flash Gordon*?

10 Who played the lead character in the 1988 film *My Stepmother is an Alien*?

11 Which member of the cast of *Star Trek: First Contact* also directed the movie?

12 Which character in the *Star Wars* films is played by the combined efforts of James Earl Jones and Dave Prowse?

13 Who you gonna call?

14 Who is the star of the 1978 remake of the 1956 film *Invasion of the Body Snatchers*?

15 From which actor's stomach does the baby creature emerge in *Alien*?

16 Who is the star of the 1993 version of *Attack of the 50 Foot Woman*?

17 Perhaps best known for his work on *ER* and *Jurassic Park*, who wrote and directed the 1973 film *Westworld*, starring Yul Brynner?

18 What is Douglas Raen's memorable contribution to *2001: A Space Odyssey*?

19 What is the name of the 1971 film starring Bruce Dern, featuring a spaceship carrying the last of Earth's flora and fauna?

20 What is the title of Mel Brooks's 1987 spoof of the *Star Wars* films?

21 From which country did the 1972 film *Solaris* originate?

22 Which film introduced the characters Marty McFly and Doc Brown?

23 Which 1985 film features a group of inhabitants of an old people's home who find a way of feeling young again?

24 Which 1982 film is set in Los Angeles in the year 2019?

25 Which 1988 film, which spawned a sequel, concerned two dim Valley boys travelling through time to research their history project?

1 Which mountain overlooks the city of Naples?

2 Aconcagua is the highest mountain in South America. In which country does it stand?

3 By which city does the Sugar Loaf Mountain stand?

4 Which mountain range spans northern Morocco, Algeria and Tunisia?

5 In which country are the Sierra Madre ranges?

6 In which state is the USA's highest mountain, Mount McKinley?

7 In which country is Mount Ararat?

8 Mont Blanc stands on the border of which two European countries?

9 Why would it be incorrect to describe this mountain as Mount Fujiyama?

10 Which mountain in the Swiss Alps is featured in a Clint Eastwood film?

11 Which East African mountain has a Swahili name meaning 'mountain of the god of cold'?

20

12 Which Australian mountain was discovered by a Polish explorer and named after one of his countrymen?

13 Which mountain in Great Britain has a railway going to its summit?

14 Which mountain was named in 1865 after the British surveyor-general of India?

15 What does the word 'Ben' mean, as in Ben Nevis?

16 In which mountain range does the country of Andorra lie?

17 Mauna Kea is an extinct volcano on which Pacific island?

18 What is the name shared by mountains in Iceland and the Isle of Man?

19 In which state is the Mount Rushmore monument, featuring the faces of four presidents?

20 By what name do most of us know the peak the French call Mont Cervin and the Italians call Monte Cervino?

21 In which American state are the Adirondack Mountains?

22 In which country are the Apennines?

23 In which country is Mount Cook, named after explorer Captain James Cook?

24 In which mountain range is the ski resort of Aspen?

25 What is the name of the flat-topped mountain overlooking Cape Town in South Africa?

1 Which common flower has the scientific name *bellis perennis* and has a connection, through song, with a bicycle?

2 Where do hydrophytic plants grow?

3 What would you find in the pods of the *pisum stativum*?

4 At three feet in diameter the rafflesia has the largest single flower of any plant in the world. In which part of the world does it grow?

5 How do procumbent plants grow?

6 What word is used to describe bell-shaped flowers?

7 In what conditions do thermophilous plants thrive?

8 What is meant by the name of saxifrage, which grows in cracks in rocks?

9 Where does bracket fungus grow?

10 Which carnivorous plant's natural habitat consists of a small coastal area between North and South Carolina?

11 Where does the edelweiss grow?

12 What colour is the flower of the Amazon lily when it opens?

13 What is the more common name of the poisonous plant *atropa belladonna*?

14 Where is the natural habitat of the cheese plant?

15 Which family of plants sends up shoots in the shape of croziers?

16 What trick does the mirror orchid play on a male bee?

17 Which shrub was introduced to England in 1598, can be used in cooking, and is also a component of Eau de Cologne?

18 From which country did the leek originate?

19 What would you be most likely to be chewing if it were flavoured with *mentha piperita* or *mentha viridis*?

20 Botanists, gardeners and chefs know their *allium cepas*. What is an *allium cepa*?

21 What is another name for the white poppy?

22 What name is given to a plant that grows from seed, and flowers and dies within a year?

23 Which flower is represented on the flag of India?

24 What type of plant is a lady's slipper?

25 Swedish botanist Anders Dahl gave his name to which flower?

1 Which British producer worked in tandem with Madonna on her *Ray of Light* album?

2 Which country singer guested with the KLF on their single 'Justified and Ancient'?

3 The drum break from 'Funky Drummer' is one of the most-used samples of all time. Who recorded the original track?

4 Who was the owner of Manchester's Hacienda Club and Factory Records?

5 With which band did Norman Cook have a UK number one in 1990?

6 Alex Gifford and Will White were joined by Shirley Bassey on their single 'History Repeating'. By what name are they known collectively?

7 What was the name of Shaun Ryder's post-Happy Mondays group?

8 Which British dance act was masterminded by Jazzie B and Nellee Hooper?

9 How are Ed Simons and Tom Rowlands better known?

10 With which spice girl did Missy 'Misdemeanor' Elliott sing on 'I Want You Back'?

11 Which techno artists' albums include *Accelerator*, *Lifeforms* and *Dead Cities*?

12 What was The Prodigy's first UK hit single?

13 Which female vocalist guested with Massive Attack on their third album, *Mezzanine*?

14 Which band named themselves after a milk drink featured in *A Clockwork Orange*?

15 Posdnous, Trugoy the Dove and PA Pasemaster Mase had their first hit in 1989. By what name are they collectively known?

16 'Ride On Time' spent six weeks at number one in the UK in 1989. For whom?

17 Which Detroit producer has used pseudonyms such as 69, Psyche, Paperclip People and Innerzone Orchestra?

18 Which singer made his first appearance on Adamski's 'Killer' in 1992?

19 From which US city did techno originate?

20 Which Chicago club gave house music its name?

21 Which DJ and recording artist is known as the 'House Godfather'?

22 Which Steve 'Silk' Hurley single was the first house record to top the UK charts in 1987?

23 Whose albums include *Better Living by Chemistry* and *You've Come a Long Way, Baby*?

24 Who released their second album *Rhythm and Stealth* in 1999?

25 Moby is a descendent of which famous author?

1 Whose life story featured in the film *Amadeus*?

2 Gilbert and Sullivan: which one wrote the music?

3 Whose operas include *Tannhäuser* and *Tristan und Isolde*?

4 Name the composer who supplied the music to such Hitchcock films as *Psycho*, *North By Northwest* and *Vertigo*.

5 Who wrote the music for the ballets *Swan Lake* and *The Sleeping Beauty*?

6 Who wrote 'White Christmas' while sunning himself in California?

7 Which Polish composer was portrayed by Cornell Wilde in the film *A Song to Remember*?

8 With what names was 'Duke' Ellington christened?

9 'Land of Hope and Glory' comes from whose *Pomp and Circumstance* marches?

10 Who was known as 'the Father of the Waltz'?

11 Who wrote the 'Firebird Suite' and the 'Ebony Concerto' for a swing band?

12 Who wrote the 'Flight of the Bumblebee', which later turned up as a pop hit called 'Nutrocker'?

13 Whose songs include 'Night and Day', 'Begin the Beguine' and 'Just One of Those Things'?

14 Which British king reputedly wrote 'Greensleeves'?

15 Name the Russian composer who wrote *Peter and the Wolf*.

16 Who worked as an arranger for Glenn Miller and later wrote the scores for *The Pink Panther* and *Breakfast at Tiffany's*?

17 One of the most prolific composers of all time, his surname means 'stream' in his native German language. Name him.

18 He was born in Cologne but shocked Paris with his rollicking music, including the famous 'Can Can' from his *Orpheus in the Underworld*. What was his name?

19 Who wrote the music to such musicals as *Cats*, *Jesus Christ Superstar* and *The Phantom of the Opera*?

20 His incomplete Eighth Symphony is world famous as the 'Unfinished'. Name this prolific Austrian composer.

21 Who wrote *Rhapsody in Blue*?

22 Name the Italian composer famous for providing the scores to such spaghetti Westerns as *The Good, the Bad and the Ugly*.

23 Which great British composer wrote *A Sea Symphony* and, at the age of 80, the score for a film about Scott's Antarctic expedition?

24 Name the 1990 Western which won John Barry an Oscar for Best Film Score.

25 Emerson Lake and Palmer had a number two UK hit with 'Fanfare for the Common Man'. Who wrote it?

1 On which island did the air disaster occur in 1977, where two Boeing 747s collided, leaving 583 people dead?

2 Which oil tanker ran aground in Prince William Sound, Alaska, in 1989?

3 What disaster occurred on the night of 14–15 April 1912?

4 What was the nature of the disaster at Bhopal, India, in December 1984, which claimed up to 3,000 lives?

5 In which country did the British airship R101 crash, killing 50 people in 1903?

6 Which Welsh village was devastated in 1966 when a huge volume of slurry slipped down into the village, engulfing the local school, killing 116 children and 28 adults?

7 Between 1918 and 1920, more than 21.5 million lives were claimed in an epidemic of which illness?

8 In which US state is Mount St Helens, which erupted in 1980?

9 What was the name of the Russian submarine that was flooded and stranded on the sea bed in August 2000?

10 What type of disaster occurred at Berlin in 1908, Brooklyn, New York in 1918 and Balham, London in 1940?

11 In which year did the *Torrey Canyon* run aground off the Scilly Isles, spilling its 120,000 tonnes of oil?

12 St Pierre, the capital of Martinique in the West Indies, was completely wiped out in 1902. What caused this catastrophe?

13 At which motor racing event in 1955 were 82 people killed when a Mercedes-Benz 300 SLR went out of control, exploded and showered wreckage into the crowd?

14 Which American city was devastated by earthquake and fire in April 1906?

15 In which year did the explosion of the Chernobyl nuclear reactor occur?

16 Off the coast of which African country did the tanker *Castillo de Belver* catch fire and split in two in August 1983?

17 At which Scottish football ground did 66 people die when barriers buckled and collapsed at the end of a game in January 1971?

18 What was the cause of 29 deaths at the village of Flixborough, Humberside, on 2 June 1974?

19 From which Belgian port did the ferry *Herald of Free Enterprise* set sail on 6 March 1987 before letting in water and capsizing?

20 Which Zeppelin caught fire at Lakehurst, New Jersey, on 6 May 1937?

21 Which military disaster of the Crimean War did Tennyson famously mourn in verse?

22 What struck Central America in 1998, killing nearly 10,000 people and leaving approximately 2.5 million people dependent on aid?

23 Which American state penitentiary caught fire in 1930, resulting in 322 deaths?

24 At which British airport did 54 people perish when a Boeing 737 engine exploded before takeoff in August 1985?

25 In which year was the Lockerbie disaster, which destroyed Pan Am flight 103, killing 270 people?

1 Which year saw the maiden flight of a US Space Shuttle?

2 The Bay of Pigs was very much in the news in 1961. Where is it located?

3 In January 1971 President Milton Obote of Uganda was overthrown by his army commander. What was his name?

4 What historic sports event happened at Iffley Road, Oxford, on 6 May 1954?

5 Who was found dead in a bungalow near Hollywood on 5 August 1962?

6 Which disaster took place in 1986?

7 Where were four men with electronic surveillance equipment arrested at gunpoint in June 1972?

8 What 200-page document was signed on 28 June 1919?

9 Where is the prison in which Nelson Mandela was held from 1964 to 1990?

10 How did a group called 'Black September' make headlines in 1972?

11 1988 saw the appointment of the first woman prime minister in the Islamic world. Who was she?

12 What event of 1963 was captured on the most famous, and most valuable, piece of amateur film footage ever shot?

13 Who were the targets of a terrorist bomb at Brighton's Grand Hotel in 1984?

14 Which historic structure was collapsed in 1989?

15 In which year did Alaska and Hawaii become the 49th and 50th states of the Union?

16 Which high-profile politician was caught on video, crackpipe in hand, by the FBI in 1990?

17 What was opened at Luxor, Egypt, in February 1924?

18 American Terry Anderson was taken hostage in Lebanon in 1984. What year was he released?

19 What happened at Cheddington, Buckinghamshire, on 8 August 1963?

20 Which American politician was shot and paralyzed by Arthur Bremer in 1972?

21 Which former Viceroy of India was murdered by a terrorist bomb in August 1979?

22 In which state is the Three Mile Island nuclear power plant, scene of a near-disaster in 1979?

23 By what name has Monday 19 October 1987 come to be remembered ?

24 In which US city was the Alfred P Murrah Building bombed in April 1995?

25 What was the name of the Salman Rushdie book, the publication of which brought about the Islamic death threat and forced him into hiding?

1 Five-time world squash champion Susan Devoy came from which country?

2 Which American tennis player won all 26 of her singles matches in Wightman Cup competitions against Britain between 1971 and 1985?

3 Who won the 100 metres at the 1984 Olympics in a then world record time?

4 Who won the javelin gold medal for Britain at the same games?

5 At which sport did Italian Deborah Compagnioni win Olympic gold medals at each of the games in 1992, 1994 and 1998?

6 Who won Australia's 100th Olympic gold medal of all time during the Sydney games?

7 Who won gold for Britain in the 1991 World Championships in Tokyo in the 10,000 metres?

8 Czech Vera Caslavska won seven Olympic titles in all, in 1964 and 1968. What was her sport?

9 With which sport do you associate Australian Karrie Webb?

10 Who won the Wimbledon singles title at the age of nineteen in 1971 and again nine years later after she had married and become a mother?

11 Which South African-born runner competed for Britain barefoot at the 1984 Olympics?

12 Which sprinter took part in the Moscow games of 1980 and was still competing at the highest level in Sydney?

13 Who won silver for Britain in the judo competition at Sydney?

14 Which Australian swimmer won Olympic gold medals in the 100 metres freestyle in 1956, 1960 and 1964?

15 How many Grand Slam titles has Steffi Graf won?

16 Who won gold at the 1987 and 1991 World Athletics Championships in the long jump and in 1993 and 1997 in the heptathlon?

17 In Sydney 2000, Australia beat Argentina to win its third Olympic gold in which sport?

18 At what sport did Hungarian Krisztina Egerszegi win Olympic gold in 1988 at the age of fourteen?

19 Who won the French Open women's singles tennis championship in 2000?

20 Who did the 100 and 200 metres sprint double in Sydney?

21 The winner of the 1971 European Three-Day Event was also voted BBC Sports Personality of the Year. Who was she?

22 With which sport do you associate American Picabo Street?

23 German Ulrike Meyfarth won gold at the 1972 Munich Olympics and repeated her triumph twelve years later in Los Angeles. What was her event?

24 Who was the last Briton to win the Wimbledon singles title before Virginia Wade in 1977?

25 Who was the first gymnast ever to score a perfect '10', doing so at the Montreal Olympics of 1976?

25

1 Where were the Winter Olympics held in 1928 and 1948?

2 Who was the first man to win Olympic gold at 200 and 400 metres?

3 In which event did Carl Lewis win his ninth and final gold medal?

4 How many gold medals did Mark Spitz win in his first Olympics?

5 Where did Steve Redgrave win his fourth gold medal?

6 Where did Linford Christie run his first Olympic race?

7 Who was the oldest Olympic 100 metres champion when he won in 1980?

8 Who was Britain's only female medallist at the Atlanta Olympics?

9 Which amazing treble did Emile Zatopek achieve at the 1952 games?

10 In which year did women first compete in the Olympics?

11 Where did Daley Thompson compete in his first Olympics?

12 Who replaced her partner Michael Hutchinson before winning gold in 1984?

13 Who won women's hockey gold in Barcelona?

14 Under what name did Mrs Erik De Bruin win gold in Atlanta?

15 Who lit the torch in the stadium at the Sydney Olympics?

16 Which Briton won the heptathlon in 1976?

17 At which games were Israeli competitors kidnapped and killed?

18 Who broke the world 100 metres record in an Olympic final only to be found guilty of drug offences?

19 How many gold medals did Britain win in the Sydney Olympics?

20 Who was Sebastian Coe's main British Olympic rival?

21 Which country does 10,000 metres world-record holder and gold medallist Haile Gebreselassie come from?

22 Who was Britain's most successful hockey playing forward who helped them win the gold medal in Seoul?

23 Which country's coxless four was nicknamed the 'Awecome Foursome' at the Sydney games?

24 Who beat Ian Thorpe in the 200 metres freestyle in the Olympics?

25 Who came third in the women's 400 metres in Sydney?

1 In which town is *The Simpsons* set?

2 Who are Miss Hoover and Ms Krabappel?

3 What was Marge's maiden name?

4 Which character's 'real name' is Herschel Krustovsky?

5 At which exclusive club did Homer have his behind smacked with wooden paddles during his initiation ritual?

6 Which occasional character's voice is supplied by *Frasier* star Kelsey Grammer?

7 Who drives the school bus?

8 Who usually reads the news on the Simpsons' TV?

9 On whose real-life TV show did the Simpsons make their first appearance?

10 Lisa had a birthday song written for her by a guest in the Simpsons' home. Who was the guest pretending to be?

11 What is the full name of Homer's boss?

12 What is the name of Chief Wiggum's son?

13 Who was the founder of the town in which the Simpsons live?

14 When Bart went on an exchange trip to France what did he see the wine makers adding to the wine?

15 Which character is nicknamed 'Spanky' by his mother?

16 Who was the inspiration for the voice of Mayor Quimby?

17 Who played the voice of Homer's half-brother, Herb?

18 Which grown man collects Malibu Stacy dolls?

19 Who is Santa's Little Helper?

20 Of what type of public vehicle did Homer become a driver?

21 On which tough-guy actor's voice did Hank Azaria base that of Chief Wiggum?

22 Whom did Barney Gumble replace in the barbershop quartet, The B Sharps?

23 What is Homer's father's first name?

24 Which of Burns and Smithers is voiced by Harry Shearer?

25 During a game of which sport did Bart and Lisa make up after they had fallen out?

6

1 What false name is used by the con man in the first episode?

2 In which seaside town is the series based?

3 Where is Basil trying to get to when his car breaks down?

4 What is the name of the French restaurant owner who comes to Basil's rescue on gourmet night?

5 Which regular character joined the hotel in the second series?

6 What is the name of the builder that Sybil wants to do the work in the hotel?

7 With whom does Basil see Polly in an embrace, from which he totally misinterprets the situation?

8 What is the name of the horse on which Basil places a bet?

9 In his muddled conversation with the deaf Mrs Richards, where does Manuel tell her that Basil comes from?

10 Which regular character is played by Ballard Berkeley?

11 What is the name of the hotel on which John Cleese and Connie Booth based *Fawlty Towers*, which actually gets mentioned in the episode with the builders?

12 What are the names of the hotel's two elderly lady residents?

13 Which member of the show's cast appeared in the 1954 David Lean film *Hobson's Choice*?

14 What falls onto Basil's head in the episode with the Germans?

15 What is Manuel's birthday present from Basil?

16 Who plays the spoon salesman whom Basil mistakes for a hotel inspector?

17 Into whom does Basil threaten to insert a garden gnome?

18 Who plays the role of the doctor in the episode with the corpse?

19 On what does Basil put rat poison on in the episode with the health inspector?

20 Who announces, rather grandly, 'I know nothing'?

21 What is poking out of the top of Basil's pullover when the doctor comes into the dead man's room?

22 Which composer's music does Sybil describe as a 'racket'?

23 How does Basil get out of the hotel at the end of the episode with the dead body?

24 What are the four ingredients of a Waldorf salad?

25 What musical instrument does Manuel play?

1 Which city was besieged by the Turks in 1453?

2 After the United States, which country supplied the most troops to fight Iraq in the Gulf War in 1991?

3 How many ships were in the Spanish Armada of 1588?

4 At which battle did the Americans, led by Major-General Horatio Coates, defeat the British under Lt General Sir John Burgoyne in 1777?

5 Whom did the Japanese defeat at the Battle of Tsushima in 1905?

6 Who led the Macedonians against the Persians at the Battle of Gaugamela in 331 BC?

7 Whose brothers, Gyrth and Leofwine, fought at the Battle of Hastings in 1066?

8 At the Battle of Blenheim in 1704, who led the allied troops against the French?

9 At which sea battle did the Americans defeat the Japanese in 1942, despite their ships being outnumbered three to one?

10 During which war did the Battle of Agincourt take place?

11 Who were the Duke of Wellington's and Napoleon's respective co-commanders at the Battle of Waterloo?

12 Which battle was fought between the Union and Confederate armies from 1–3 July 1863?

13 Who led the Israelis in the Sinai campaign against Egypt at the time of the Suez crisis?

14 Who was the Japanese commander at the Battle of Singapore in 1942?

15 Where, in September 1950, did General MacArthur's troops land prior to the recapture of Seoul?

16 Which man led the British, Portuguese and Sepoys against the Bengalis at Plassey in 1757?

17 Who put Vienna under siege in 1529?

18 Where did Cromwell's New Model Army defeat the Royalists in 1651 to end the Civil War?

19 Which of the Solomon Islands was regained from the Japanese by the Americans in May 1942?

20 Who became King of England after the Battle of Bosworth Field in 1485?

21 Which battle against the Austrians and the Russians in 1805 is regarded as Napoleon's greatest victory?

22 Who led the Americans to victory against the British at Princeton in 1777?

23 Who inspired the French to resist the English at Orléans in 1429?

24 Who was head of RAF Fighter Command at the Battle of Britain?

25 Which English king was defeated by the Scots at the Battle of Bannockburn in 1314?

1 Which goddess was the Greek equivalent of Juno?

2 Who is the elephant-headed Hindu god of good luck?

3 Into what was Daphne changed as a means of avoiding the advances of the god Apollo?

4 In Germanic religions, Ragnarök was a term used to describe an impending apocalyptic disaster. What does it translate as in English?

5 Who was the wife of Osiris?

6 What is the native religion of Japan, the name of which translates as 'the way of the gods'?

7 Who fell into the ocean because he could not keep control of his father the sun's chariot?

8 Whose was Valhalla, the heavenly great hall for slain warriors in Norse myth?

9 What common theme unites Helios, Sol and Re?

10 The tale of a musician who failed to bring his love back from the underworld because he looked back at her was the inspiration for a well-known Tennessee Williams play. What was it?

11 In what form did Zeus come to Danae?

12 Who is the Hindu god of creation?

13 Who spent six months of every year in the underworld, a symbolic reference to the germination of seeds and their rebirth every spring?

14 What was the name of the murderer that the crowds told Pilate to free rather than Jesus?

15 Which name is shared by the Greek goddess of victory and an international sportswear manufacturer?

16 Which Egyptian deity murdered Osiris?

17 Who was pope from c. AD 33–67?

18 What name did Freud give to the complement to the Oedipus complex in which a woman fixates on her father?

19 Who pined away out of unrequited love for Narcissus until only her voice was left?

20 In which war is Shakespeare's *Troilus and Cressida* set?

21 The Greek god of love has a statue in central London dedicated to a 19th-century philanthropist. Who is the god?

22 After which Norse god is the day Thursday named?

23 Purcell based an opera on the subject of Dido's abandonment by her lover. What was the lover's name?

24 ... and what city was he believed to have been the founder of, according to Virgil's *Aeneid*?

25 The Muslim calendar starts from July 622. What event does the date mark?

ANSWERS TO QUIZ 9

Famous Families
1 The Marx Brothers
2 Franklin D Roosevelt
3 Osbert
4 Fonda
5 The Borgias
6 Al Joyner
7 Bing Crosby
8 Montgolfier
9 Joan Fontaine
10 Steve and Mark
11 The Osmonds
12 The Medicis
13 One
14 Pierre Auguste Renoir and Jean Renoir
15 Film direction
16 Michael; the others are all part of the American acting family
17 The Bunkers
18 Tennis
19 Bridges
20 Saxe-Coburg-Gotha
21 The Partridge Family
22 The Montagues and the Capulets
23 Strauss
24 Gaye married Gordy's sister, Anna
25 Joseph and Rose

People and Animals
1 Eddie the dog
2 Mr Ed
3 Crufts
4 Clyde
5 Three-day eventing
6 Roddy McDowell and Elizabeth Taylor
7 An Alsatian
8 Ronald Reagan
9 David Copperfield
10 Norway and Japan
11 The Bull Run
12 The Piazza Race
13 Benji
14 Dian Fossey
15 Schrödinger's cat
16 Joy Adamson
17 Dr Dolittle
18 Brigitte Bardot
19 Percy
20 'Martha My Dear'
21 Bastet
22 Linda McCartney
23 Corgis
24 Tarzan
25 Bubbles

Cult Films
1 Dennis Hopper
2 A circus
3 In a hall of mirrors
4 Anita Ekberg
5 He removed it
6 Brian Cox
7 *The Devils*
8 Jerry Lewis
9 Jean Paul Gaultier
10 *Badlands*
11 Kevin Spacey
12 Dirk Bogarde
13 *The Producers*
14 *The Man with Two Brains*
15 *The Wicker Man*
16 *Touch of Evil*
17 *The Hustler*
18 *This is Spinal Tap*
19 *The Texas Chain Saw Massacre*
20 *Reservoir Dogs*
21 *Se7en*
22 *Withnail and I*
23 Richard O'Brien
24 Béatrice Dalle
25 *A Clockwork Orange*

Science Fiction Films
1 *Nostromo*
2 *The Black Hole*
3 *Barbarella*
4 Jules Verne
5 *Mars Attacks!*
6 *Independence Day*
7 *The Man Who Fell to Earth*
8 Fritz Lang
9 Queen
10 Kim Basinger
11 Jonathan Frakes
12 Darth Vader
13 *Ghostbusters*
14 Donald Sutherland
15 John Hurt
16 Daryl Hannah
17 Michael Crichton
18 He is the voice of HAL
19 *Silent Running*
20 *Spaceballs*
21 Russia
22 *Back to the Future*
23 *Cocoon*
24 *Blade Runner*
25 *Bill and Ted's Excellent Adventure*

Mountains
1 Mount Vesuvius
2 Argentina
3 Rio de Janeiro
4 The Atlas Mountains
5 Mexico
6 Alaska
7 Turkey
8 France and Italy
9 Yama means 'mountain', so it should be Fujiyama or Mount Fuji
10 The Eiger
11 Kilimanjaro
12 Mount Kosciusko
13 Snowdon
14 Everest, after Sir George Everest
15 Mountain
16 The Pyrenees
17 Hawaii
18 Snaefell
19 South Dakota
20 The Matterhorn
21 New York
22 Italy
23 New Zealand
24 The Rocky Mountains
25 Table Mountain

Plants
1 Daisy
2 In or around water
3 Peas
4 Borneo and Sumatra
5 They spread over the ground
6 Campanulate
7 Warm or sunny
8 Stone-breaker
9 On the trunk of a tree
10 The Venus flytrap
11 In the Alps at high altitude
12 White
13 Deadly nightshade
14 Central America's rainforest
15 The fern
16 Its flower resembles a female bee
17 Rosemary
18 Switzerland
19 Chewing gum – peppermint or spearmint
20 An onion
21 Opium poppy
22 An annual
23 The lotus
24 An orchid
25 The dahlia

Dance Music
1 William Orbit
2 Tammy Wynette
3 James Brown
4 Tony Wilson
5 Beats International
6 Propellerheads
7 Black Grape
8 Soul II Soul
9 Chemical Brothers
10 Mel B/Scary Spice
11 Future Sound of London
12 'Charly'
13 Elizabeth Fraser
14 Moloko
15 De La Soul
16 Black Box
17 Carl Craig
18 Seal
19 Detroit
20 The Warehouse Club
21 Frankie Knuckles
22 'Jack Your Body'
23 Fatboy Slim
24 Leftfield
25 Herman Melville

Composers
1 Mozart
2 Sir Arthur Sullivan
3 Wagner
4 Bernard Hermann
5 Tchaikovsky
6 Irving Berlin
7 Fryderyk Chopin
8 Edward Kennedy Ellington
9 Sir Edward Elgar
10 Johann Strauss Sr
11 Igor Stravinsky
12 Nicolai Rimsky-Korsakov
13 Cole Porter
14 Henry VIII
15 Sergei Prokofiev
16 Henry Mancini
17 Johann Sebastian Bach
18 Jacques Offenbach
19 Andrew Lloyd-Webber
20 Franz Schubert
21 George Gershwin
22 Ennio Morricone
23 Ralph Vaughan Williams
24 *Dances With Wolves*
25 Aaron Copland

Disasters
1 Tenerife
2 The *Exxon Valdez*
3 The sinking of the *Titanic*
4 The Union Carbide plant leaked poisonous gas
5 France
6 Aberfan
7 Influenza
8 Washington
9 The *Kursk*
10 Underground rail disasters
11 1967
12 Volcanic eruption
13 Le Mans
14 San Francisco
15 1986
16 South Africa
17 IBROX (Glasgow Rangers)
18 An explosion at a chemical plant

19 Zeebrugge
20 The *Hindenburg*
21 The Charge of the Light Brigade
22 Hurricane Mitch
23 Ohio
24 Manchester
25 1988

News Events
1 1981
2 Cuba
3 Idi Amin
4 Roger Bannister ran the first sub-four-minute mile
5 Marilyn Monroe
6 Chernobyl
7 The Watergate complex, Washington, DC
8 The Treaty of Versailles
9 Robben Island, off Cape Town
10 They were Arab terrorists who stormed the Israeli building in the Olympic village near Munich
11 Benazir Bhutto
12 The assassination of President Kennedy
13 The British Government
14 The Berlin Wall
15 1959
16 Marion Barry, Mayor of Washington, DC
17 The coffin of Tutankhamun
18 1991
19 The Great Train Robbery
20 George Wallace
21 Earl Mountbatten
22 Pennsylvania
23 Black Monday, due to the stock market crash
24 Oklahoma City
25 *The Satanic Verses*

Sportswomen
1 New Zealand
2 Chris Evert
3 Evelyn Ashford
4 Tessa Sanderson
5 Slalom skiing
6 Cathy Freeman
7 Liz McColgan
8 Gymnastics
9 Golf
10 Evonne Cawley née Goolagong
11 Zola Budd
12 Merlene Ottey
13 Dawn Fraser
14 Kate Howey
15 22
16 Jackie Joyner-Kersee

17 Hockey
18 Swimming (200 metres backstroke)
19 Mary Pierce
20 Marion Jones
21 Princess Anne
22 Skiing
23 High jump
24 Ann Jones, 1969
25 Nadia Comaneci

Olympics
1 St Moritz
2 Michael Johnson
3 Long jump
4 Two
5 Atlanta
6 Seoul
7 Alan Wells
8 Denise Lewis
9 10,000, 5,000, marathon
10 1900
11 Montreal
12 Jayne Torvill
13 Spain
14 Michelle Smith
15 Cathy Freeman
16 Mary Peters
17 Munich
18 Ben Johnson
19 Eleven
20 Steve Ovett
21 Ethiopia
22 Sean Curly
23 Australia's
24 Peter Van Den Hoogenband
25 Katherine Merry

The Simpsons
1 Springfield
2 Lisa's and Bart's schoolteachers
3 Bouvier
4 Krusty the Klown
5 The Stonecutters
6 Sideshow Bob
7 Otto
8 Kent Brockman
9 Tracey Ullman
10 Michael Jackson (who provided the voice)
11 Charles Montgomery Burns
12 Ralph
13 Jebediah Springfield
14 Antifreeze
15 Principal Seymour Skinner
16 John F Kennedy
17 Danny DeVito
18 Waylon Smithers
19 The Simpsons' dog
20 The monorail

21 Edward G Robinson
22 Chief Wiggum
23 Abraham
24 Both
25 Ice hockey

Fawlty Towers
1 Lord Melbury
2 Torquay
3 Back to the hotel with food for gourmet night
4 André
5 Terry the chef
6 Stubbs
7 Her friend's stepfather
8 Dragonfly
9 Swanage
10 Major Gowen
11 Gleneagles
12 Miss Gatsby and Miss Tibbs
13 Prunella Scales
14 A moose's head
15 An umbrella
16 Bernard Cribbins
17 Mr O'Reilly
18 Geoffrey Palmer
19 A slice of veal
20 Manuel
21 A kipper
22 Brahms
23 In the linen basket when it is collected
24 Apple, celery, walnuts, grapes
25 The guitar

Famous Battles
1 Constantinople
2 Saudi Arabia
3 130
4 Saratoga
5 The Russians
6 Alexander the Great
7 King Harold II's
8 The Duke of Marlborough and Prince Eugene of Savoy
9 The Battle of Midway
10 The Hundred Years' War
11 Field Marshal Blucher and Marshal Ney
12 The Battle of Gettysburg
13 Moshe Dayan
14 General Yamashita
15 Inchon
16 Robert Clive
17 The Turks
18 Worcester
19 Guadalcanal
20 Henry Tudor (Henry VII)
21 Austerlitz
22 George Washington
23 Joan of Arc

24 Air Chief Marshal Sir Hugh Dowding
25 Edward II

Religion & Myth
1 Hera
2 Ganesh
3 A laurel tree
4 'Twilight of the Gods'
5 Isis
6 Shinto
7 Phaethon
8 Odin's
9 They are all sun gods
10 *Orpheus Descending*
11 A shower of gold
12 Brahma
13 Persephone (Proserpine in Roman myth)
14 Barabbas
15 Nike
16 Seth
17 St Peter
18 Electra complex
19 Echo
20 The Trojan War
21 Eros
22 Thor
23 Aeneas
24 Rome
25 Muhammad's flight from Mecca to Medina

THE ULTIMATE BOOK OF TRIVIA

OF TRIVIA

QUIZ

10

1 Who did Lauren Bacall marry after the death of Humphrey Bogart?

2 Catherine of Aragon was a widow when she married Henry VIII. Who was her first husband?

3 By today's standards, Cleopatra's marriage to Mark Antony was bigamous and her first marriage would have been frowned on. Who was her first husband?

4 Who was the comic partner of the man born Arthur Jefferson?

5 Leofric, Earl of Mercia, was married to a woman famous for an act of protest. What was her name?

6 Shakira Baksh is married to which screen superstar?

7 Which pop songwriting couple were behind the hits 'Will You Love Me Tomorrow?' and 'Do The Loco-Motion'?

8 In which year did Queen Victoria marry Prince Albert of Saxe-Coburg-Gotha?

9 *Tristran und Isolde* is an opera by which composer?

10 He was once a British monarch; she once ran a hotel. Which British acting couple?

11 'Sock it to me!' girl Judy Carne was the first and Loni Anderson the second wife of which film star?

12 Which duo, who became Universal's top box-office draw in the 1940s, made their film debut in 1940's *One Night in the Tropics*?

13 In which building were Prince Charles and Lady Diana married?

14 Who was Frank Sinatra's third wife?

15 Anne Hayes, Britt Ekland, Miranda Quarry and Lynne Frederick were the four wives of which comedian and actor?

16 Ronnie Bennett was married to which famous record producer?

17 Who are actress Jamie Lee Curtis's famous parents?

18 What were the surnames of the men who discovered insulin?

19 Who was married to Adolf Hitler for one day?

20 'Nutbush City Limits' was a hit for which troubled couple?

21 Which famous couple was the subject of an opera by Engelbert Humperdinck?

22 Which famous partnership called their circus 'The Greatest Show on Earth'?

23 Which famous writer, author of *The Second Sex*, was the partner of Jean-Paul Sartre?

24 Sir David Frost was once married to which of the four ladies mentioned in question 15?

25 Who is the film producer/director husband of Julie Andrews?

1 Which four presidents are depicted on Mount Rushmore?

2 How many American presidents were there before Abraham Lincoln?

3 Which former US general became president in 1869?

4 Which president instigated the 'New Deal' for the USA?

5 Which future president was chief military assistant to General Douglas MacArthur in the Philippines during World War II?

6 What is the US president's anthem?

7 Who succeeded William McKinley as US president on his assassination?

8 Whom did Abraham Lincoln defeat in the 1861 election?

9 Who was the first US vice-president?

10 Which president ordered the dropping of the first atomic bomb on Japan?

11 Which president was awarded the Nobel Peace Prize in 1919?

12 Ronald Reagan proposed a Strategic Defense Initiative to create a defensive 'shield' of weapons in space. By what name is it popularly known?

13 Were Theodore Roosevelt and Franklin D Roosevelt related?

14 Which of John F Kennedy's brothers became embroiled in controversy in 1969 after his female companion drowned at Poucha Pond bridge, Chappaquiddick?

15 With which foodstuff is Jimmy Carter associated?

16 What was Richard Nixon's middle name?

17 ... and which US president controversially granted Nixon a full pardon over the Watergate scandal?

18 John F Kennedy was the first president of what religious ilk?

19 Whom did George Bush senior defeat to become president in 1988?

20 What record did Bill Clinton set when he became Governor of Arkansas in 1978?

21 Who drafted the Declaration of Independence?

22 What was Andrew Jackson's nickname?

23 What relation was William Henry Harrison, the ninth president, to Benjamin Harrison, the 23rd president?

24 Where and what is the actual 'Watergate'?

25 How long had Republicans held the presidential office before Bill Clinton was elected in 1992?

1 In what competition did Connery represent Scotland in 1953?

2 Who co-starred with Connery in the 1975 film *The Man Who Would Be King*?

3 In 1989's *Family Business*, Connery plays Matthew Broderick's grandfather. Who bridges this generation gap?

4 In which 1973 film does Connery give one of his most powerful performances, as a policeman investigating a case of child abuse?

5 Which Alfred Hitchcock film stars Connery as a rich publisher who falls in love with a girl who steals from him?

6 On whose novel was the 1993 film *Rising Sun* based, in which Connery stars with Wesley Snipes?

7 For his performance in which film did Sean Connery win an Oscar in 1988?

8 In which 1996 film does he provide the voice of a creature called Draco?

9 How many times has he starred as James Bond?

10 In which 1988 San Francisco-based film does Connery star with Mark Harmon and Meg Ryan?

11 Which party approached Sean Connery in 1969 with an invitation to run for Parliament?

12 Which famous explorer is portrayed by Connery in the 1971 film *The Red Tent*?

13 In the 1976 film *Robin and Marian*, who plays Maid Marian?

14 In which 1977 war film does Connery star as Major General Robert Urquhart?

15 Which Terry Gilliam film features Sean Connery as King Agamemnon?

16 In which fifteenth-century murder mystery does he play a character called William of Baskerville?

17 Who wrote the novel on which the 1990 film *The Russia House* is based?

18 Which prison features in the movie *The Rock*?

19 Which French actress stars with Connery in the 1968 Western *Shalako*?

20 Which 1965 film stars Connery as one of a group of soldiers at the mercy of sadistic officers in a desert prison camp?

21 Who was originally offered Connery's lead role in John Boorman's *Zardoz*?

22 Sean Connery plays King Arthur in *First Knight*. Who plays Sir Lancelot?

23 In the 1990 thriller *The Hunt for Red October*, what is the subject of the film's title?

24 What is Dr Jones's (father of Indiana) Christian name in *Indiana Jones and the Last Crusade*?

25 Which film of an Agatha Christie story features Sean Connery as a character called Colonel Arbuthnot?

1 Which tsar built St Basil's Cathedral?

2 What is the name for a Russian summer home?

3 What was the name of Gorbachev's predecessor?

4 Who ordered the Russian nobility to become more 'European' by shaving off their beards?

5 What is a soviet?

6 Which Siberian monk was the greatest inspiration of Tsar Nicholas and his wife Alexandra?

7 How many cathedrals are there inside the Kremlin?

8 Why is Red Square so called?

9 What was the name of the prison in the KGB's Moscow HQ?

10 What does Bolshoi mean?

11 What city has formerly been known as both Petrograd and Leningrad?

12 How many islands make up St Petersburg?

13 What is the name of the State Museum in St Petersburg?

14 Whose collection was originally exhibited there?

15 Which famous shopping street, linking St Petersburg to Novgorod, is almost 5 km long and features in the work of Gogol?

16 In which town is *The Brothers Karamazov* set?

17 Which Russian river is the longest in Europe?

18 Which mountain range marks the divide between Europe and Asian Siberia?

19 In which town were Tsar Nicholas II and his family executed during the Russian Revolution?

20 Which famous citizen of this town became Russia's first president?

21 Which sea is home to the sturgeon, source of the world's best caviar?

22 What is the name for the remote forest landscape of Siberia?

23 Which lake is known as the 'Pearl of Siberia'?

24 How many time zones does the Trans-Siberian Railway cross?

25 Which Pacific city is known as the 'San Francisco of Russia'?

1 Which famous restaurant is housed inside Grand Central Station?

2 Who designed the Houses of Parliament?

3 For what purpose was Crystal Palace constructed?

4 Which building's proposed extension did Prince Charles describe as 'a great carbuncle'?

5 When Sir Laurence Olivier founded the National Theatre Company, where did it perform?

6 In which prison was the first treadmill erected?

7 Which baseball team plays at Shea Stadium?

8 In which year were the Olympic Games held at Wembley Stadium?

9 Where is Jose Marti International Airport?

10 Where is the Pirelli skyscraper?

11 Why was the Eiffel Tower built?

12 In which city is the space needle?

13 In which town is the Royal Mint?

14 Who designed Coventry Cathedral?

15 Where are the headquarters of UNESCO?

16 Where is O'Hare airport?

17 Which church contains Napoleon's tomb?

18 Which is the largest palace in the world?

19 Caernarfon Castle was one of the many castles constructed by which king?

20 Where is the largest hotel in the world?

21 What is the most common pub name in Britain?

22 Every fort in India contains a Diwan-I-Am. What does the phrase mean?

23 What is the Queen's official residence in Edinburgh?

24 Who designed the Glasgow School of Art?

25 Which Madrid art gallery opened in 1993 after an industrial magnate's Spanish wife chose the city in preference to London?

1 In which town was Elvis born on 8 January 1935?

2 Which two songs were on Elvis's first single on the Sun label in the United States?

3 What was the name of Elvis's vocal backing group?

4 What was Elvis's first UK hit?

5 Which guitarist and which bass player accompanied Elvis on his first recording session, and on many subsequent sessions?

6 What was Elvis's first feature film?

7 Prior to his posthumous number one, 'Way Down', what was Elvis's last UK chart-topping single?

8 In which city did Elvis marry Priscilla Beaulieu on 1 May 1967?

9 What was the name of Elvis's twin brother, who was stillborn?

10 What is the significance of the number US53310761?

11 Which songwriting team was responsible for such hits as 'Hound Dog', '(You're So Square) Baby I Don't Care', 'Trouble' and 'King Creole'?

12 How much did RCA pay Sun for Elvis's recording contract in November 1955?

13 What event happened on 1 February 1968?

14 Which Elvis song was based on the German folk song 'Muss Ich Denn Zum Stadtele Hinaus'?

15 What links Dr John Carpenter, Guy Lambert, Danny Fisher, Walter Gulick and Lt Josh Morgan?

16 Whom did Elvis receive as guests at his Beverley Hills home on 27 August 1965?

17 Who played Elvis in *Elvis: The Movie* in 1979?

18 What was Elvis's first UK number one single?

19 Which Elvis single had two spells at the top of the UK charts in 1965?

20 By what name was Dutchman Andreas Cornelius van Kuijk better known?

21 In the song 'Trouble', what does Elvis say is his middle name?

22 In which two consecutive years did Elvis score four UK number one hit singles?

23 Which United States president made Elvis a special agent of the Bureau of Narcotics and Dangerous Drugs?

24 Who, along with Elvis, made up the 'Million Dollar Quartet'?

25 In the song 'Jailhouse Rock', which instrument is played by Spider Murphy?

22

1 Where were Typically Tropical going to?

2 The Chipmunks were the brainchild of David Seville. But what was Seville's real name?

3 Which song urged you to 'Push pineapple, shake the tree'?

4 Who had a hit with 'Mah-Na, Mah-Na'?

5 Who had a hit in 1979 with a super-speedy version of 'Banana Splits (The Tra La La Song)'?

6 Who had hits with 'I'm Walking Backwards For Christmas' and 'The Ying Tong Song'?

7 What was the name of Benny Hill's fastest milkman in the west?

8 Name The Scaffold's first chart single.

9 Cash and Carry first recorded 'The Birdie Song'. But who had the hit?

10 Which football team had a top five record with 'Ossie's Dream'?

11 Peter Sellers recorded a spoof of which Beatles song in the style of Laurence Olivier's Richard III?

12 What was the name of Spike Jones's comedy band?

13 Who had hits with parodies of 'Sh-Boom', 'Rock Island Line' and 'Heartbreak Hotel'?

14 What was unusual about the Archies, who had a number one hit with 'Sugar Sugar'?

15 What was Rolf Harris's first hit?

16 ... and what war was his 1969 hit 'Two Little Boys' about?

17 What distinguished Bobby McFerrin's 1988 hit 'Don't Worry Be Happy'?

18 'Weird Al' Yankovic had a hit with a parody of a Michael Jackson song. What was it called?

19 Which wrestler had a hit with 'I'm the Leader of the Gang' in 1993?

20 Who had a hit with 'Long-Haired Lover From Liverpool'?

21 Which glam rocker had a hit with the quirky 'Laughing Gnome' in 1973?

22 What was Chuck Berry's only number one?

23 Name Paul McCartney's back-up group on his 'We All Stand Together' single.

24 Monty Python's Flying Circus proved a one-hit wonder act – with which song?

25 What was Ray Stevens's 1974 hit, based on a phenomenon that was occurring at sports events at the time?

1 Who starred as Claus von Bulow in the film version of his life after von Bulow was acquitted of murdering his wife?

2 Who led the team of criminal defence lawyers representing O. J. Simpson?

3 Whose note addressed to Oscar Wilde led to his doomed libel trial?

4 Which adjective was used by the trial judge to describe Lady Mary Archer during her husband's libel case?

5 What did Ian Hislop, editor of *Private Eye*, famously say about the British legal system after the Sonia Sutcliffe libel trial?

6 Which Australian camper claimed that a dingo ate her baby after she went on trial for the baby's murder?

7 Which American heiress was captured by the FBI and tried as an urban guerilla after her kidnapping by the Symbionese Liberation Army?

8 Who returned to claim his wife and life after nine years away at war, only to be tried as an impostor?

9 Who was convicted of selling military secrets to the Germans on 22 December 1894?

10 Of which scandalous book were the jury famously asked: 'Is it a book you would wish your wife or servants to read?'?

11 During her evidence in cross-examination, who famously said, 'Well, he would, wouldn't he?'?

12 Which doctor was tried at the Old Bailey for chopping off his wife Cora's head in 1910?

13 At which court did Henry Fielding sit as a magistrate?

14 Based on a real case, 'The Winslow Boy' was written by which author?

15 Which pop star received a record £1 million libel damages from the *Sun*?

16 Whom did Scott Thorson sue for palimony in 1983?

17 For what crime was Yigal Amir put on trial on 23 January 1996?

18 Whose dalliance with Brazilian model Luciana Morad led him to the divorce court in July 1999?

19 Which English nanny had her original conviction of second-degree murder changed to one of involuntary manslaughter in November 1997?

20 Who coined the term 'sosumi'?

21 Which philosopher's punishment was to drain a bowl of hemlock after being found guilty of corrupting the young?

22 Which star of the silent screen was tried for the murder of 25-year-old starlet Virginia Rappe in 1922?

23 Who chaired South Africa's Truth and Reconciliation Commission from 1995 to 1998?

24 Which 1692 witchcraft trial became a major 20th-century American play?

25 Which fictional Czech bank manager was arrested but never charged for a crime after 'someone must have been telling lies' about him?

12

1 Who invented the Spinning Jenny in 1764?

2 Who took the first practical photograph?

3 In 1888, what did George Eastman call his hand-held box camera, the first of its kind?

4 In 1447 Johannes Gutenberg invented the printing press. What was the first book he produced?

5 The perfection of which invention led to the Industrial Revolution?

6 What did Jesse Reno invent using traditional conveyor-belt principles to pull folding steps up a slope?

7 Whose job as a bookbinder on an edition of the *Encyclopaedia Britannica* led to the discovery of electricity?

8 What was invented by an American firm called Texas Instruments in 1958?

9 Where was the first alarm clock produced?

10 Secret research into what was codenamed the 'Manhattan Project'?

11 What did a professor of vocal physiology at Boston University use his deaf students to help him invent in 1876?

12 And what did Thomas Edison later invent in the lab set up with prize money awarded to the above invention?

13 Where was the potter's wheel first used?

14 Who first demonstrated television in 1926?

15 Who invented the lift?

16 Name the American who patented a burglar-proof lock described as 'magic' and 'infallible'.

17 Who was the first director of the atomic lab at Los Alamos, New Mexico?

18 Which nation first invented the wheelbarrow?

19 Which British city street had the first gas lamps?

20 Who invented nylon?

21 Where and when did people first use spectacles?

22 Who invented the self-lighting match?

23 What did Sir John Harrington invent in 1589?

24 Which significant beverage did Dr John Pemberton of Atlanta, Georgia invent in 1886?

25 Who opened the first cinema in Paris in 1895?

1 Which Frenchman, born in 1871, is synonymous with the World Cup?

2 Which country hosted the first World Cup in 1930?

3 What was significant about Rob Rensenbrink's goal for Holland against Scotland in the 1978 World Cup?

4 What connects Tunisian Mr Ali Bennaceur to England's exit from the 1986 World Cup quarterfinal?

5 Against which team did Pele score three goals in the 1958 semifinal?

6 What did teams use for the first time at the World Cup in Mexico in 1970?

7 How many goals did Gary Lineker score in World Cup final stages?

8 Which two teams were victorious on the first day of the first World Cup in 1930?

9 Which was the first final to go into extra time?

10 The infamous clash between Chile and Italy in 1962 has gone down in history – what is it known as?

11 For which country did Said Owarian score a sensational individual goal against Belgium in the 1994 tournament?

12 Stuart Pearce and Chris Waddle are remembered for their penalty misses in the 1990 semifinal shoot-out against West Germany, but which three Englishmen scored from the spot?

13 Which was the first African nation to play in the final stages?

14 Michael Owen scored a stunning second goal for England against Argentina in the 1998 tournament. Who scored England's first goal in the match proper?

15 Who scored the most goals in a single tournament?

16 Who was Scotland's manager in the 1978 competition in Argentina?

17 Who scored in every game of Brazil's 1970 World Cup tournament?

18 Who was top scorer in the 1966 competition held in England?

19 Which country was beaten 9-0 by Yugoslavia in the 1974 tournament?

20 Against whom did Pele score his first goal in the final stages of a World Cup, in 1958?

21 Which was the first country to win a World Cup on home soil?

22 Who scored West Germany's last-minute equalizer in the 1966 final against England?

23 In which Californian city was the 1994 final played?

24 Which was the first team to be eliminated from a World Cup without losing a match?

25 1998 was the second time that France hosted the World Cup. Which two other countries have also hosted it twice?

6

14 Who took 19 wickets in one test match?

15 Which county has the most cricket County Championship titles?

16 Who broke Bob Beamon's long jump record?

17 Who holds the men's 200 metres record?

18 Who holds the record for the women's 100 metres and 200 metres?

1 Which team scored the most goals in an FA Cup game?

2 Who has won the most tennis men's singles titles?

3 Who has won the most women's titles?

4 Who have won the most men's doubles titles?

5 Who won the most snooker world titles?

6 Who has won the most Olympic gold medals in an endurance event?

7 What nationality was Paavo Nurmi who set world records at distances ranging from 1,500 metres to 10,000 metres?

8 Which motoracing champion has won the most F1 titles?

9 Which golfer was the youngest ever US Masters winner?

10 Who has won the most world darts championships?

11 Who has won the most Cricket World Cups?

12 Who has the highest Test score?

13 Who scored the highest domestic cricket score?

19 Stacey Dragila held the world record in which field event?

20 How many times did Lester Piggot win the Derby?

21 Who was champion jockey a record 26 times?

22 Which country has won the America's Cup most often?

23 Which baseball team has won the World Series the greatest number of times?

24 Who is the only cyclist to have won the Tour de France in five successive years?

25 Who broke the first four-minute mile?

1 By what name was Peggy Hookham better known?

2 Who was a founder and first director of the New York City Ballet?

3 Which French artist produced a succession of pastel drawings of ballerinas?

4 Which ballet was originally entitled *Chopiniana*?

5 In which film does Gene Kelly dance with a cartoon mouse?

6 Who choreographed *West Side Story*?

7 Who formed the Dance Theater of Harlem?

8 Who originally choreographed *Chicago*?

9 Which Tyneside lad took up dancing lessons with Julie Walters against his miner father's wishes?

10 In 1905, who first danced 'The Dying Swan'?

11 Who first choreographed Stravinsky's *Rite of Spring*?

12 Whose final season as artistic director of the Royal Ballet was 2000–1?

13 Which 1914 ballet was composed by Satie and designed by Picasso?

14 When Judy Garland dropped out, which film gave Ginger Rogers the chance to star with Fred Astaire one last time?

15 In 1986, which director made *Ginger and Fred*, about a pair of geriatric imitators who come out of retirement for one last show?

16 Of which Petipa ballet did Rudolf Nureyev make a film, starring himself?

17 Which Australian dance spectacular, choreographed by Dein Perry, won an Olivier Award in 1996?

18 Which experimental choreographer presented his first solo New York show with John Cage in 1944 and went on performing with his life partner for the next 50 years?

19 With which famous dancer did Ballets Russes impresario Diaghilev have a doomed affair?

20 Which child star's father starred in *The Nutcracker* in the 1950s alongside Bonnie Bedelia?

21 What was unusual about Adventures in Motion Pictures' version of *Swan Lake*?

22 What colour were Moira Shearer's shoes in Powell and Pressburger's classic film?

23 Which Spanish director has filmed dance versions of Lorca's *Blood Wedding* and the life of Goya?

24 Which male dancer shot to fame with *Riverdance*?

25 Which ballerina at the Royal Ballet became its youngest ever principal with her performance as Rose in *The Prince of the Pagodas*?

1 Which Poet Laureate was sacked as film critic of the *Evening Standard*?

2 Which poet's experiences in the First World War expressed themselves in his *Satirical Poems* and his *Memoirs of a Fox-Hunting Man*?

3 Which poet, an icon of counter-culture's first collection of poetry was called *Howl*?

4 Which Nobel Prize-winning poet was born in County Derry?

5 'It took the whole of Creation to produce my foot, my each feather' – whose foot?

6 Who wrote the poem which was read at the funeral in *Four Weddings and a Funeral*?

7 Who wrote The Rime of the Ancient Mariner?

8 With whom did W H Auden collaborate on *Letters from Iceland*?

9 Which French surrealist poet hid in a mental hospital during the Second World War, pretending to be one of the patients?

10 What kind of symmetry did the Tyger possess, according to William Blake?

11 Who was the love of Dante Alighieri's life?

12 Which cleric poet told Death not to be proud 'though some have called thee Mighty and dreadful'?

13 Which female Greek poet was born on the island of Lesbos and wrote love lyrics to women?

14 To whom did Elizabeth Barrett Browning address the words 'How do I love thee? Let me count the ways'?

15 Which romantic Italian poet became the subject of a play by Goethe?

16 Which 17th-century Dublin poet wrote various 'improved' versions of Shakespeare's plays?

17 According to T S Eliot, which month is the cruellest?

18 Which American poet was escorted home from Italy in 1945, but was never tried and instead was placed in a mental asylum where he won the Bollingen Prize for poetry?

19 Whose advice was 'When I am dead, my dearest, sing no sad songs for me'?

20 Who succeeded Ted Hughes as Poet Laureate?

21 Which Trinidadian poet won the Nobel Prize for Literature in 1992?

22 Which poet's father was exiled from Florence with Dante?

23 According to Andrew Marvell, when would coyness be no crime?

24 Of whom are the seasons of mist and mellow fruitfulness a close bosom friend?

25 Six of his greatest 'flowers of evil' were banned and he was fined for offences against public morals. Who was he?

1 Which author wrote *The Sound and the Fury*, *The Wild Palms* and *As I Lay Dying*?

2 What did A E Housman's initials stand for?

3 Which E M Forster novel features the Schlegel sisters?

4 How do we better know Mrs William Heelis?

5 Which novel deals with the events of one day in Dublin in June 1904?

6 Whose first collection of short stories, entitled *In Our Time*, was published in 1925?

7 Which of Jane Austen's novels was published posthumously?

8 Who is Pip's benefactor in Dickens's *Great Expectations*?

9 In Swift's *Gulliver's Travels*, what is Gulliver's profession?

10 Which writer, archaeologist and soldier joined the RAF after the First World War and changed his name to Shaw in 1927?

11 What are the March sisters' names in Louisa M Alcott's *Little Women*?

12 Which French author's novel *Germinal* depicts life in a mining community?

13 Which English writer divided his novels into three categories: Novels of Character and Environment, Romances and Fantasies, and Novels of Ingenuity?

14 How many tales are there in Chaucer's *Canterbury Tales*?

15 Which Nobel Prize winner wrote *A History of the English-speaking Peoples*?

16 Which St Louis-born novelist and poet became a British subject in 1927?

17 What is the surname of Cathy in *Wuthering Heights*?

18 What was the name of William Wordsworth's sister?

19 Whose works, *The Ballad of Reading Gaol* and *De Profundis*, were written from his experiences in prison?

20 Which thriller writer's works include *The Dark Eyes of London*, *Four Just Men* and *Sanders of the River*?

21 For which novel was Boris Pasternak awarded the 1958 Nobel Prize, an award he declined?

22 Which Algerian-born French author's works included *L'Etranger* and *La Peste*?

23 Which of the Brontë sisters married the Reverend A B Nicholls in 1854?

24 Whose life was the subject of James Boswell's biography, published in 1791?

25 Who wrote the Barsetshire novels?

1 In which film did Dustin Hoffman play a single-parent advertising executive?

2 Which advertising executive founded an important modern art collection in St John's Wood, London?

3 Which product was, controversially, advertised with the slogan 'Hello boys'?

4 Which advertising creative went on to direct *Blade Runner*?

5 Who controversially modelled for Calvin Klein under the slogan 'Nothing gets between me and my Calvins'?

6 In the early 1970s, Coca Cola produced a massively successful advertising campaign in which the lyrics to 'I'd like to teach the world to sing' were amended ... to what?

7 What Booker Prize-winning novelist wrote the slogan 'That'll do nicely' for American Express?

8 Who invented the Guinness toucan?

9 Who left ad agency JWT to found the Chicago Pizza Pie Factory?

10 In January 1984, Michael Jackson was hospitalized with second-degree burns after his hair caught fire while he was making a commercial. For which company was the commercial?

11 Victor Kiam thought it was so good that he did what?

12 What was the title of Vance Packard's seminal work on advertising in 1957?

13 The star of a Levi's jeans commercial went on to have a top 10 UK hit with 'Each Time You Break My Heart', co-written and produced by Madonna. Who was he?

14 After their falling out with Saatchi & Saatchi, what did its two founding members start up next?

15 Who is credited with developing the FCUK Fashion campaign?

16 William Crawford produced a booklet that became a bible for advertising: what was it called?

17 Which actress has portrayed the car-driving Nicole?

18 For which airline did 60s star Terence Stamp appear in a commercial?

19 Oliviero Toscarini's photographs for a Benetton advertising campaign bore the slogan 'Looking Death In The Face'. What was the subject of the photographs?

20 Madonna's sponsorship by Pepsi lasted less than a month. Which song, originally featured in a Pepsi commercial, prompted the company to drop her?

21 Which British supermodel featured in the Calvin Klein CKOne campaign?

22 Which Avenue in New York is most closely associated with advertising?

23 Who directed *How to Get Ahead in Advertising* in 1989?

24 An advert for which product appeared in the middle of Monica Lewinsky's only British TV interview (with Jon Snow) after the Clinton affair?

25 Which campaign did the American trade paper *Advertising Age* controversially name as its 'ad of the 20th century'?

ANSWERS TO QUIZ 10

Famous Couples
1 Jason Robards, Jr
2 Henry's brother Arthur
3 Ptolemy XIII (her brother)
4 Oliver Hardy
5 Lady Godiva
6 Michael Caine
7 Gerry Goffin and Carole King
8 1840
9 Richard Wagner
10 Timothy West and Prunella Scales
11 Burt Reynolds
12 Abbott and Costello
13 St Paul's Cathedral
14 Mia Farrow
15 Peter Sellers
16 Phil Spector
17 Tony Curtis and Janet Leigh
18 Banting and Best
19 Eva Braun
20 Ike and Tina Turner
21 Hansel and Gretel
22 Barnum and Bailey
23 Simone de Beauvoir
24 Lynne Frederick
25 Blake Edwards

US Presidents
1 George Washington, Thomas Jefferson, Theodore Roosevelt and Abraham Lincoln
2 Fifteen
3 Ulysses Simpson Grant
4 Franklin D Roosevelt
5 Dwight Eisenhower
6 'Hail to the Chief'
7 Theodore Roosevelt
8 James Buchanan
9 John Adams
10 Harry S Truman
11 Woodrow Wilson
12 Star Wars
13 Yes, they were distant cousins
14 Edward Kennedy
15 Peanuts
16 Milhous
17 Gerald Ford
18 John F Kennedy
19 Michael Dukakis
20 He became the youngest person ever to hold the office
21 Thomas Jefferson
22 'Old Hickory'
23 He was his grandfather
24 Washington, DC. It's a hotel and office complex where the Democratic Party

had its headquarters
25 Twelve years

Sean Connery
1 Mr Universe
2 Michael Caine
3 Dustin Hoffman
4 *The Offence*
5 *Marnie*
6 Michael Crichton
7 *The Untouchables*
8 *Dragonheart*
9 Seven
10 *The Presidio*
11 The SNP
12 Roald Amundsen
13 Audrey Hepburn
14 *A Bridge Too Far*
15 *Time Bandits*
16 *The Name of the Rose*
17 John le Carré
18 Alcatraz
19 Brigitte Bardot
20 *The Hill*
21 Burt Reynolds
22 Richard Gere
23 A nuclear submarine
24 Henry
25 *Murder on the Orient Express*

Russia
1 Ivan the Terrible
2 A dacha
3 Konstantin Chernenko
4 Peter the Great
5 A workers' council
6 Gregory Rasputin
7 Three
8 The Russian word for 'red' is the same as 'beautiful'. It has nothing to do with Communism
9 Lubyanka Prison
10 Big
11 St Petersburg
12 101 islands
13 The Hermitage
14 Catherine the Great
15 Nevsky Prospekt
16 Staraya Russa
17 The Volga
18 The Urals
19 Yekaterinburg
20 Boris Yeltsin
21 Caspian
22 Taiga
23 Lake Baikal
24 Seven
25 Vladivostock

Public Buildings
1 The Oyster Bar
2 Charles Barry and Augustus Pugin
3 To house the Great Exhibition of 1851
4 The National Gallery
5 The Old Vic
6 Brixton Prison
7 New York Mets
8 1948
9 Havana, Cuba
10 Milan, Italy
11 To celebrate the 100th anniversary of the French Revolution in 1889
12 Seattle
13 Llantrisant, Wales
14 Sir Basil Spence
15 Paris
16 Chicago
17 St Louis's Church in the Hôtel des Invalides, Paris
18 The Chinese Imperial Palace which covers 178 acres
19 Edward I
20 The MGM Grand Hotel in Las Vegas, Nevada opened in 1993 and has 5,009 rooms
21 The Red Lion
22 Hall of Public Audience
23 Holyrood Palace
24 Charles Rennie Mackintosh
25 Museo Thyssen-Bornemisza

Elvis Presley
1 Tupelo, Mississippi
2 'That's All Right' and 'Blue Moon of Kentucky'
3 The Jordanaires
4 'Heartbreak Hotel'
5 Scotty Moore and Bill Black
6 *Love Me Tender*
7 'The Wonder of You' (August 1970)
8 Las Vegas
9 Jessie
10 It was Elvis's army number
11 Jerry Lieber and Mike Stoller
12 $35,000
13 Lisa Marie Presley was born
14 'Wooden Heart'
15 They are all movie characters played by Elvis
16 The Beatles
17 Kurt Russell
18 'All Shook Up' (July 1957)
19 'Crying in the Chapel'
20 Colonel Tom Parker,

Elvis's manager
21 Misery
22 1961 and 1962
23 Richard Nixon
24 Carl Perkins, Jerry Lee Lewis and Johnny Cash
25 Tenor saxophone

Novelty Records
1 Barbados
2 Ross Bagdasarian
3 'Agadoo'
4 Piero Umiliani
5 The Dickies
6 The Goons
7 Ernie
8 'Thank U Very Much'
9 The Tweets
10 Tottenham Hotspur
11 'A Hard Day's Night'
12 The City Slickers
13 Stan Freberg
14 They were cartoon characters; the group didn't exist in real life
15 'Tie Me Kangaroo Down Sport'
16 The American Civil War
17 He performed it a cappella
18 'Eat It'
19 Hulk Hogan
20 Jimmy Osmond
21 David Bowie
22 'My Ding-A-Ling'
23 The Frog Chorus
24 'Always Look on the Bright Side of Life'
25 'The Streak'

Court Cases
1 Jeremy Irons
2 Johnny Cochran
3 The Marquess of Queensbury, father of Lord Alfred Douglas
4 'Fragrant'
5 'If that's justice, I'm a banana.'
6 Lindy Chamberlain
7 Patty Hearst
8 Martin Guerre
9 Alfred Dreyfus
10 *Lady Chatterley's Lover*
11 Mandy Rice-Davies
12 Dr H H Crippen
13 Bow Street
14 Terence Rattigan
15 Elton John
16 Liberace
17 The assassination of Israel's prime minister Yitzhak Rabin

18 Mick Jagger
19 Louise Woodward
20 Apple computers
21 Socrates, in 399 BC
22 Fatty Arbuckle
23 Archbishop Desmond Tutu
24 The Salem witches trial
25 Joseph K

Inventions
1 James Hargreaves
2 Louis Daguerre in 1826
3 The Kodak camera
4 A Latin edition of the Bible
5 The Watt Steam Engine
6 The escalator
7 Michael Faraday
8 The silicone chip
9 In Germany in 1360
10 The atom bomb
11 The telephone (invented by Alexander Graham Bell)
12 The gramophone
13 In Mesopotamia c.3000 BC
14 John Logie Baird
15 Elisha Otis
16 Linus Yale
17 J Robert Oppenheimer
18 The Chinese, c. AD 200
19 Pall Mall, London, in 1807
20 An American chemist named Wallace H Carothers
21 In China in the 1200s
22 John Walker in 1827
23 The flushing toilet
24 Coca-Cola
25 The Lumière brothers

The World Cup
1 Jules Rimet
2 Uruguay
3 It was the 1,000th goal at World Cup final stages
4 He was the referee who allowed the 'hand of God' goal
5 France
6 Substitutes
7 Ten (six in 1986, four in 1990)
8 France and the USA
9 Italy v Czechoslovakia, 1934
10 The Battle of Santiago
11 Saudi Arabia
12 Lineker, Beardsley and Platt
13 Egypt, 1934
14 Alan Shearer
15 Just Fontaine of France with 13 in 1958
16 Ally MacLeod
17 Jairzinho
18 Eusebio, Portugal

19 Zaire
20 Wales
21 Italy, 1934
22 Wolfgang Weber
23 Pasadena
24 Scotland, 1974
25 Italy (1934 and 1990) and Mexico (1970 and 1986)

Sporting Records
1 Preston
2 Pete Sampras
3 Martina Navratilova
4 Todd Woodbridge and Mark Woodforde ('The Woodies')
5 Joe Davis
6 Steve Redgrave
7 Michael Schumacher
8 Juan Manuel Fangio
9 Tiger Woods
10 Phil Taylor
11 West Indies
12 Brian Lara
13 Graham Hick
14 Jim Laker
15 Yorkshire
16 Mike Powell
17 Michael Johnson
18 Finnish
19 Pole vault
20 Nine
21 Sir Gordon Richards
22 USA
23 New York Yankees
24 Miguel Indurain
25 Roger Bannister

Dance
1 Dame Margot Fonteyn
2 George Balanchine
3 Edgar Degas
4 *Les Sylphides*
5 *Anchors Aweigh* (1945)
6 Jerome Robbins
7 Arthur Mitchell
8 Bob Fosse
9 Billy Elliot
10 Anna Pavlova
11 Nijinsky
12 Anthony Dowell
13 *Parade*
14 *The Barkleys of Broadway*
15 Federico Fellini
16 *Don Quixote*
17 *Tap Dogs*
18 Merce Cunningham
19 Nijinsky
20 Macaulay Culkin's father
21 It had an all-male cast of swans
22 Red
23 Carlos Saura

24 Michael Flatley
25 Darcey Bussell

Poets
1 Sir John Betjeman
2 Siegfried Sassoon
3 Allen Ginsberg
4 Seamus Heaney
5 'Hawk Roosting' – Ted Hughes
6 W H Auden
7 Samuel Taylor Coleridge
8 Louis MacNeice
9 Paul Eluard
10 'Fearful symmetry' – *Songs of Experience*
11 Beatrice Portinari
12 John Donne
13 Sappho
14 Robert Browning
15 Torquato Tasso
16 Nahum Tate
17 April
18 Ezra Pound
19 Christina Rossetti
20 Andrew Motion
21 Derek Walton
22 Francesco Petrarch
23 'Had we but world enough and time' – 'To His Coy Mistress' (1681)
24 The maturing sun – 'To Autumn', John Keats
25 Charles Baudelaire

Literature
1 William Faulkner
2 Alfred Edward
3 *Howard's End*
4 Beatrix Potter
5 *Ulysses* by James Joyce
6 Ernest Hemingway
7 *Persuasion*
8 Abel Magwitch
9 Surgeon
10 T E Lawrence
11 Jo, Meg, Beth and Amy
12 Emile Zola
13 Thomas Hardy
14 23
15 Winston Churchill
16 T S Eliot
17 Earnshaw
18 Dorothy
19 Oscar Wilde
20 Edgar Wallace
21 *Dr Zhivago*
22 Albert Camus
23 Charlotte
24 Samuel Johnson
25 Anthony Trollope

Advertising
1 *Kramer vs Kramer*
2 Charles Saatchi
3 The Wonderbra
4 Ridley Scott
5 Brooke Shields
6 'I'd like to buy the world a Coke'
7 Salman Rushdie
8 Dorothy L Sayers
9 Bob Payton
10 Pepsi
11 He bought the company
12 *The Hidden Persuaders*
13 Nick Kamen
14 M & C Saatchi
15 Trevor Beattie
16 *How to Succeed in Advertising*
17 Estelle Skomik
18 Virgin
19 Convicted murderers on Death Row
20 'Like a Prayer'
21 Kate Moss
22 Madison Avenue
23 Bruce Robinson
24 Vanish stain remover
25 Marlboro Man

THE ULTIMATE BOOK OF TRIVIA

QUIZ 11

1 Who said, on being refused membership of an exclusive golf club, 'I'm not an actor, and I enclose my press cuttings to prove it'?

2 Of which Shakespeare role did Laurence Olivier say, 'When you've the strength for it, you're too young; when you've the age you're too old. It's a bugger, isn't it?'?

3 Who is credited with, 'A woman drove me to drink and I never even had the courtesy to thank her'?

4 Which boxer used to 'float like a butterfly, sting like a bee'?

5 Which actress is reported to have said, 'I'm as pure as the driven slush'?

6 Who, when asked what his epitaph should read, replied, 'He was an average guy who could carry a tune'?

7 At the 1963 Royal Variety Performance who said, 'Will the people in the cheaper seats clap your hands? All the rest of you, if you'll just rattle your jewellery'?

8 Which newsreader said, 'Let's face it, there are no plain women on television'?

9 Which United States president said, 'Read my lips, no new taxes'?

10 On learning that he was described as an Irishman because he was born in Dublin, who said, 'Being born in a stable does not make a man a horse'?

11 Which British Prime Minister is said to have commented to friends when first appointed, 'I have climbed to the top of the greasy pole'?

12 Which TV show featured the catchphrases 'very interesting, but stupid' and 'here come de judge'?

13 When asked what his handicap was during a game of golf, which entertainer replied, 'I'm a coloured, one-eyed Jew'?

14 Which movie mogul supposedly said, 'A verbal contract isn't worth the paper it's written on'?

15 Who said, 'Of course, America had often been discovered before Columbus, but it had always been hushed up'?

16 Who described a performance by Katharine Hepburn as running 'the entire gamut of emotions from A to B'?

17 Which American comedian said, 'Too bad all the people who know how to run the country are busy driving cabs and cutting hair'?

18 Who commented 'I used to be Snow White...but I drifted'?

19 What did politician and broadcaster Austin Mitchell describe as 'an ermine-lined dustbin, an upmarket geriatric home with a faint smell of urine'?

20 Who said 'All I need to make a comedy is a park, a policeman and a pretty girl'?

21 Which British monarch said of King Lear, 'A strange, horrible business, but I suppose good enough for Shakespeare's day'?

22 Which film director said, 'Actors should be treated like cattle'?

23 Which American comedienne said, 'Boy George is all England needs – another queen who can't dress'?

24 Who said, 'An actor's a guy who, if you ain't talking about him, ain't listening'?

25 When asked his view of Western civilisation, who replied, 'I think it would be good idea'?

1

1 Who was Kurt Cobain referring to when he said 'I'd rather be dead than cool'?

2 Of whom did Leo Rosten observe, 'Any man who hates dogs and babies can't be all bad'?

3 About whom was it said, 'He can't act, can't sing and can dance a little'?

4 'Between us, we cover all knowledge; he knows all that can be known, and I know the rest.' To which famous 19th- and early 20th-century writer was Mark Twain referring?

5 Who 'cried at all his weddings and with good reason'?

6 About whom did Ronald Reagan say, 'I don't resent his popularity'?

7 Who did Reagan describe as 'the mad dog of the Middle East'?

8 Who was Pyrrhus talking about when he said, 'One more such victory and we're lost'?

9 Of whom did author Albert Goldman comment: 'One of the greatest problems was trying to find something positive to say about this man.'?

10 About whom was Yitzhak Rabin talking when he said 'Enough blood and tears'?

11 'Let them eat cake.' Let who eat cake?

12 With whom did Margaret Thatcher say 'we can do business'?

13 About whom did President Eisenhower say 'I just will not – I *refuse* – to get into the gutter with that guy'?

14 Whose 'normal career was one glorious defeat after another'?

15 Who did Woody Allen describe as 'the funniest woman on the planet'?

16 Who, when told that Lord Astor denied knowing her, replied, 'He would, wouldn't he?'?

17 Whom did Decca A & R Dick Rowe tell that guitar groups were 'on the way out'?

18 Which politician did Thatcher describe as 'not even able to leave his house'?

19 About whom did Hitler say, 'I'd rather have teeth pulled than meet him again'?

20 Who was Thatcher referring to when she said, 'There's no sympathy in politics'?

21 Of whom did Mark Twain say, 'Once you've put one of his books down, you simply can't pick it up again'?

22 Of whom did Jim Murray say, 'I'd like to borrow his body for just 48 hours. There are three guys I'd like to beat up and four women I'd like to make love to'?

23 Of whom did Churchill say, 'I can't deal with two shits at once'?

24 Who, according to Churchill, was 'in defeat unbeatable, in victory unbearable'?

25 Of whom did Joe Pasternak say, 'Wet, she was a star – dry she ain't'?

1 Who played the part of The Beatles' manager in *A Hard Day's Night*?

2 In whose films was Margaret Dumont sometimes cast as a put-upon society figure?

3 Who played the scientist's assistant, Igor, in *Young Frankenstein*?

4 Which Scottish-born actor is best remembered for his exaggerated double takes in Laurel and Hardy movies?

5 Who played Gene Hackman's police partner in *The French Connection*?

6 Who was the third sailor on shore leave with Gene Kelly and Frank Sinatra in *On the Town*?

7 In which film did Fred MacMurray appear as Jack Lemmon's boss, Mr Sheldrake?

8 Which film featured singer Al Martino who, as singer Johnny Fontane, makes an appearance at a family wedding?

9 In which film did George Segal and Sandy Dennis support the leads Richard Burton and Elizabeth Taylor?

10 Who won an Academy Award for best supporting actor in Stanley Kubrick's *Spartacus*?

11 Who appeared as a blind hermit in *Young Frankenstein*?

12 Which stalwart of British horror films played Grand Moff Tarkin in *Star Wars*?

13 Which film director played a small but significant role in *Chinatown*?

14 Who provided the love interest for Jack Lemmon and Walter Matthau in *Grumpy Old Men*?

15 Which future *Baywatch* star was one of Elliott's classmates in *ET, The Extra-Terrestrial*?

16 In the 1967 film *To Sir with Love*, starring Sidney Poitier, which pop singer appeared as one of the pupils in addition to singing the theme song?

17 In the 1963 film version of Edgar Allan Poe's 'The Raven', which future Oscar-winning actor played Peter Lorre's son?

18 In which James Bond film did German actor Gert Frobe play the title role?

19 Which actor played supporting roles in *Jerry Maguire* and *As Good as it Gets*?

20 Which future stars of the comedy series *Taxi* played hospital patients in *One Flew Over the Cuckoo's Nest*?

21 In one of her earliest screen roles, which actress appeared with the Marx Brothers in the 1950 film *Love Happy*?

22 Which singer made his screen debut in *Catch-22* in 1970?

23 A star of Coppola's *Godfather* movies, who played the unbilled part of a businessman in *The Conversation*, under the same director?

24 What is the significance of Gregory Peck and Robert Mitchum's cameo appearances in the 1991 version of *Cape Fear*?

25 Who was nominated for a best supporting actor Oscar in *JFK*?

1 Who has the title role in the 1931 film *Little Caesar*?

2 Which film features a trio of characters called Jimmy Conway, Henry Hill and Tommy De Vito?

3 Who plays Bob Hoskins's moll in *The Long Good Friday*?

4 What title is common to a 1932 film starring Paul Muni and one made in 1983 starring Al Pacino?

5 Which 1973 Martin Scorsese film centres on the lives of small-time hoods in New York's Little Italy?

6 Who plays hot-headed Sonny Corleone in *The Godfather*?

7 In which film does James Cagney cry on his way to the electric chair as a favour to his priest friend?

8 At 200 minutes, which is the longest of the three *Godfather* films?

9 Which stylized comic-book character faces villains such as Big Boy Caprice and Lips Manlis in the 1990 film starring Warren Beatty?

10 In which film do James Cagney and Humphrey Bogart appear together for the third and final time?

11 In which film does Michael Caine appear as a mob boss who assigns Bob Hoskins the job of chauffeuring a high-class call girl?

12 Who plays Al Capone in *The Untouchables*?

13 Which big star of today is billed as '1st Irishman' in *The Long Good Friday*?

14 The gang members in *Reservoir Dogs* are named after colours. Who plays Mr Orange?

15 Which American rap star, a real-life victim of gang violence, appears in several films, such as *Poetic Justice* in 1993 and *Bullet* in 1995?

16 Which 1984 film follows the fortunes of a group of Jewish boys on Manhattan's Lower East Side from the 1920s to the 1960s?

17 Which Woody Allen film features a playwright, a gangster's moll and a hitman with a talent for writing?

18 Who directed the 1993 film *Carlito's Way*?

19 Which Dennis Hopper-directed film features Robert Duvall and Sean Penn as policemen caught up in Los Angeles youth gang violence?

20 Who directed and is also star of the 1991 film *Bugsy*, about the life of legendary gangster Benjamin 'Bugsy' Siegel?

21 Which sequel also serves as its predecessor's prequel?

22 What does James Cagney push into Mae Clarke's face in the 1931 film *The Public Enemy*?

23 Which 1993 film marked the debut of Robert De Niro as director?

24 Which double Oscar-winning actress appeared as Tallulah in the all-juvenile *Bugsy Malone* in 1976?

25 In which 1995 film does John Travolta play Chili Palmer, a Miami-based loan collector with Mafia connections?

1 What mammal of northern Europe, Asia and North America is sometimes called a glutton?

2 What sort of animal is a fer-de-lance?

3 Which large feline of Asia is sometimes called an ounce?

4 Which rodent has given its name to a mean-spirited or bad-tempered woman?

5 What apparently inappropriate name is used for a gathering and breeding place for seals?

6 What is the main diet of the pangolin?

7 Which is the largest land-living carnivore?

8 The word 'ophidian' refers to what sort of animal?

9 Which large rodent's fur is known as nutria?

10 Americans call it a caribou. What is it called in Europe?

11 Dugongs and manatees belong to which family of animals?

14

12 The echidna, or spiny anteater, and the duck-billed platypus share a characteristic which does not apply to any other mammal. What is it?

13 Which is the largest living rodent?

14 Which two islands are the natural habitat of the orang - utan?

15 Which small breed of cattle is found wild in the Tibetan plateau, north of the Himalayas?

16 Which small rodent, highly valued for its fine, silky fur, lives almost exclusively high in the Andes?

17 Which is the largest member of the cat family that is indigenous to the New World?

18 Which animal is the symbol of the World Wide Fund for Nature?

19 What is the name of the wild pig of Central and South America that has three species called collared, white-lipped and chaco?

20 Hyraxes, which grow to weigh a maximum of 5 kg and are the Conies mentioned in the Bible, have a shared ancestry with which large mammal?

21 Which is the smallest mammal in Europe?

22 Which snake is also known as a hamadryad?

23 The vicuña is a member of which family of mammals?

24 The tenrec is a small insectivore that is only found on which large island?

25 What is the largest mammal?

1 In which country is Europe's highest mountain, Mt Elbrus?

2 Which metallic element has the symbol Eu?

3 In which century was the Canal du Midi opened, connecting the Atlantic Ocean to the Mediterranean Sea?

4 What nationality was the chemist Alfred Nobel?

5 If you drove in a straight line from Moscow to Madrid how many countries would you drive in altogether?

6 Which mountain range lies in the north of Spain, west of the Pyrenees?

7 Created by German scientists in 1876, what was the first artificial flavouring?

8 Which European country generates the highest proportion of its electricity by hydroelectric power stations?

9 Where is the Glenveagh National Park?

10 Between which two countries would you find Lake Olirid?

11 In 1904 Danish biologist Johannes Schmidt discovered the Sargasso Sea in the North Atlantic to be the breeding ground of which fish?

12 Which European country is the world's largest producer of cork?

13 What forms the natural border between Europe and Asia?

14 What nationality was Christian Schonbein, who discovered ozone in 1840?

15 Which two countries have coastlines on the Bay of Biscay?

16 Into where does the Volga, Europe's longest river, flow?

17 Which country is the world's leading exporter of salmon?

18 Artificial PKN fertilisers were introduced in Britain in 1926. What are the constituent parts?

19 What is the second official language spoken in Germany?

20 What separates Spain from Morocco?

21 Lake Ladoga is the largest lake in which country?

22 In which country are the Apennine Mountains?

23 Which country has borders with France, Germany, Austria, Lichtenstein and Italy?

24 Between which two countries would you find the Gulf of Bothnia?

25 What is common to the Republic of Ireland, Northern Ireland, Scotland, Wales, Monaco, Denmark and Portugal?

1 Which American soprano became the first singer to give a solo Proms recital in August 2000?

2 By what name is Beethoven's sixth symphony known?

3 Whose 'Variations on a Theme by Paganini' is a standard part of the piano repertoire?

4 Which Suffolk town was the birthplace of Benjamin Britten?

5 Which composer was baptised with the forenames Johannes Chrysostamus Wolfgangus Theophilus?

6 What is meant by the musical instruction largo?

7 In a standard orchestra line-up, which musicians sit immediately to the conductor's left?

8 Who was asked in 1874 by Henrik Ibsen to write incidental music to *Peer Gynt*?

9 Which male vocal range is pitched between tenor and bass?

10 Whose ballet music includes *Petrushka* and *The Rite of Spring*?

11 How many keys are on a standard concert piano?

12 Which knight is conductor with the Berlin Philharmonic Orchestra?

13 In 1932 Edward Elgar recorded his violin concerto. Who was the sixteen-year-old soloist?

14 Which opera overture is used as a background to post-Grand Prix champagne celebrations?

15 Which hymn traditionally closes the last night of the Proms?

16 In 1922, which composer scored Mussorgsky's piano piece *Pictures at an Exhibition* for full orchestra?

17 Who was the first American-born principal conductor of the New York Philharmonic Orchestra?

18 What connects composers such as Haydn, Mozart, Beethoven and Schubert with the city of Vienna?

19 What was Richard Wagner composing intermittently between 1848 and 1874?

20 Which British opera festival was started in 1934?

21 What function did the composer Franz Schubert perform at Beethoven's funeral?

22 Which movie is synonymous with the Adagietto from Mahler's fifth symphony?

23 What do the initials FRAM stand for?

24 By what name is Antonin Dvorák's ninth symphony known?

25 Which pianist/composer/conductor was born in Berlin in 1929, took American citizenship in 1943 and became a well-known face on British TV in the 1970s?

1 What was Frank Sinatra's middle name?

2 Name Nat King Cole's hit-making daughter.

3 What is Doris Day's real name?

4 The 1960s television show *Flying Colours* featured a singer named Gerry Dorsey.
Who did he become?

5 Who sang the opening song in the film *The Italian Job*?

6 Dean Martin used to box under the name Kid Crochet. True or false?

7 Johnny Mathis was once a world-class athlete. In which event?

8 Glenn Miller received the first-ever gold record award. For which single?

9 Name all three Andrews sisters.

10 Bandleader James Last started out playing which instrument?

11 Which Henry Mancini song does Andy Williams employ as his theme tune?

12 'Route 66' composer Bobby Troup was married to which sultry singer?

13 Apart from singing, what occupation is Tony Bennett famous for?

14 Who was The Velvet Fog?

15 Which musician actually created Mantovani's unique sound?

16 Name the arranger/orchestra leader on Frank Sinatra's *Songs For Swinging Lovers* album.

17 Who had a multi-million best-seller with 'How Much Is that Doggie in the Window?'?

18 How was Norma Dolores Egstrom better known?

19 In which film does Julie London sing 'Cry Me a River'?

20 Who duetted with Celine Dion on the 1997 hit 'Tell Him'?

21 Who partnered David Bowie on a Christmas hit in 1982?

22 Name Neil Diamond's first British hit.

23 Name the hit-making Three Tenors.

24 Which American singer was married to Debbie Reynolds, Elizabeth Taylor and Connie Stevens?

25 His hits include 'I'll Be Home', 'Friendly Persuasion' and 'Love Letters in the Sand'. Who is he?

1 Who was the first Catholic president of the United States?

2 In 1960 Penguin books announced that they would be publishing which controversial novel?

3 Which government post was held by John Profumo at the time of the affair involving Christine Keeler?

4 Who was shot dead in Dallas on 24 November 1963?

5 With which band did The Jimi Hendrix Experience's record producer/manager Chas Chandler make his name?

6 Who moved into his 'Factory' on New York's East 47th Street in 1963?

7 In which year was the Berlin Wall constructed?

8 Whose death in 1965 prompted President Johnson to order that all American flags the world over be flown at half-mast, a mark of respect never before accorded to a foreigner?

9 Which revolutionary icon was killed on 9 October 1967?

10 Who directed Terence Stamp in his first starring role in the film *Billy Budd* in 1962?

11 To what did the chant 'Hell, no! We won't go!' refer?

12 What happened at Max Yasgur's dairy farm in New York state during 15–17 August 1969?

13 What did Frenchman André Turcat do on 2 March 1969?

14 What happened to the Apollo I spacecraft on 27 January 1967?

15 Which founder of the Organisation for Afro-American Unity was murdered in Harlem on 21 February 1965?

16 When was the abolition of the death penalty made permanent in Great Britain?

17 In 1969 Richard Cawston made a documentary film for the BBC about which famous family?

18 Where did Harold Macmillan make his famous 'Winds of Change' speech in 1969?

19 In which year did the oil tanker Torrey Canyon come aground near Land's End, causing a major environmental disaster?

20 Who, in 1963, became the first film star to earn a million dollars for a single film?

21 What connects Richard Nixon, Lyndon B Johnson, Hubert Humphrey and Spiro Agnew?

22 In which year did a Soviet cosmonaut make the first spacewalk?

23 In December 1967, 53-year-old Louis Washkansky became the first person to undergo what?

24 How did UN Secretary-General Dag Hammarskjoeld die in September 1961?

25 In which month of which year was the six-day war between the Arabs and the Israelis?

1 Which future world heavyweight boxing champion won gold in the middleweight division at the 1976 games in Montreal?

2 Klaus Dibiasi won three consecutive platform diving medals in 1968, 1972 and 1976. Which country did he represent?

3 In which years were the Olympics held in Los Angeles?

4 At which event did swimmers Duncan Goodhew and Adrian Moorhouse win gold at Moscow and Seoul respectively?

5 Which nation won the gold medal in the Association Football event at the 1964 Tokyo games and again at Mexico City in 1968?

6 At which Olympic games did the British men's hockey team win gold?

7 How many nations were represented at the first modern games in Athens in 1896?

8 Who won Great Britain's first gold at the Sydney 2000 games?

9 At which games was the women's 400 metres hurdles first included?

10 Where and when did the games take place in the southern hemisphere for the first time?

11 At the time of writing, the men's 100 metres world record stands to Maurice Greene at 9.79 seconds. What was the winning time for the event at the 1896 games in Athens?

12 Which Ethiopian athlete won the marathon at the Rome and Tokyo games in 1960 and 1964?

13 Who lit the torch and later won a gold medal at the Sydney games?

14 Which gymnast won gold on the beam discipline at both the Montreal and Moscow games in 1976 and 1980?

15 Between 1920 and 1928, how many gold medals were won by Finnish distance runner Paavo Nurmi?

16 Which French athlete walked out of the Sydney games on the eve of the competition?

17 How did Russian Sacha Belov break American hearts at the Munich games in 1972?

18 Who was Steven Redgrave's rowing partner when he won his first two golds at Los Angeles and Seoul?

19 In which games did archery first become an Olympic sport?

20 Which Atlanta athlete broke the 200 metres world record in his home-town in 1996?

21 Which two future heavyweight boxing champions of the world won Olympic golds at that weight in 1964 and 1968 respectively?

22 Apart from being gold medallists, what did American swimmers Johnny Weissmuller and Buster Crabbe have in common?

23 Who won seven gold medals, all with world records, in the swimming pool at the 1972 Munich games?

24 What did Swedish modern pentathlon competitor Hans-Gunnar Liljenvall have the dubious distinction of being first to do at an Olympic games in Mexico City, 1968?

25 Marion Jones was expected to win five gold medals at the Sydney Olympics. How many did she actually win?

1 Who was the 2000 World Rally champion?

2 Which British Formula One champion went on to win in Indie Cars?

3 What distinction does Brazilian driver Felipe Massa hold in the 2002 Formula One season?

4 When did James Hunt win Formula One?

5 Which father and son won the Formula One Championship?

6 Which British motorcyclist had to be rebuilt?

7 Who was the 2001 World Superbike champion?

8 What did Murray Walker do before commentating?

9 What is Martin Brundle's other job?

10 Who won the 2001 Constructors' Championship?

11 Who won Formula One in 2001?

12 Who was Ferrari's number two in 2001?

13 Which British driver retired from Formula One in 2000?

14 Who died and had an Formula One track named after him?

15 Where did Ayrton Senna die?

16 Who is Michael Schumacher's younger brother?

17 What job did Damon Hill do before he got involved in motor sport?

18 Who finished second in the Driver's Championship in the year 2000?

19 Who survived a plane crash that killed the pilot?

20 Where is the British Grand Prix held?

21 Which ex-champion owned the team which became Jaguar?

22 Who was co-commentator with Murray Walker when Murray retired?

23 What is the lowest class of race?

24 Which team's colours are orange?

25 Which team's colours are green?

1 Which easy-listening crooner had a hit hour-long weekly variety show from 1955–1963?

2 Who topped the bill at the 1963 Royal Variety Performance?

3 Bob Horn's Bandstand began in 1952 as a local show in the Philadelphia area. By what name was it known when it went national in 1957?

4 By the time the above programme went national who was its host?

5 Which US DJ hosted the *Moondog's Rock 'n' Roll Party*?

6 Which BBC/WGBH co-production serialised the history of pop music in ten parts?

7 The Rolling Stones changed the lyrics of their 1967 single 'Let's Spend the Night Together' for *The Ed Sullivan Show*. What was the new title?

8 'The Pre-Fab Four' were the stars of a TV series that debuted in 1966. What was it called?

9 In which year did *Top of the Pops* begin?

10 Which band performed covers of songs by David Bowie, Leadbelly and the Meat Puppets during their appearance on 'Unplugged'?

11 On which TV show did the Beatles make their US TV debut?

12 How did the Sex Pistols cause outrage during an appearance on British TV in 1976?

13 Whose appearance at the 1996 Brit Awards prompted a stage invasion by Pulp's Jarvis Cocker?

14 By what name was Monkee Mickey Dolenz known in his days as a child star in *Circus Boy*?

15 Which former presenter of *The Tube* died in 2000?

16 In what way were many of Elvis Presley's early TV performances censored?

17 Who provided the voices for both Beavis and Butthead?

18 Which event dominated TV screens on 13 July 1985?

19 John Lennon became the first Beatle to appear solo when he sang his 1970 hit single on *Top of the Pops*. What was it called?

20 Which giant of easy listening once had his own show in which, amongst other things, a bear kept asking him for cookies?

21 Which show gave a backdrop of music from the charts to footage of news events beginning in the fifties?

22 Which singer, second in popularity only to Elvis Presley in the late 1950s, had his own TV show between 1957–1960?

23 Giving rise to several albums, which channel has featured artists in an 'unplugged' setting?

24 Which member of the Rat Pack had a hit TV series from 1965–74?

25 Who was prevented from singing 'Talkin' John Birch Paranoid Blues' on the *Ed Sullivan Show* because the network thought it too controversial?

20

1 Which supersoap had the working title 'Oil'?

2 Which US soap was mentioned in *Friends*, in connection with Joey's acting career?

3 What was *Soap*'s catchphrase?

4 What was America's first prime-time TV soap opera?

5 What was the spin-off series from *Dallas*?

6 Which supersoap featured actors who had previously starred in *I Dream of Jeannie* and *The Man from Atlantis*?

7 Which American soap features various members of the Foster family?

8 What is the name of the setting for Australian soap *Home and Away*?

9 Which soap, a spin-off from *Dynasty*, starred Charlton Heston, Katharine Ross and Barbara Stanwyck?

10 Which American soap starred Jane Wyman and was set in California's wine region?

11 Who wrote the script for an unmade movie in 1974 that later became the TV series *ER*?

12 What part did John Forsythe, *Dynasty*'s Blake Carrington, play in the hit TV series *Charlie's Angels*?

13 What was Dr Kildare's Christian name?

14 What is the world's longest-running television soap opera?

15 Who did Aaron Spelling cast as Donna Martin in *Beverly Hills 90210*?

16 Which soap was set in Wentworth Detention Centre, Melbourne?

17 Which TV show saw the first appearance of the character Lou Grant?

18 In which US state was *Knots Landing* set?

19 Why are soap operas so called?

20 Complete the name of this US soap: *Sunset *****?

21 Which star of a famous soap went on to appear in several mini-series, including *Shogun*?

22 The UK's first indigenous medical soap was also the country's first twice weekly serial. What was it called?

23 How many Emmys did *ER* win in its first year?

24 In the final episode of *Dallas*, who owned Ewing oil?

25 In a 1983 episode of which soap did former US president Gerald Ford and former Secretary of State Henry Kissinger appear at a ball?

1 What frightened Miss Muffet away?

2 Which false idol was worshipped by the Hebrews at the foot of Mount Sinai?

3 In Edward Lear's poem, which bird sang to the Pussycat?

4 In *The Wizard of Oz,* what was the lion looking for?

5 Name Tin Tin's canine companion.

6 Which bird brought back a twig to Noah to signal the end of the Flood?

7 What killed Cleopatra?

8 What did Prokofiev's Peter catch and take to the zoo?

9 Which birds were kept on the Capitol and, allegedly, saved Rome from attack by the Gauls?

10 Which bird is an emblem of the French nation?

11 Onto whose back should the Gingerbread Man not have jumped?

12 Who did Jean de Brunhoff create?

13 In the 1933 film, which actress is held aloft by King Kong?

14 Which flightless bird from Mauritius is now extinct?

15 In Wonderland, who took a watch out of his waistcoat pocket only to discover that he was late?

16 Rimsky-Korsakov composed a short piece of music about whose flight?

17 Which bird was the emblem of Prussia?

18 Which gentle creature did Walt Disney create in 1942?

19 Who was the first animal in space?

20 Which detective tries to find out who framed Roger Rabbit?

21 What sort of animal was Tarka?

22 What was Joy Adamson's lion cub called?

23 What kind of animal was Willy in *Free Willy*?

24 Which cross-eyed lion in a 1965 film spawned the *Daktari* television series?

25 In which 1986 film did Michael Hutchence star as a truly terrible punk singer?

ANSWERS TO QUIZ 11

Quotations

1 Victor Mature
2 King Lear
3 W C Fields
4 Muhammad Ali (Cassius Clay)
5 Tallulah Bankhead
6 Bing Crosby
7 John Lennon
8 Anna Ford
9 George Bush
10 The Duke of Wellington
11 Benjamin Disraeli
12 *Rowan and Martin's Laugh-In*
13 Sammy Davis, Jr
14 Sam Goldwyn
15 Oscar Wilde
16 Dorothy Parker
17 George Burns
18 Mae West
19 The House of Lords
20 Charlie Chaplin
21 Queen Victoria
22 Alfred Hitchcock
23 Joan Rivers
24 Marlon Brando
25 Mahatma Gandhi

About Whom?

1 Courtney Love
2 W C Fields
3 Fred Astaire
4 Rudyard Kipling
5 Humphrey Bogart
6 Mikhail Gorbachev
7 ColonelGaddafi
8 The Romans
9 Elvis Presley
10 The Palestinians
11 The French
12 Gorbachev
13 Senator Joseph McCarthy
14 Earl Mountbatten
15 Diane Keaton
16 Mandy Rice-Davies
17 Brian Epstein, the Beatles' manager
18 Neil Kinnock
19 General Franco
20 Ted Heath
21 Henry James
22 Muhammad Ali
23 Clement Attlee
24 Viscount Montgomery
25 Swimmer-turned-actress Esther Williams

Also Starring

1 Norman Rossington
2 The Marx Brothers

3 Marty Feldman
4 James Finlayson
5 Roy Scheider
6 Jules Munshin
7 *The Apartment*
8 *The Godfather*
9 *Who's Afraid of Virginia Woolf?*
10 Peter Ustinov
11 Gene Hackman
12 Peter Cushing
13 Roman Polanski, *Chinatown*'s director
14 Ann-Margret
15 Erika Eleniak
16 Lulu
17 Jack Nicholson
18 *Goldfinger*
19 Cuba Gooding, Jr
20 Danny DeVito and Christopher Lloyd
21 Marilyn Monroe
22 Art Garfunkel
23 Robert Duvall
24 They were the stars of the 1962 version
25 Tommy Lee Jones

Gangsters

1 Edward G Robinson
2 *Goodfellas*
3 Helen Mirren
4 *Scarface*
5 *Mean Streets*
6 James Caan
7 *Angels with Dirty Faces*
8 *The Godfather, Part II*
9 *Dick Tracy*
10 *The Roaring Twenties*
11 *Mona Lisa*
12 Robert De Niro
13 Pierce Brosnan
14 Tim Roth
15 Tupac Shakur
16 *Once Upon a Time in America*
17 *Bullets over Broadway*
18 Brian De Palma
19 *Colors*
20 Warren Beatty
21 *The Godfather, Part II*
22 A grapefruit (probably half of one)
23 *A Bronx Tale*
24 Jodie Foster
25 *Get Shorty*

Wild Animals

1 Wolverine
2 Snake
3 Snow leopard
4 Shrew

5 Rookery
6 Ants and termites
7 Brown or grizzly bear
8 Snake
9 Coypu
10 Reindeer
11 Sirenia or sea cows
12 They lay eggs
13 Capybara
14 Borneo and Sumatra
15 Yak
16 Chinchilla
17 Jaguar
18 Giant panda
19 Peccary
20 Elephant
21 Pygmy shrew
22 King cobra
23 Llama
24 Madagascar
25 Blue whale

Europe

1 Russia
2 Europium
3 Seventeenth (1681)
4 Swedish
5 Eight (Russia, Belarus, Poland, Czech Republic, Germany, Switzerland, France and Spain)
6 The Cantabrian Mountains
7 Vanilla essence
8 Norway
9 County Donegal, Republic of Ireland
10 Albania and Macedonia
11 European eel
12 Portugal
13 The Ural Mountains
14 German
15 France and Spain
16 The Caspian Sea
17 Norway
18 Phosphorus, potash and nitrogen
19 Turkish
20 The Straits of Gibraltar
21 Russia
22 Italy
23 Switzerland
24 Sweden and Finland
25 They all have a coastline and a land border with only one other country

Classical Music

1 Jessye Norman
2 The Pastoral Symphony
3 Rachmaninoff
4 Lowestoft
5 Mozart

6 Slow, dignified in style
7 First violins
8 Edvard Grieg
9 Baritone
10 Stravinsky
11 88
12 Sir Simon Rattle
13 Yehudi Menuhin
14 Bizet's *Carmen*
15 'Jerusalem'
16 Ravel
17 Leonard Bernstein
18 They all died there
19 The *Ring* cycle
20 Glyndebourne
21 He was a pallbearer
22 *Death in Venice*
23 Fellow of the Royal Academy of Music
24 *From the New World*
25 André Previn

Easy Listening

1 Albert
2 Natalie Cole
3 Doris von Kappelhoff
4 Engelbert Humperdinck
5 Matt Monro
6 True
7 High jump
8 'Chattanooga Choo Choo'
9 Patti, Maxine and LaVerne
10 Double bass
11 'Moon River'
12 Julie London
13 Painting
14 Mel Tormé
15 Ronald Binge
16 Nelson Riddle
17 Patti Page
18 Peggy Lee
19 *The Girl Can't Help It*
20 Barbra Streisand
21 Bing Crosby
22 'Cracklin' Rosie'
23 Jose Carreras, Placido Domingo and Luciano Pavarotti
24 Eddie Fisher
25 Pat Boone

The 1960s

1 Catholic F
2 *Lady Chatterley's Lover*
3 Secretary of State for War
4 Lee Harvey Oswald
5 The Animals
6 Andy Warhol
7 1961
8 Winston Churchill
9 Che Guevara
10 Peter Ustinov

11 The war in Vietnam
12 The Woodstock festival
13 He flew Concorde on her maiden flight
14 It caught fire on the launch pad, killing all three crew
15 Malcolm X
16 1969
17 The Royal Family
18 Cape Town, South Africa
19 1967
20 Elizabeth Taylor in *Cleopatra*
21 They were the four US vice presidents during the 1960s
22 1965
23 A heart transplant operation
24 In an air crash
25 June 1967

The Olympics
1 Michael Spinks, USA
2 Italy
3 1932 and 1984
4 100 metres breaststroke
5 Hungary
6 Seoul, 1988
7 Fourteen
8 Jason Queally, 1 km cycling time trial
9 Los Angeles, 1984
10 Melbourne, 1956
11 Twelve seconds
12 Abebe Bikila
13 Cathy Freeman
14 Nadia Comaneci, Romania
15 Nine
16 Marie-José Perec
17 He scored the last-second winning basket to inflict the first ever defeat of the USA Olympic basketball team
18 Andrew Holmes
19 Munich, 1972
20 Michael Johnson
21 Joe Frazier and George Foreman
22 They both went on to movie careers
23 Mark Spitz
24 Fail a drugs test
25 Three

Motor Sports
1 Colin McRae
2 Nigel Mansell
3 Youngest driver

4 1976
5 The Hills
6 Barry Sheen
7 Troy Bayliss
8 Advertising
9 He sells cars
10 Ferrari
11 Michael Schumacher
12 Barichello
13 Johnny Herbert
14 Gilles Villeneuve
15 Monza
16 Ralph
17 A motorcycle courier
18 Mika Hakkinen
19 David Coulthard
20 Silverstone
21 Jackie Stewart
22 Jim Rosenthal
23 Karting
24 Arrows
25 Jaguar

Music Shows
1 Perry Como
2 The Beatles
3 *American Bandstand*
4 Dick Clark
5 Alan Freed
6 *Dancing in the Street*
7 'Let's spend *some time* together'
8 *The Monkees*
9 1964
10 Nirvana
11 *The Ed Sullivan Show*
12 By swearing
13 Michael Jackson
14 Mickey Braddock
15 Paula Yates
16 He was shown only from the waist up
17 Mike Judge
18 Live Aid
19 'Instant Karma!'
20 Andy Williams
21 The Banana Splits
22 Pat Boone
23 MTV
24 Dean Martin
25 Bob Dylan

Soap Operas
1 *Dynasty*
2 *Days of Our Lives*
3 'Confused? You will be!'
4 *Peyton Place*
5 *Knots Landing*
6 *Dallas*
7 *The Bold and the Beautiful*
8 Summer Bay
9 *The Colbys*

10 *Falcon Crest*
11 Michael Crichton
12 He was the voice of Charlie
13 James
14 *Coronation Street*
15 His daughter Tori
16 *Prisoner: Cell Block H*
17 *The Mary Tyler Moore Show*
18 California
19 Because soap manufacturers used to sponsor them
20 *Beach*
21 Richard Chamberlain
22 *Emergency Ward 10*
23 Eight
24 Cliff Barnes
25 *Dynasty*

Famous Animals
1 A spider
2 The Golden Calf
3 The Owl
4 Courage
5 Snowy
6 The dove
7 An asp
8 A wolf
9 The geese
10 The rooster
11 The sly fox
12 Babar the Elephant
13 Fay Wray
14 The dodo
15 The White Rabbit
16 The Bumblebee
17 The eagle
18 Bambi, the fawn
19 Laika the dog
20 Eddie Valiant, played by Bob Hoskins
21 An otter
22 Elsa
23 A killer whale
24 Clarence
25 *Dogs in Space*

THE ULTIMATE BOOK OF TRIVIA

OF TRIVIA

QUIZ

12

1 Who became Prime Minister of Israel in 1969?

2 With which political movement is the name Emmeline Pankhurst associated?

3 Who learnt English at an abbey in Dublin in order to teach Indian and Anglo-Saxon girls in Calcutta, where she worked prior to taking her vows as a nun in 1931?

4 Which Burmese politician, winner of the 1991 Nobel Peace Prize, was under house arrest from 1988 to 1995?

5 Which female scientist received the Nobel Prize for Chemistry in 1911?

6 Of whom did Charlotte Brontë say, 'Stronger than a man, simpler than a child, her nature stood alone'?

7 Which co-founder of the Social Democratic Party was the party's first elected MP?

8 What is Hillary Clinton's maiden name?

9 Edith Head's name appeared many times on movie credits. What was her contribution?

10 What was Mrs Beeton's Christian name?

11 Which woman was one of the founders of United Artists in 1919?

12 Soprano Maria Callas was born Maria Kalogeropoulos in 1923 in which city?

13 Who wrote *Sex and the Single Girl* in 1962 and later revitalised *Cosmopolitan* magazine?

14 By what title do we now know the woman born Margaret Hilda Roberts in 1925?

15 Which major event of 1936 was documented by German filmmaker Leni Riefenstahl?

16 By what nickname was American all-round sports star of the 30s, 40s and 50s Mildred Didrikson better known?

17 Whose diary was written as a series of letters to an imaginary friend called Kitty?

18 Who succeeded Lal Shastri as India's Prime Minister in 1966?

19 Who was canonised in 1920, 489 years after her death?

20 By what name is Princess Sophia of Anhalt-Zerbst better remembered?

21 What did Russian Valentina Tereshkova become the first woman to do in 1963?

22 Which American actress is married to Baron Haden-Guest?

23 Of which country was Benazir Bhutto prime minister between 1988–90 and 1993–97?

24 Which writer, lecturer, broadcaster and champion of feminism was born in Melbourne in 1939?

25 Who, at the age of 87, became the first woman to receive the Order of Merit in 1907?

1 Which actor, who died in 1999, didn't pick up his Oscar for *Patton*?

2 In which year did Princess Diana die?

3 How many Jews perished in the Holocaust?

4 Which British comedian died, aged 57, in Hampstead in 1995?

5 Which legendary jazz pianist and bandleader died in 1984?

6 Who died in a car crash from which his friend Gene Vincent escaped?

7 When did George VI die?

8 Which playwright, the author of 'I'll Leave It To You', died in 1973?

9 How many died at Hillsborough?

10 What happened at Heysel in 1985?

11 Whose wife was killed by Charles Manson?

12 How did Jackson Pollock die?

13 Who killed Lee Harvey Oswald?

14 Where did John Lennon die?

15 Which Labour leader died after one year in office?

16 In which city was John F Kennedy assassinated?

17 Where was Martin Luther King killed?

18 When did Elvis die?

19 Name the INXS singer who died in 1997.

20 Apollonaire is said to have coined the word 'surrealist' to describe the work of which painter, who died in 1985?

21 What was the name of the Nirvana singer who killed himself?

22 Who, on her deathbed, said, 'Get my "Swan" costume ready!'?

23 Who was the most recent Kennedy to die prematurely?

24 Which golfer's plane lost control, killing him and the crew?

25 Which blue-eyed singer died in 1998?

1 In which series of films from 1984 onwards did Robert Englund star as Freddy Krueger?

2 Which film first featured a character later called Pinhead?

3 Who played the title role in *The Abominable Dr Phibes*?

4 In 1951 Howard Hawks produced *The Thing*. Who directed the 1982 remake, starring Kurt Russell?

5 Which 1922 German vampire film starred the genuinely scary-looking Max Schreck in the title role?

6 Who played Jack Nicholson's wife in *The Shining*?

7 Who directed the 1968 film *Rosemary's Baby*?

8 Which of Courteney Cox's co-stars from the *Scream* films is now her husband?

9 Who played the monster in the 1931 film *Frankenstein*?

10 What particular gimmick was used in the 1958 film *House of Wax*?

11 Who played the title role in the 1960 Hammer production *The Curse of the Werewolf*?

12 Which 1945 Ealing film is a sequence of supernatural stories told by a group of people in a country house?

13 Which horror film star was portrayed in an Oscar-winning performance by Martin Landau in Tim Burton's 1994 film about cult filmmaker Ed Wood?

14 Which mother and daughter both appeared in John Carpenter's *The Fog*?

15 Which 1976 film is about a persecuted schoolgirl with psychokinetic powers?

16 Which actor of the silent era was known as 'The Man of a Thousand Faces'?

17 What was the contribution of actress Mercedes McCambridge to Linda Blair's performance in *The Exorcist*?

18 Apart from Anthony Perkins, which other performer from *Psycho* also appeared in *Psycho II* 23 years later?

19 What is the title of the 1992 Belgian film about a film crew following the exploits of a serial killer?

20 Which series of films features a habitual killer called Michael Myers?

21 What is the significance of the 1976 film *To the Devil . . . A Daughter*?

22 Which director's films include *Shivers*, *Videodrome* and *The Fly*?

23 What is the name of the summer camp in the *Friday the Thirteenth* movies?

24 Who played the title role in the 1965 British film *The Nanny*?

25 In which Tim Burton film did Johnny Depp's character have to confront the legend of an axe-wielding headless horseman?

1 Who produced David Lean's first four films as director?

2 Who plays Fagin in *Oliver Twist*?

3 Which film features a spiritualist called Madame Arcati, played by Margaret Rutherford?

4 For which film does Carnforth railway station provide an unlikely romantic setting?

5 Which Italian city is the setting for the 1955 film *Summertime*?

6 Who worked for four days in the title role of *Lawrence of Arabia* before quitting?

7 Which film stars Charles Laughton as a widowed Lancashire bootmaker with three daughters?

8 Which actor is the first person to appear on screen in *Dr Zhivago*?

9 In which film did John Mills win an Oscar for his portrayal of a village idiot?

10 Which Joseph Conrad novel was David Lean planning to film after *A Passage to India*?

11 Which Frenchman composed the music for every Lean film from *Lawrence of Arabia* onwards?

12 What took eight months to plan and build, required 45 elephants to drag 1,500 tree trunks into place, and stood 90 ft high and 245 ft wide?

13 Who made his film debut in *In Which We Serve*, playing a stoker who deserts his post?

14 Which film follows the lives of a lower-middle-class London family in the period between the two World Wars?

15 Who plays the part of Lara in *Dr Zhivago*?

16 What is the name of the actor who plays Dr Aziz in *A Passage to India*?

17 For which film did Ralph Richardson win the New York Film Critics' Award as best actor, playing the part of an aircraft manufacturer?

18 Which actor first appears as a dot on the horizon and rides towards the camera in *Lawrence of Arabia*?

19 For which film did David Lean become the first British director to be nominated for an Academy Award?

20 What part did Anthony Newley play in *Oliver Twist*?

21 Which actor received ten per cent of the gross box-office receipts on top of his salary for *The Bridge on the River Kwai*?

22 Who won an Oscar as best supporting actress for *A Passage to India*?

23 In addition to acting in David Lean films, what connects actresses Kay Walsh and Ann Todd?

24 Which actress starred in *In Which We Serve*, *This Happy Breed* and *Brief Encounter*?

25 What connects *Oliver Twist* with *Monty Python's Flying Circus*?

1 What is the Aborigine name for Ayers Rock?

2 What year was Sydney Opera House completed?

3 What is the capital of South Australia?

4 What is the name of Sydney's bohemian quarter?

5 Where did Captain Cook set foot on Australian soil?

6 Which famous Australian author wrote *Oscar and Lucinda*?

7 Which famous Australian model appeared in the opening ceremony of the Sydney Olympic Games?

8 In 1866, where did Mother Mary MacKillop establish the first school in Australia for all children regardless of race or income?

9 Which valley is the vineyard of the nation?

10 Where is Australia's Parliament House?

11 Which penal settlement was home to 12,500 convicts and connected to Tasmania by a strip of land known as Eaglehawk Neck?

12 What is the capital of Tasmania?

13 How many time zones are there within Australia?

14 Australia produces over 90 per cent of one of the earth's semi-precious stones. Which one?

15 What are the highest waterfalls in Australia?

16 What does Wagga Wagga mean?

17 Melbourne is situated on the banks of which river?

18 Which National Park features natural landmarks called London Bridge and the Twelve Apostles?

19 What sport is played by the West Coast Eagles and Essendon Bombers?

20 Who discovered Darwin Harbour?

21 In 1974, how many of Darwin's 8,000 homes were destroyed by Cyclone Tracy?

22 Which wildlife park was used to film *Crocodile Dundee*?

23 Which town is situated close to the geographic centre of Australia?

24 What is the largest sand island in the world?

25 Which famous Australian pop singer once had a television wedding to Jason Donovan?

1 In the Scorsese movie of the same name, who sang 'New York, New York'?

2 Which 60s band had a hit with 'Waterloo Sunset'?

3 Who went for a stroll down 'Baker Street'?

4 In 1965 who went to 'Maggie's Farm'?

5 On which interstate highway did Chuck Berry get his kicks?

6 Which band released the song 'Breakfast in America'?

7 Who sang 'The Girl from Ipanema'?

8 Who did the 'Harlem Shuffle' in 1969?

9 To where did Steely Dan bid 'toodle-oo'?

10 Who boogied on down to the Funky Nassau?

11 Who Funked for Jamaica?

12 To which city did Dionne Warwick ask the way in 1968?

13 The Lovin' Spoonful were cats from which town in 1967?

24

14 Which group were 'Drowning In Berlin' in 1982?

15 Which famous album included the tracks 'Maxwell's Silver Hammer' and 'Carry that Weight'?

16 Which theme tune, sung by Matt Monro and composed by John Barry, came to us with love?

17 Where in Mayfair did a nightingale sing?

18 Who fell in love with 'my little China Girl'?

19 Which beautiful capital by the sea is 'wonderful'?

20 Which beach was far away in time?

21 Where was Lola a showgirl?

22 Where did George and Ira Gershwin experience 'A Foggy Day'?

23 Which fair was the subject of a Simon and Garfunkel song?

24 Who sang 'My Jamaican Guy'?

25 For whom did David Byrne produce an album called *Mesopotamia* in 1981?

1 Who is the youngest member of Boyzone?

2 Whose debut hit 'No No No' featured ex-Fugee Wyclef Jean?

3 Which teen boy band did Johnny Wright manage before Backstreet Boys?

4 At which summer event in 2000 did Christina Aguilera make her live UK debut?

5 What was Robbie Williams' first solo UK number one?

6 How were New Kids on the Block billed after a two-year absence from the charts with their 1994 efforts 'Dirty Dawg' and 'Never Let You Go'?

7 Which American vocal group scored their first UK top-ten hit in 1996 with 'We've Got It Goin' On'?

8 Robbie Williams has had by far the most success of the former members of Take That. Gary Barlow and Mark Owen have enjoyed some measure of success, but what are the names of the other two?

9 With which boy band did Mariah Carey cover the Phil Collins hit 'Against All Odds'?

10 Boyzone's first UK hit was 'Love Me for a Reason' in 1994. In which year did the Osmonds take the song to number one in Britain?

11 Released in May 1999, what was Geri Halliwell's first solo single?

12 Which song gave Hanson a transatlantic number one in 1997?

13 Which girl group had hits with 'Give It Up, Turn It Loose', 'Whatta Man' and 'Don't Let Go (Love)'?

14 Which American R&B/pop quintet released the album *No Strings Attached* in 2000?

15 Ace of Base come from which country?

16 The ever-changing Latin teen group Menudo saw one of their old boys enjoy worldwide success in 1999. Who is he?

17 With which teen band did Bobby Brown sing before going solo?

18 What was the first Spice Girls single not to top the UK charts?

19 Which artist topped the US Billboard singles chart, the Latino singles and Latino album chart all in the same week in October 2000?

20 Which band sang Britney Spears' 'Baby One More Time' at Glastonbury 2000?

21 Which group was put together for a TV programme based in Miami?

22 With whom did Boyz II Men record the single 'One Sweet Day' in 1995?

23 Which trio released the album *Crazysexycool*?

24 Which film featured R Kelly's 'I Believe I Can Fly'?

25 All Saints' hit 'Pure Shores' was taken from the soundtrack of which film?

1 Who replaced guitarist Mick Taylor in the Stones line-up?

2 Name Mick's first solo album.

3 What was the name of the television show that featured Mick Jagger as a ringmaster?

4 What is Mick's middle name?

5 Brian Jones came from which Gloucestershire town?

6 'Come On' was the Stones' first single. But who first wrote and recorded the song?

7 Which festival was notoriously captured on film in *Gimme Shelter*?

8 Name the legendary Australian outlaw portrayed on film by Mick.

9 Which album cover had to be reshot because it featured unauthorized shots of various personalities?

10 In which year did the band play a free concert in London's Hyde Park?

11 Bryan Jones died in a swimming pool at Cotchford Farm, Sussex. But which author once owned the farm?

12 Name the production credit that Jagger and Richards adopted from 1974 onwards.

13 What is the name of Bill Wyman's Knightsbridge restaurant?

14 Charlie Watts's book *Ode to a High Flying Bird* is a tribute to which jazzman?

15 Which Stones hit was reputedly based on Martha and the Vandellas' 'Dancing in the Street'?

16 A daughter was born to Mick and Bianca Jagger in October 1970. What did they name her?

17 Name the Carly Simon US number one (number three in the UK) for which Mick supplied a back-up vocal.

18 The Rolling Stones haven't topped the UK singles charts since 1969. What was the title of that final chart-topper?

19 Which album was dedicated to the late Ian Stewart, the pianist who played on so many Stones dates?

20 Which Stones album title parodied that of a Beatles release?

21 The Stones took their name from a song by a blues giant. Name him.

22 What was the name of the club at Richmond's Station Hotel where the Stones first really came to prominence?

23 Who wrote 'I Wanna Be Your Man', the Stones' second UK hit?

24 Which album opened with 'Start Me Up'?

25 Name the album that resulted from a 1972 jam session with Ry Cooder and Nicky Hopkins.

1 Where did Wyatt Earp's most notorious shoot-out take place?

2 What was the Wild West?

3 Which Apache chief surrendered in 1886?

4 Who led the first complete continental crossing?

5 Which Sioux chief was present at the incident which kickstarted the Sioux Wars?

6 Who brought cattle to America?

7 Which famous hunter killed 4,280 buffalo in eighteen months when asked to supply meat for the workers on the Kansas Pacific Railroad?

8 The USA grew rapidly when it purchased which area from France in 1803?

9 Which purpose-built railway with corrals and stockyards led to the success of the Texas cattle industry?

10 Where did Texan settlers led by Davy Crockett meet the Mexican forces head on in 1836?

11 Who took out his first patent for a revolver in 1836?

12 What did the Native Americans call the dried meat of a buffalo?

13 Who invented the broad-brimmed cowboy hat?

14 Who were the first American cowboys?

15 Why were Gold Rush prospectors called 'Forty-niners'?

16 How fast did wagon trains generally move westwards?

17 What was adobe?

18 What was the mobile headquarters of a cowboy crew called?

19 Approximately how many people on wagon trains were actually killed by Native Americans?

20 And roughly how many died from disease?

21 Who made jeans from tent canvas which became all the rage for cowboys in 1850?

22 What was the name given to farmers on the Great Plains who broke up turf to use for construction?

23 Who was defeated at Little Big Horn in 1876?

24 What did an Illinois farmer invent in 1874 to keep dogs away from his wife's flowers?

25 Who played Butch Cassidy and the Sundance Kid in the 1969 film version of their lives?

1 Who found the true source of the River Nile?

2 What nationality was the first person to sail round northern Canada through the Bering Strait?

3 Who accidentally sailed around the Cape of Good Hope in 1488?

4 On whose real-life exploits is James Clavell's novel *Shogun* based?

5 Why did David Livingstone go to Africa?

6 Who paid for Christopher Columbus's first voyage across the Atlantic?

7 Which famous Egyptian queen ordered the expedition to Punt and insisted on dressing as a king while wearing a false beard?

8 What was the name of Sir Francis Drake's most famous ship?

9 From 1835 to 1843, 14,000 Dutch Boers moved inland to set up new colonies. What was this journey called?

10 Who employed Henry Hudson to search for the North-west Passage?

11 How did Henry Stanley carry his boat, the *Lady Alice*, overland?

12 Which continent did Captain Cook discover in 1768?

13 Who were the first Europeans to reach Mount Kilimanjaro in Tanzania?

14 For which newspaper did Henry Stanley work?

15 What was the first town founded by Europeans in southern Africa?

16 Which Carthaginian navigator founded six colonies along the African coast and reached the Bight of Benin?

17 What nationality was Vasco da Gama?

18 Which Viking chief, banished from Iceland, founded the norse colonies on Greenland?

19 Of which settlement did local people invite Sir Francis Drake to become the king?

20 Which French explorer of West Africa convinced many African leaders to cede power to France?

21 Where was Henry Stanley when he uttered the phrase 'Dr Livingstone, I presume?'?

22 Who established a colony at Roanoke Island and christened it 'Virginia' in honour of Elizabeth I, the Virgin Queen?

23 Which woman lived with natives in West Africa and became the first European to visit parts of Gabon in 1894?

24 Which king hired Henry Stanley to carve out an empire for him in central Africa?

25 Which country sent the most explorers to Africa?

1 What are the four majors in men's golf?

2 Who won his first major via a playoff at the 1975 Open at Carnoustie?

3 In which year did Nick Faldo come from six shots behind Greg Norman on the last day to win his third US Masters title?

4 Who captained America to Ryder Cup victory in 1999?

5 Who achieved the first televised hole in one on British TV?

6 In which year did Arnold Palmer win his first Masters title?

7 Which women's tournament is played annually at Rancho Mirage, California?

8 At which course would you (hopefully) find the Road Hole?

9 What nationality is golfer Vijay Singh?

10 What is the term for a hole played in three shots below par?

11 The Open is always played on a links course. What is the main characteristic of a links?

12 Which British player won the women's US Open in 1987?

13 Whose real first name is Eldrick?

14 In what type of event do two players play against each another as opposed to playing against the entire field?

15 Which British-based tournament has had Weetabix as a sponsor?

16 When the flight of a golf ball curves slightly right to left it is called 'draw'. What is a slight curve of flight from left to right called?

17 Which golfer won the Open in 1987, 1990 and 1992?

18 Which is the only one of the majors to be staged at the same course every year?

19 How many majors have been won by Jack Nicklaus?

20 Ben Hogan was the last man before Tiger Woods to do what?

21 What is the trophy awarded to the winner of the Open?

22 What name is given to the area containing the 11th, 12th and 13th holes at the Augusta National championship course?

23 What name is given to a score, decided on by the tournament organisers, above which a player may not progress into the next round?

24 What is the women's equivalent of the Ryder Cup?

25 What separates the Muirfield course from the Muirfield Village course?

25

1 Who were the first winners?

2 Who were the first losers?

3 When was the first final?

4 Who were the last team to win before the Second World War?

5 Why did Manchester United not take part in the FA Cup in the 1999/2000 season?

6 Who has won the most FA Cup finals?

7 Who scored a hat-trick in the 1953 final?

8 What's the biggest win in the final?

9 Who have lost the most finals?

10 Who scored Arsenal's winning goal in the 1971 final?

11 When was the last game at Wembley?

12 What was the name of the white horse who helped clear the pitch at the 1923 final?

13 At which ground was the 1970 Cup Final replay?

14 Who scored Ipswich's goal in the 1978 final?

15 Who scored the only goal of the 1980 final with his head?

16 Who dribbled his way around Manchester City's defence to score a memorable goal in the 1981 final?

17 How many teams did Gary Lineker play for in cup finals?

18 In 1994, by what score did Manchester United beat Chelsea?

19 Who beat Manchester United in 1995?

20 Who did Chelsea beat in 1997?

21 Who were the losing finalists in both 1998 and 1999?

22 Which is the only team to have beaten Tottenham in the final?

23 How many ties are there in the third round?

24 Who is the oldest player to play in a final?

25 Who scored the fastest goal in a final?

1 Which English painter is considered the precursor of the French Impressionists?

2 Whose painting of Lola de Valence inspired a poem by Baudelaire?

3 Which Impressionist painter, according to Don Maclean, painted his 'palette blue and grey'?

4 About whom was the term 'Impressionist' used for the first time in 1872?

5 Whose favourite subject was a mountain east of Aix-en-Provence?

6 Which English Impressionist is best known for his images of fog, rain and snow?

7 Which of Manet's favourite models married his brother in 1876?

8 Who said, 'I want to establish the right to dare everything'?

9 In Robert Altman's 1990 film, who played Vincent Van Gogh?

10 Who developed a style of separate small dots of pure colour in 1884?

11 Whose favourite model was Gabrielle, his housekeeper?

12 Whose nude *Olympia* in 1863 outraged the Paris Salon?

13 Of whom did Marcel Proust write that his work 'makes the viewer cross the magic mirror of reality'?

14 Who abandoned the law in favour of art, with a special predilection for painting ballet dancers and circus folk?

15 Who died in the Marquesas Islands in 1903?

16 Whose water lilies made his garden at Giverny famous?

17 Whose last great painting was *A Bar at the Folies-Bergère*?

18 Who narrated the life of Vincent Van Gogh in the Paul Cox film of 1987?

19 Which son of a nobleman, associated with the Impressionists, became permanently stunted during childhood and grew up to illustrate scenes of the Moulin Rouge and other low life?

20 Who was the only one of the Impressionists to have exhibited at all eight of their exhibitions?

21 Which English artist worked in Paris with Degas but came home to form the Camden Town Group from his studio in Fitzroy Square?

22 The photographer Nadar loaned his studio in 1874 to which group of painters for tier first notorious exhibition?

23 In the Vincente Minnelli film *Lust for Life*, who played Vincent Van Gogh?

24 Who depicted a *Sunday Afternoon on the Island of La Grande Jatte*?

25 And who wrote an entire musical inspired by this painting?

24

1 Who played Agatha Christie in Michael Apted's 1978 film *Agatha*?

2 In which year did David Suchet first appear as Hercule Poirot?

3 In which novel did Miss Marple first appear?

4 In Guy Hamilton's film version of *The Mirror Crack'd*, who played Miss Marple?

5 What was Hercule Poirot's secretary called?

6 Which of Agatha Christie's plays is now the longest continually running drama in the West End?

7 How many Miss Marple books are there?

8 In which book did she kill off Hercule Poirot?

9 In which novel did Hercule Poirot first appear?

10 In Sidney Lumet's *Murder on the Orient Express*, who plays Hercule Poirot?

11 On which train was Miss Marple travelling when she saw a woman being strangled?

12 In John Guillermin's film of *Death on the Nile*, who played Hercule Poirot?

13 What was Miss Marple's first name?

14 Which massive clue was held back from the reader in *The Body in the Library*?

15 *Why Didn't They Ask —?* Ask whom?

16 What was Hercule Poirot's brother called?

17 Who directed all of Margaret Rutherford's Miss Marple films?

18 In which novel did Hercule Poirot first talk about his little grey cells?

19 Which novel was turned into a film directed by Billy Wilder and starring Marlene Dietrich?

20 Which Agatha Christie play became a film called *And Then There Were None* when its original title was deemed to be distasteful?

21 In which village did Miss Marple live?

22 What nationality was Hercule Poirot?

23 What was unusual about the narrator of *The Murder of Roger Ackroyd*?

24 What was the name of the television series in which Angela Lansbury starred as Miss Marple?

25 Which was the last Miss Marple novel?

1 What is the rubber or metal tip of a walking stick or umbrella called?

2 What originally came in an 8" size, then $5\frac{1}{4}$", and then $3\frac{1}{2}$"?

3 What name is given to the lens or combination of lenses forming the image in a camera or projector?

4 From which material is a snooker cue tip made?

5 On what can music or data be recorded as a series of metallic pits enclosed in PVC to be read by an optical laser?

6 What aid to vision was invented by Benjamin Franklin?

7 Which saying originates from the name given to a small metallic knob acting as the sight of a firearm?

8 What word of Italian origin describes the lower part of an interior wall that is decorated differently from the upper part?

9 What is a tabor?

10 Which small handtool shares its name with a cocktail consisting of half gin or vodka and half lime juice?

11 What collective noun for finches is also a small object worn or kept for magical powers of protection?

12 The name of which popular spirit is also a machine for separating cotton from its seeds?

13 What does the Australian term 'to pass in one's marble' mean?

14 What is a sneck?

15 What is the name of the small wooden or plastic peg used in golf?

16 What is the name of a small rod originally designed to get rid of carbon dioxide from fizzy drinks?

17 Which part of a drill or lathe can be a 'three jaw' or 'four jaw'?

18 Which rodent is also a computer control device?

19 What is made in a cafetière?

20 On what would you find an aglet?

21 What is a 'waiter's friend'?

22 What is an ice hockey puck generally made from?

23 Which household appliance is driven by a magnetron?

24 A 'bertha' could be which part of an item of clothing?

25 What are the metal strips on the neck of a guitar called?

1 Which nuclear treaty did Jimmy Carter sign?

2 What did Anzac stand for?

3 Give one of the two meanings of the acronym SAT.

4 In computer-speak, what is 'WYSIWYG'?

5 The letters SOS were chosen as a mayday call because they were the simplest to transmit and receive in Morse code. What phrase have they subsequently been taken to stand for?

6 In computing, what does WORM stand for?

7 What is a dinky?

8 What is the acronym for a computer screen?

9 What does RADAR stand for?

10 What does NIMBY mean?

11 From which two letters is the word Jeep derived and why?

12 What have you done if you've gone AWOL?

13 What does MASH stand for?

14 What does NATO stand for?

15 What is a laser?

16 In e-speak, what does BAK signify?

17 For what organization did the Men from UNCLE work?

18 What is LIFFE?

19 What was a Nazi?

20 Who are the members of BLESMA?

21 What is NASDAQ?

22 If you write SWALK on an envelope, what have you done?

23 What was the Russian for 'death to spies' shortened to by Ian Fleming in the Bond books?

24 What is a WAP phone?

25 What apocalyptic threat did Ronald Reagan try to persuade Americans to sign up to?

ANSWERS TO QUIZ 12

Famous Women
1 Golda Meir
2 The campaign for universal suffrage
3 Agnes Bojaxhiu, later Mother Teresa of Calcutta
4 Aung San Suu Kyi
5 Marie Curie
6 Her sister Emily
7 Shirley Williams
8 Rodham
9 Costume design
10 Isabella
11 Mary Pickford
12 New York
13 Helen Gurley Brown
14 Baroness Thatcher
15 The Berlin Olympics
16 Babe Zaharias
17 Anne Frank
18 Indira Gandhi
19 Joan of Arc
20 Catherine the Great
21 Travel in space
22 Jamie Lee Curtis
23 Pakistan
24 Germaine Greer
25 Florence Nightingale

Died in the 20th Century
1 George C Scott
2 1997
3 Six million
4 Peter Cook
5 Count Basie
6 Eddie Cochran
7 1952
8 Noël Coward
9 97
10 46 Italians were crushed to death
11 Roman Polanski's
12 In a car crash
13 Jack Ruby
14 New York
15 John Smith
16 Dallas
17 Memphis
18 1977
19 Michael Hutchence
20 Marc Chagall
21 Kurt Cobain
22 Anna Pavlova
23 John F Kennedy, Jr
24 Payne Stewart
25 Frank Sinatra

Horror Films
1 The *Nightmare on Elm Street* series
2 *Hellraiser*
3 Vincent Price
4 John Carpenter
5 *Nosferatu*
6 Shelley Duvall
7 Roman Polanski
8 David Arquette
9 Boris Karloff
10 It was made in 3-D
11 Oliver Reed
12 *Dead of Night*
13 Bela Lugosi
14 Janet Leigh and Jamie Lee Curtis
15 *Carrie*
16 Lon Chaney
17 She provided the Devil's voice
18 Vera Miles
19 *Man Bites Dog*
20 The *Halloween* series
21 It was the last horror film made by Hammer
22 David Cronenberg
23 Camp Crystal Lake
24 Bette Davis
25 *Sleepy Hollow*

David Lean
1 Noël Coward
2 Alec Guinness
3 *Blithe Spirit*
4 *Brief Encounter*
5 Venice
6 Albert Finney
7 *Hobson's Choice*
8 Alec Guinness
9 *Ryan's Daughter*
10 *Nostromo*
11 Maurice Jarre
12 The bridge in *The Bridge on the River Kwai*
13 Richard Attenborough
14 *This Happy Breed*
15 Julie Christie
16 Victor Bannerjee
17 *The Sound Barrier*
18 Omar Sharif
19 *Brief Encounter*
20 The Artful Dodger
21 William Holden
22 Peggy Ashcroft
23 Lean married them both
24 Celia Johnson
25 Oliver was played by child actor John Howard Davies, who went on to produce *Monty Python*

Australia
1 Uluru
2 1973
3 Adelaide
4 Kings Cross
5 Botany Bay
6 Peter Carey
7 Elle McPherson
8 Penola, South Australia
9 Barossa Valley
10 Canberra
11 Port Arthur
12 Hobart
13 Three
14 Opal
15 The Wollomombi Falls, New South Wales
16 Wagga is the Aborigine word for 'crow'. Wagga Wagga means 'two crows'
17 The Yarra
18 Port Campbell National Park
19 Australian Rules Football
20 The first officer of HMS *Beagle*, who named it after Charles Darwin, who had led the ship on a previous voyage
21 7,500
22 Yarrawonga Wildlife Park
23 Alice Springs
24 Fraser Island, Queensland
25 Kylie Minogue

Places in Songs
1 Liza Minnelli
2 The Kinks
3 Gerry Rafferty
4 Bob Dylan
5 Route 66
6 Supertramp
7 Stan Getz
8 Bob and Earl
9 East St Louis
10 Beginning of the End
11 Tom Browne
12 San José?
13 Nashville
14 The Mobiles
15 *Abbey Road*
16 'From Russia With Love'
17 Berkeley Square
18 David Bowie
19 'Wonderful, Wonderful Copenhagen'
20 'Echo Beach', Martha and the Muffins
21 'At the Copacabana', Barry Manilow
22 London Town
23 Scarborough
24 Grace Jones
25 B52s

Teen Pop
1 Ronan Keating
2 Destiny's Child
3 New Kids on the Block
4 London's Party in the Park
5 'Millennium'
6 NKOTB
7 Backstreet Boys
8 Howard Donald and Jason Orange
9 Westlife
10 1974
11 'Look at Me'
12 'Mmmbop'
13 En Vogue
14 N'Sync
15 Sweden
16 Ricky Martin
17 New Edition
18 'Stop'
19 Christina Aguilera
20 Travis
21 S Club 7
22 Mariah Carey
23 TLC
24 *Space Jam*
25 *The Beach*

Rolling Stones
1 Ronnie Wood
2 *She's the Boss*
3 The Rolling Stones' *Rock and Roll Circus*
4 Philip
5 Cheltenham
6 Chuck Berry
7 Altamont
8 Ned Kelly
9 *Some Girls*
10 1969
11 A A Milne, author of *Winnie the Pooh*
12 The Glimmer Twins
13 Sticky Fingers
14 Charlie Parker
15 '(I Can't Get No) Satisfaction'
16 Jade
17 'You're So Vain'
18 'Honky Tonk Women'
19 *Dirty Work*
20 Let It Bleed
21 Muddy Waters
22 The Crawdaddy
23 Lennon–McCartney
24 *Tattoo You*
25 *Jammin' With Edward*

Wild West
1 The OK Corral
2 The western frontier of North America between 1780 and 1900
3 Geronimo
4 Meriwether Lewis and William Clark in 1803
5 Conquering Bear
6 The Spanish
7 William F 'Buffalo Bill' Cody
8 Louisiana
9 The Kansas Pacific Railroad
10 The Alamo, a mission near

San Antonio, Texas
11 Samuel Colt
12 Jerky
13 John B Stetson
14 Texans who stole cattle from Mexican ranches
15 Because the Gold Rush took place in 1849
16 About 20 km a day
17 Mud bricks out of which ranches were made
18 The chuckwagon
19 Around 400
20 Around 10,000
21 Levi Strauss
22 Sod busters
23 General Custer
24 Barbed wire
25 Paul Newman and Robert Redford

Exploration
1 Sir Richard Burton and John Speke
2 Norwegian, Roald Amundsen, in 1906
3 Bartolomeu Dias
4 Will Adams, an Elizabethan adventurer
5 He was a missionary
6 Ferdinand and Isabella of Spain
7 Hatshepsut
8 The *Golden Hind*
9 The Great Trek
10 The Dutch East India Company
11 He divided it into eight sections
12 Australia
13 Two Germans called Johannes Rebmann and Ludwig Krapf
14 The *New York Herald*
15 Cape Town, South Africa
16 Admiral Hanno, who set sail in 425 BC
17 Portuguese
18 Erik the Red
19 San Francisco (which he called New Albion)
20 Pierre Ne Brazza
21 Ujiji, on the shores of Lake Tanganyika
22 Sir Walter Raleigh
23 Mary Kingsley
24 King Leopold II of Belgium
25 Scotland

Golf
1 US Masters, US Open, The Open and the US PGA
2 Tom Watson
3 1996

4 Ben Crenshaw
5 Tony Jacklin
6 1958
7 The Nabisco Dinah Shore
8 The Old Course, St Andrews
9 Fijian
10 An albatross
11 It is by the sea
12 Laura Davies
13 Tiger Woods
14 Match play
15 The Women's British Open
16 Fade
17 Nick Faldo
18 US Masters, Augusta
19 18 (6 Masters, 4 US Open, 3 Open, 5 US PGA)
20 He won three of the four majors in one calendar year
21 The claret jug
22 Amen Corner
23 The cut
24 The Solheim Cup
25 Over 4,000 miles (Muirfield is in Scotland, Muirfield Village in Columbus, Ohio)

FA Cup
1 Wanderers
2 Royal Engineers
3 1872
4 Portsmouth
5 They chose to play in the World Club Championship in Brazil
6 Manchester United
7 Stan Mortensen
8 6–0, 1903, Bury beat Derby County
9 Leicester City
10 Charlie George
11 2000
12 Billy
13 Old Trafford
14 Roger Osborne
15 Trevor Brooking
16 Ricky Villa
17 Two
18 4-0
19 Everton
20 Middlesbrough
21 Newcastle United
22 Coventry City
23 32
24 Stanley Matthews
25 Roberto Di Matteo

Impressionists
1 Joseph Turner
2 Edouard Manet
3 Vincent (Van Gogh)
4 Claude Monet
5 Paul Cézanne
6 Alfred Sisley

7 Berthe Morisot
8 Paul Gauguin
9 Tim Roth
10 Georges Seurat
11 Pierre Auguste Renoir
12 Edouard Manet
13 Claude Monet
14 Edgar Degas
15 Paul Gauguin
16 Claude Monet
17 Edouard Manet
18 John Hurt
19 Henri de Toulouse-Lautrec
20 Camille Pissarro
21 Walter Sickert
22 Impressionists
23 Kirk Douglas
24 Georges Seurat
25 Stephen Sondheim (*Sunday in the Park with George*)

Agatha Christie
1 Vanessa Redgrave
2 1988
3 *Murder at the Vicarage* (1930)
4 Angela Lansbury
5 Miss Lemon
6 *The Mousetrap*
7 Twelve
8 *Curtain*
9 *The Mysterious Affair at Styles* (1920)
10 Albert Finney
11 The 4.50 from Paddington
12 Peter Ustinov
13 Jane
14 The characters' marriages
15 *Why Didn't They Ask Evans?*
16 Achille
17 George Pollock
18 *The Mysterious Affair at Styles*
19 *Witness for the Prosecution*
20 *Ten Little Niggers*
21 St Mary Mead
22 Belgian
23 He was also the murderer
24 *Murder She Wrote*
25 *Miss Marple's Final Cases*

Objects
1 A ferrule
2 Floppy disc
3 Objective or object glass
4 Suede
5 A compact disc
6 Bifocal lens
7 To draw a bead
8 Dado
9 A small drum
10 A gimlet
11 A charm
12 Gin

13 To die
14 A latch on a door or window
15 A tee
16 A swizzle stick
17 A chuck
18 A mouse
19 Coffee
20 A shoelace
21 Combined knife, corkscrew and bottle-opener
22 Vulcanized rubber
23 A microwave oven
24 A collar
25 Frets

Acronyms
1 SALT
2 The Australian and New Zealand Army Corps
3 Scholastic Aptitude Test or South Australian Time
4 What You See (on the screen) Is What You Get (in the printout)
5 Save Our Souls
6 Write Once Read Many times
7 Dual income no kids
8 VDU
9 Radio Detection and Ranging
10 Not In My Backyard
11 *G* and *P* – General Purpose vehicle
12 Absent without leave (from the army)
13 Mobile Army Service Hospital
14 North Atlantic Treaty Organization
15 Light amplification by stimulated emission of radiation
16 Back At Keyboard
17 United Network Command for Law and Enforcement
18 London International Financial Futures and Options Exchange
19 A member of the German National Socialist Party (from the first word in German <u>Na</u>tionalso<u>zi</u>alistische Deutsche Arbeiterpartei)
20 The British Limbless Ex-Servicemen's Association
21 National Association of Securities Dealers Automated Quote System
22 Sealed With A Loving Kiss
23 SMERSH
24 Wireless Application Protocol phone
25 MAD – mutually assured destruction

THE ULTIMATE BOOK OF TRIVIA

QUIZ 13

1 What name is given to the last man in a team to compete or, in a tug-of-war team, the man furthest from the opposition?

2 Which team was founded by one Abe Saperstein and is not unfamiliar with 'Sweet Georgia Brown'?

3 In Australia, in which sort of team might you find a 'belt man'?

4 Still down under, what was the job of a 'bullocky'?

5 By what name was the US basketball team that won the 1992 and 1996 Olympic finals known?

6 What name is given to the word game in which one team says a rhyme or rhyming line for a word or line given by the other team?

7 Who won the first Superbowl, in 1967?

8 Can you name one of the two French words which are often used to describe a motor racing team?

9 Traditionally, which order is given to a team of dogs to make them start or go faster?

10 By what name were the group of young actors including Sean Penn, Emilio Estevez and Demi Moore known?

11 What is the name of the NFL team based in the city of Seattle?

12 Teams from which country wear the silver fern?

13 In American football what name is given to the predetermined sets of players used at kickoffs and when an attempt is made at a field goal?

14 Which member of the Magnificent Seven was also a Man from U.N.C.L.E.?

15 What is a 'dog train'?

16 How many players are there in a netball team?

17 Which word is often used for a member of a team who is a burden to the rest of the team?

18 Which term is used for a team that has not qualified for a competition but is allowed to take part, at the organisers' discretion?

19 Which country won the first football World Cup?

20 Which city's American football team is called the Bears?

21 What is the name given to the annual international lawn tennis championship for men's teams?

22 How many substitutes are allowed in a basketball team?

23 What collective name was given to Frank Sinatra, Peter Lawford, Joey Bishop, Dean Martin and Sammy Davis, Jr?

24 Forever linked with The Beatles, Shea Stadium is home to which baseball team?

25 Which 1993 movie was based on the true story of the Jamaican bobsleigh team which amused the world at the 1988 Olympics?

1 Who led the British forces at El Alamein?

2 Who was Commander, US Forces in the Pacific in March 1942?

3 Who was ambushed by the Indians?

4 Who was the last military emperor of Russia?

5 What was the nickname of Manfred von Richthofen?

6 Which Jamaican became Joint Chief of Staff?

7 Who flew with false legs in the Second World War?

8 Which Parachute Regiment colonel was killed in an Argentine trench?

9 Which Greek conquered the civilized world in the 4th century BC?

10 Who led the Spartans in the Peloponnesian War?

11 Where was Nelson born?

12 What nationality was Che Guevara?

13 Who was born in Temujin in AD 1167?

14 Which British hero died on his motorbike?

15 Who became Lord Protector of England in 1653?

16 Which French leader died in 1821?

17 Who was Genghis Khan's grandson?

18 Which city did Bomber Harris flatten?

19 Who led the Greek siege of Troy for nine years?

20 Whose wrath helped end the Trojan War?

21 Who was the Trojans' finest warrior?

22 Who was Mason Patrick?

23 Who was 'Stormin' Norman'?

24 Which Cabinet post did Winston Churchill hold at the start of the First and Second World Wars?

25 What was the only major naval battle of the First World War?

1 How does Hitchcock appear in *Strangers on a Train*?

2 What was the first film Hitchcock directed in America?

3 In which psychological thriller did Sean Connery star alongside Tippi Hedren?

4 In which film is James Stewart convinced that a murder has been committed by Raymond Burr?

5 Who wrote the novel on which Hitchcock's 1936 film *Secret Agent* is based?

6 Who rejected the lead role in the 1940 film *Foreign Correspondent* before it was given to Joel McCrea?

7 Which artist was behind Gregory Peck's dream sequence in *Spellbound*?

8 Which film was Hitchcock's first voluntary experiment with a single setting?

9 What does Cary Grant discover in some wine bottles in *Notorious*?

10 Who plays the evil Uncle Charlie in *Shadow of a Doubt*?

11 In which film does Hitchcock appear walking out of a pet shop with some dogs?

12 How much money does Janet Leigh steal from her employer before checking in at the Bates Motel?

13 Leslie Banks played the male lead in Hitchcock's original version of *The Man who Knew Too Much* in 1934. Who was the male lead in the 1956 version?

14 In which film do John Laurie and Peggy Ashcroft appear as a farmer and his wife?

15 Hume Cronyn appears in the 1943 film *Lifeboat*, but what was his contribution to the 1948 film *Rope*?

16 Which film ends with a gripping (literally) scene at the top of the Statue of Liberty?

17 Which actor stars in *Rope* and *Strangers on a Train*?

18 From which Shakespeare play is the title *North by Northwest* indirectly taken?

19 In which year did Hitchcock receive the Irving Thalberg Award from the Academy of Motion Picture Arts and Sciences?

20 What is significant about the 1925 film *The Pleasure Garden*?

21 In which Hitchcock film does Doris Day sing the Oscar-winning song 'What Will Be, Will Be'?

22 Who made her screen debut in the 1956 film *The Trouble with Harry*?

23 In which 1955 film does Cary Grant star with Grace Kelly?

24 What was the first of Grace Kelly's three films for Hitchcock?

25 Who played the part of Father Michael Logan in the 1952 film *I Confess*?

4

1 Who plays the chief villain Hans Gruber in the 1988 film *Die Hard*?

2 Who was nominated for an Academy Award in the 1947 film *Kiss of Death*, in which he pushes a wheelchair-bound old lady down the stairs to her death?

3 In which film does Laurence Olivier take sadistic pleasure in drilling Dustin Hoffman's teeth?

4 In which Hitchcock film does Godfrey Tearle lead a spy ring and kill a music-hall memory man?

5 In which film does Rebecca de Mornay star as a crazed nanny consumed with a desire for revenge on her employer?

6 With which song is Frank Booth (Dennis Hopper at his nastiest) obsessed in the film *Blue Velvet*?

7 In which film does Jack Nicholson play the Devil incarnate, Daryl van Horne?

8 Which film director plays corrupt city official Noah Cross in the 1974 film *Chinatown*?

9 Who plays Nazi 'Angel of Death' Josef Mengele in the 1978 movie *The Boys from Brazil*?

10 Which character appears in a doorway in Vienna in one of the great moments in cinema?

11 Robert De Niro plays Max Cady, released from prison and terrorising the family of the lawyer who secured his conviction in the 1991 remake of *Cape Fear*. Who played the part in the original 1962 version?

12 Who is the killer tracked down by FBI trainee Clarice Starling (Jodie Foster) in *The Silence of the Lambs*?

13 What expression is sometimes used to describe a vengeful, wronged woman, following Glenn Close's performance in *Fatal Attraction*?

14 Who plays the violent Bill Sikes in David Lean's *Oliver Twist*?

15 In which film did Louise Fletcher win an Academy Award for her performance as the destructive Nurse Mildred Ratched?

16 What does preacher Robert Mitchum have tattooed on his fingers in *The Night of the Hunter*?

17 In which 1992 film does a disturbed Jennifer Jason Leigh answer an advertisement placed by Bridget Fonda?

18 Who leads a group of men who take people hostage on a New York subway train in *The Taking of Pelham One Two Three*?

19 Which two wrongdoers were played by Faye Dunaway and Warren Beatty in the eponymous 1967 film?

20 In which film does Julia Roberts fake her own death to get away from her bullying, manipulative husband, played by Patrick Bergin?

21 Who plays the 'Bad' in *The Good, the Bad and the Ugly*?

22 Which Disney cartoon horror was brought to life by Glenn Close in 1996?

23 Which character has been played by Brian Cox and Anthony Hopkins?

24 Then aged 24, who played the teenaged thug Pinkie Brown in the 1947 film of Graham Greene's *Brighton Rock*?

25 Which real-life murderer is portrayed by Tony Curtis in the 1968 film which bears his nickname?

1 Which African country is the largest in area?

2 In which country are the Central Kalahari Game Reserve and the Gemsbok National Park?

3 Which river separates Zimbabwe from South Africa?

4 How many African countries do not have a coastline?

5 Which snake has distinctive orange and black bands the length of its body?

6 From which lake does the White Nile begin its course?

7 What is the more common name of the large, odd-looking bird variously called boatbill or whalebill?

8 With more than 11.5 million inhabitants, which African city has the greatest population?

9 Adopted as a national emblem, what species of gazelle is found in the southern drylands?

10 What makes up roughly one-fifth of the continent's surface area?

11 Would you see a zebra in western Africa?

12 Which stretch of water lies to the north of Somalia, on the horn of Africa?

13 Zanzibar lies off the coast of which country?

14 What natural feature lies to the south and east of the Ethiopian plateau, and extends down through Kenya and Tanzania?

15 What is significant about the Banc D'Arguin National Park in Mauritania in the northwest?

16 How many types of seal are resident to African shores?

17 Which types of bird gather in millions on the shallow soda lakes of East Africa?

18 At 2,900 miles, what is Africa's second-longest river, seventh longest in the world?

19 By what name do we more commonly know *Panthera leo*?

20 In Africa, which breed of crocodile thrives over the widest area: the dwarf, the African slender-snouted or the Nile?

21 What type of animal has species named Grant's and Thompson's?

22 How many African countries lie on the equator?

23 Which country protrudes inland from the Atlantic coast, and is otherwise completely surrounded by Senegal?

24 In which country are the Maasai-Mara National Reserve and the Serengeti National Park?

25 The camelopard is an old European name for which African animal?

1 Palaeontologist Sir Richard Owen is credited with coining the name 'dinosaur' in 1841. From Greek origin, what is the rough translation of the term?

2 What were pterosaurs?

3 Which creature had two rows of plates running down its neck, back and tail, culminating in large spikes at the tail end?

4 Why was the Seismosaurus so named?

5 As stipulated by the International Code of Zoological Nomenclature, dinosaur names are in two parts, the first part being the genus. What is denoted by the second part?

6 Which creature had a short nose horn and two larger horns on its brow?

7 Which creature's name has passed out of usage after it was discovered that its fossils proved to be identical to the previously named Apatosaurus?

8 Why was the Edmontosaurus so named?

9 What is the significance of the Megalosaurus?

10 What was the largest of all the carnivorous dinosaurs?

11 Dinosaurs lived in the Mesozoic Era, between 65 and 290 million years ago. Split into three periods, which came between the Triassic and Cretaceous periods?

12 Which British pop group had a hit with 'Brontosaurus'?

13 As their names would suggest, where were the Mamenchisaurus and the Tuojiangosaurus found?

14 Archaeopteryx differed from its modern counterparts in that it had teeth, clawed fingers and a bony tail core. Otherwise it bore the characteristics of which group of creatures?

15 Which creature got its name because scientists felt that it fed on eggs?

16 Why do fossils of long-necked dinosaurs appear to show the head pulled back over the body?

17 Which is the smallest living relative of the dinosaur?

18 Which came off better in a fight, Tyrannosaurus rex or Iguanadon?

19 On which modern continent did Tyrannosaurus live?

20 In which period did the Diplodocus live?

21 In which American state is the Dinosaur Valley Museum?

22 In what environment did ichthyosaurs live?

23 Which cartoon family have a pet dinosaur called Dino?

24 Why was the Psittacosaurus so called?

25 Featured in the film *Jurassic Park*, which creature's name means 'quick plunderer'?

1 For what do the letters SYSLJFM stand in Joe Tex's 'The Letter Song'?

2 Which British female singer recorded an album in Memphis with Jerry Wexler producing?

3 Who is regarded as 'The Godfather of Soul'?

4 Which singer was the father of Linda Womack?

5 By what collective name were Steve Cropper, Donald 'Duck' Dunn and Al Jackson known?

6 Lou Rawls, Sam and Dave, Wilson Pickett, Otis Redding: who is next in line and why?

7 Which soul artist died at the very end of 1999, having been confined to a wheelchair since 1990 after a stage lighting rig fell on him?

8 What instrument was played by King Curtis?

9 Who had a hit in 1966 with 'Tell It Like It Is'?

10 Who is known as 'Lady Soul'?

11 What colour onions were the subject of a Booker T and the MGs tune?

12 Which area of New York City was immortalised in a dance song by Bob and Earl?

13 Who was lead singer with Harold Melvin and the Bluenotes on such songs as 'The Love I Lost' and 'If You Don't Know Me By Now'?

14 Whose magnificent bald head featured on the cover of his *Hot Buttered Soul* album?

15 Which singer is known as 'The Wicked'?

16 Maurice White was a session drummer playing on Chess hits such as 'Rescue Me' by Fontella Bass. Which soul/funk band did he go on to form in the 1970s?

17 How do we better know Messrs Moore and Prater?

18 What is the rest of this James Brown song title: 'Say it Loud…'?

19 Which family group had hits on the Stax label with 'Respect Yourself' and 'I'll Take You There'?

20 In which comedy film does Aretha Franklin, cast as a proprietress of a soul food joint, sing her 1968 hit 'Think'?

21 Which songwriters formed Philadelphia International Records?

22 Which soul artist was the surprise hit of the otherwise flowery 1967 Monterey pop festival?

23 Who picked up an Academy Award in 1971 for best film song?

24 Who had a heart attack on stage in 1975 and remained in a coma until his death in 1984?

25 When Aretha Franklin got married in 1978, which Stevie Wonder song did the Four Tops sing as she walked down the aisle?

1 Name the thrash metal kings headed by guitarist Dave Mustaine.

2 Who underwent treatment for rabies following an incident in which he bit the head off a live bat?

3 Who were Mark Farner, Mel Schacher and Don Brewer?

4 In whose band is Madonna Wayne Gacy the keyboardist?

5 Name Black Sabbath's debut hit.

6 Who was lead singer with Van Halen, but went solo in 1985?

7 Which heavy-metal guitarist provided the soundtrack to the film *Death Wish II*?

8 Who was lead guitarist with Mountain?

9 Name Iron Maiden's famous mascot (depicted on the cover of *Sanctuary* standing over Margaret Thatcher's decapitated body).

10 Eddie Vedder is lead singer with which band?

11 Who had a UK top twenty hit in 1990 with 'No More Mr Nice Guy'?

12 Who did the New Yardbirds become?

13 Their most famous single is '[Don't Fear] The Reaper'. Who are they?

14 Name the Kiss member whose solo album featured Cher, Bob Seger, Donna Summer, Helen Reddy and Janis Ian.

15 Who wrote a book titled *The Adventures of Lord Iffy Boatrace*?

16 Name the group that linked with Motorhead on the *St Valentine's Day Massacre* EP.

17 Judas Priest took their name from a Bob Dylan song. True or false?

18 Which Jimi Hendrix classic features the line 'Scuse me while I kiss the sky'?

19 Name the band formed by Ace Frehley after he left Kiss.

20 Who had a massive hit in 1993 with 'I'm Easy/Be Aggressive'?

21 From which metal band was Dave Mustaine fired in 1982?

22 Name the group that had a hit with 'Inside', the musical backdrop to a Levi's TV ad.

23 Whose first chart album was called *Concerto for Group and Orchestra*?

24 Which member of Guns N' Roses was born in Stoke, England?

25 The label is Bludgen Riffola. Name the band.

1 In which decade did people in Britain over the age of 65 first receive state pensions?

2 Who said in 1960 that politicians 'are the same all over. They promise to build a bridge even when there is no water'?

3 What was signed by the Soviet Union, Poland, Hungary, Czechoslovakia, Romania, Bulgaria, Albania and East Germany in 1955?

4 Who won the Fermanagh and South Tyrone by-election from his prison cell in April 1981?

5 Of which organisation was Yuri Andropov leader before becoming Soviet president in 1982?

6 What was the principal reason for the British Government's introduction of 'daylight saving time' in 1916?

7 Which country issued a Unilateral Declaration of Independence from Britain, on Remembrance Day 1965?

8 Which country's parliament was opened by King George V in 1921?

9 In 1971, which British Secretary of State for Education refused to allow local councils to supply free milk to schoolchildren?

10 A group from which political party organised a 'Stop Kennedy' campaign during the 1960 presidential election campaign?

11 By what name was Mao Tse-tung's purge on liberal dissidents in China between 1966–69 known?

12 In which year was the Israeli prime minister Yitzhak Rabin assassinated?

13 In which European city was the cease-fire agreement to end the war in Vietnam signed?

14 Who was ousted from power by hard-line Soviet communists in 1991?

15 What was the name given to the demonstration in Washington, DC led by the Nation of Islam's leader, Louis Farrakhan, in 1995?

16 Where did Nelson Mandela spend the majority of his time as a political prisoner?

17 Who introduced a scheme for a Nationalised Health Service in 1946?

18 Which businessman was behind the United Empire Party in Britain in the 1930s?

19 Which Irish party's name translates as 'Soldiers of Destiny'?

20 What do the initials of the ZANU party stand for?

21 Which Democratic Party candidate ran against George Bush in the 1988 presidential election campaign?

22 Who was prime minister when the British Government imposed direct rule on Northern Ireland in 1972?

23 Who shared the Nobel Peace Prize in 1993?

24 Who led the Khmer Rouge from 1962–1985?

25 When were women first admitted to the House of Lords?

1 Imprisoned since 1962, who walked free from captivity in February 1990?

2 Which pop star died from an AIDS-related illness in November 1991?

3 Who opened the Channel Tunnel in 1994?

4 In which year did Germany celebrate reunification?

5 In which year was John McCarthy released by his Lebanese captors?

6 Which world-famous musician died on 1 December 1997?

7 Who became Russia's first democratically elected president in 1991?

8 In which city was George Michael arrested for lewd behaviour in a public toilet?

9 Whom did Elvis Presley's daughter Lisa Marie marry in 1994?

10 In 1997, Zaire was renamed by its president, Laurent Kabila. What is its current full title?

11 Which Indian premier was assassinated in 1991?

12 Which former Mrs Phillips became a Mrs Laurence in 1992?

13 To what name did the city of Leningrad revert in 1991?

14 Of which organisation did Boutros Boutros-Ghali become secretary-general in 1992?

15 Who was at the centre of a televised trial lasting 266 days in 1995?

16 In which year was the Warsaw Pact dissolved?

17 Released in 1995, what was the first entirely computer-generated feature film?

18 In which year was Hong Kong passed back to China?

19 What sparked the 1992 riots in Los Angeles?

20 In which year did the Spice Girls first enter the UK charts?

21 What significant action was taken in the Middle East on 2 August 1990?

22 In which year was Nelson Mandela elected president of South Africa?

23 What was opened on 6 May 1994?

24 Who recorded the biggest-selling single of all time in 1997?

25 Which Israeli leader was assassinated by a Jewish extremist in 1995?

1 In which round did the last bare-knuckle heavyweight title fight end in 1889?

2 Which boxer was the first to have oxygen administered to him at a fight in 1903?

3 What distinction did referee Stan Christodoulou achieve in 1991?

4 Who was on the canvas for the infamous 'long count' in 1927?

5 At what age did Puerto Rican Wilfred Benitez win the world junior middleweight title in 1976?

6 By what name is John Sholto Douglas better remembered?

7 Which world middleweight champion added the epithet 'Marvellous' to his name?

8 Which British boxer is known as the Fleetwood Assassin?

9 Who was the only fighter to defeat Sugar Ray Leonard in his professional career?

10 Whose professional career started and ended with fights against Tunney Hunsaker and Trevor Berbick respectively?

11 Who did Rocky Marciano defeat to become world heavyweight champion in 1952?

12 Which British middleweight won the world title from Sugar Ray Robinson in July 1951, but lost the rematch two months later?

13 Which famous fight is the subject of the movie *When We Were Kings*?

14 Which middleweight champion was portrayed by Robert De Niro in the film *Raging Bull*?

15 What was so distinctive about the Corbett v Fitzsimmons heavyweight title fight in 1897?

16 Who was the first heavyweight to regain the world title?

17 Which British fighter's entrance into the ring prompted commentator Reg Gutteridge to announce, 'The ego has landed'?

18 Which Mexican fighter won 97 of his 100 professional fights between 1980 and 1996?

19 Which fighter was known as 'The Hitman'?

20 At what age did Naseem Hamed become WBO world featherweight champion?

21 What distinction is held by Eva Shain of New Jersey?

22 At which weight did Audley Harrison win Olympic gold in Sydney?

23 Who beat Trevor Berbick in 1986 to win his first heavyweight title, the WBC?

24 Which Scottish boxer did Alexis Arguello beat to win the world lightweight title in 1980?

25 What achievement is shared by Hungarian Laszlo Papp and Cuban Teofilio Stevenson?

1 Who is the notorious bad boy opposite?

2 Which footballer famously slept with several Miss Worlds before leaving Manchester United and moving to Fulham?

3 Who said, of touring Pakistan, 'I wouldn't even send my mother-in-law there'?

4 Who was sent off in both opening premiership games of the 2000 season?

5 Who was the last English player to be sent off in the world cup?

6 Who was the first player to be sent off in the FA Cup final?

7 Which cricketing bad boy is known as The Cat?

8 Who was at the centre of cricket's match-fixing scandal?

9 Which Romanian tennis player was famous for his tantrums?

10 Who did McEnroe play three times in Wimbledon finals?

11 Who was Maradona playing for when he was first caught taking cocaine?

12 Of what were Lee Bowyer and Jonathan Woodgate of Leeds accused?

13 Which bad boy is Arsenal's top scorer ever?

14 For which club does Paul Merson now play?

15 What is the title of Tony Adams's biography?

16 Which manager clipped a couple of hooligans round the ear?

17 Which Aussie wicketkeeper bet against his own team at 500–1 and won the bet?

18 Which television presenter and ex-Spurs and England footballer became an alcoholic?

19 Who spent a year in prison for sleeping with an under-age girl?

20 Who batted with an aluminium bat?

21 Which Argentine prop was sent off for knocking out an English second row with a punch?

22 Where was Mike Tyson born?

23 Whose ear did Tyson bite off?

24 Who famously said 'You cannot be serious'?

25 Which footballer drop-kicked a fan at Crystal Palace?

1 Who is Shaggy's canine companion?

2 Which cartoon series is set in Arlen, Texas?

3 What is the name of Barney and Betty Rubble's son in *The Flintstones*?

4 With which character do you associate Elmer Fudd and Yosemite Sam?

5 Which series features a family with an evil baby and a talking dog?

6 In which cartoon series was Harry Boyle the central character?

7 Who provided the voices for Warner Bros cartoon characters such as Bugs Bunny, Daffy Duck and many others?

8 How many digits do the Simpsons have on each hand?

9 Which member of the Peanuts gang plays the piano?

10 From which country does Asterix originate?

11 Which glamorous character drove the Compact Pussycat in the Wacky Races?

12 Who is the puddy tat that Tweety Pie tawt he taw?

13 Which park is the home of Yogi Bear?

14 On which TV character was Top Cat based?

15 Jason Alexander is the voice of Duckman. On which sitcom was he a regular cast member?

16 What is the name of the vacuum cleaner in *Teletubbies*?

17 What is the connection between the Teenage Mutant Hero Turtles and the ceiling of the Sistine Chapel?

18 Who is Top Cat's long-suffering uniformed adversary?

19 Whose co-stars were a muskrat and a mole?

20 What is the Flintstones' home-town?

21 Who created Beavis and Butthead?

22 Which cartoon pop group had a UK number one hit in 1969?

23 What was the cat's name in Pixie and Dixie?

24 Which series features a character who is always getting killed?

25 Which producer is best known for his association with Tom and Jerry?

1 Which legendary frontiersman did Fess Parker play on TV in the late 1950s?

2 In which 1980s soap opera did a woman once married to Ronald Reagan play Angela Channing?

3 Billy Crystal played a transvestite in which US sitcom first transmitted in the late 1970s?

4 Who played Zorro in the 1958–60 TV series?

5 James Drury, Lee J Cobb and Doug McClure starred in the first TV western to run for 90 minutes per episode. What was it called?

6 Ted Cassidy played which family's butler?

7 Before *The X-Files*, David Duchovny had appeared in another cult TV series that dealt with the paranormal. What was it called?

8 Only one cast member of the movie *M*A*S*H* reprised his role in the TV series. Who?

9 Tom Selleck played Lance White, a rival of which US private eye?

10 After restoring his ears to normal, Leonard Nimoy played a character with the name of a capital city in which adventure series?

11 Actress Rhea Perlman married her husband Danny DeVito during a lunchbreak on which TV series?

12 Ralph James provided the voice of Orson in which 70s/80s sitcom?

13 Edward Asner first played Lou Grant in which 1970s show?

14 Ron Ely starred as Tarzan on TV between 1967–69, but who provided the Lord of the Jungle's famous jungle yell for the series?

15 Which husband-and-wife team appeared in *Space 1999*?

16 The narrator of 1980s sci-fi TV series *Buck Rogers in the 25th Century* played a top TV detective in the previous decade. Who was he?

17 Burgess Meredith occasionally appeared as a 'pompous, waddling perpetrator of foul play' in which classic TV series?

18 Honor Blackman and Diana Rigg played two of Patrick Macnee's sidekicks in the 1960s TV series *The Avengers*. Who played the third?

19 Raymond Francis played Tom Lockhart in *Murder Bag*, *Crime Sheet* and which other series?

20 Veteran British actor Wilfrid Hyde-White played scientist Dr Goodfellow in which 1980s space opera?

21 One actor appeared in both the *A-Team* and *Battlestar Galactica*. Who was he?

22 Sharon Gless, later to find fame in *Cagney & Lacey*, played nurse Kathleen Feverty in which 60s/70s medical series?

23 Before he became known for providing the voices on Hanna-Barbera cartoons, Mel Blanc regularly appeared on a famous 1950s comedy show. What was it?

24 In which 50s/60s classic comedy series did Paul Ford play Colonel John Hall?

25 The novelist Colin Dexter appeared as an extra in every episode of which TV series?

1 What type of product is made by the company founded in Chicago in 1901 by Henry Williamson Gossard?

2 Scotsman John Lawson Johnston produced a 'fluid extract of beef' mixed with caramel, salt and spices in the 1870s. What is it called?

3 Who started a company called the General Seafoods Corporation in Massachusetts in 1924 and whose name is synonymous with frozen food?

4 Which drink was first sold at Jacob's Pharmacy in Atlanta, Georgia in 1886?

5 In which year did the first Dr Martens boots come off the UK production line?

6 What is the full name of the company known as 3M?

7 What product got its name from a slogan for Wrigley's saying 'Packed tight – Kept right'?

8 For what did Lewis Edson Waterman, a New York insurance broker, take out a patent in 1884?

9 For which product were people persuaded to 'Stop me and Buy one'?

10 To protect it from imitation, which Swiss chocolate bar was granted a patent in 1909?

11 What car manufacturer was founded in 1903?

12 Who patented the first revolver in 1836?

13 Which company began manufacturing their tennis rackets in 1881?

14 Who was Pretty Polly, from whom the stockings and tights manufacturer got its name?

15 Which drink product got its name from two of its ingredients, eggs and malt extract?

16 Who started a wholesale candy business in 1910 which has grown into a company that exports to 150 countries worldwide?

17 Which Polish-born immigrant started manufacturing and selling make-up in 1916?

18 Who invented the ball-point pen?

19 Which company came about from the merger between Lever Bros Ltd and the Dutch Margarine Union?

20 Which product was named by its founder, Ole Christiansen, after the Danish for 'play well'?

21 How did the name Kodak come about?

22 What everyday household item did Jacques Brandenberger invent in 1908?

23 Which headwear manufacturer took its name from the raw materials silk, angora and wool?

24 In 1925 Grace Scurr, a temporary secretary, named which product, now synonymous with the 1980s?

25 Which brothers made their first milk chocolate in 1897?

1 What was the first Broadway musical?

2 Who composed the score for *Gentlemen Prefer Blondes* and *Funny Girl*?

3 Which musical concerned a strike at the Sleep-Tite Factory in Iowa?

4 Which row was sung about in *Porgy and Bess*?

5 What were the names of the two gangs in *West Side Story*?

6 Which musical opens at Uncle Jocko's Kiddie Show in Seattle?

7 Who wrote the collection of short stories on which *Fiddler on the Roof* was based?

8 Which 1961 movie, directed by Bryan Forbes and starring Hayley Mills and Alan Bates, provided the inspiration for Andrew Lloyd Webber's last musical of the 20th century?

9 Which former *Daily Mail* television critic wrote the lyrics for *Les Misérables*?

10 Which musical featured a giant Fabergé egg containing a hologram of Laurence Olivier's head?

11 On whose short stories was *Guys and Dolls* based?

12 Which former Cambridge Footlights comedian made a mint out of *Me and My Girl*?

13 In 1994, who returned to *Hello Dolly* for its 30th anniversary revival?

14 Which Oxford University professor of poetry had his lyrics for *Les Misérables* rejected?

15 Who played Eliza Doolittle in the original stage production of *My Fair Lady*?

16 What, in 1966, was a secretary not, according to Frank Loesser?

17 Who thanked heaven for little girls in *Gigi*?

18 About which jazz player was *Ain't Misbehavin'*?

19 Which musical was based on H G Wells's novel *Kipps*?

20 Maya Angelou made herself unavailable for rehearsals after working on which musical?

21 Which musical was built around the songs of the pop group Abba?

22 Who co-wrote *Stop the World, I Want to Get Off* with Anthony Newley in 1960?

23 Which musical was the first to feature a mixed black and white cast on stage?

24 Who directed the stage version of *The Lion King*?

25 Who choreographed *Cats*?

ANSWERS TO QUIZ 13

Teams
1 Anchorman
2 Harlem Globetrotters
3 Life-saving (he swims out with a line attached to his belt)
4 Driving a bullock team
5 The Dream Team
6 Crambo
7 Green Bay Packers
8 Ecurie or Equipe
9 'Mush'
10 The Brat Pack
11 Seahawks
12 New Zealand
13 Special teams
14 Robert Vaughn
15 A sled pulled by dogs
16 Seven
17 A passenger
18 Wild card (entry)
19 Uruguay
20 Chicago
21 Davis Cup
22 Seven
23 The Rat Pack
24 New York Mets
25 *Cool Runnings*

Military Leaders
1 Montgomery
2 McArthur
3 General Custer
4 Mikhail Romanov
5 The Red Baron
6 Colin Powell
7 Douglas Bader
8 'H' Jones
9 Alexander
10 Leonidas
11 Norfolk
12 Argentine
13 Genghis Khan
14 T E Lawrence
15 Oliver Cromwell
16 Napoleon
17 Kublai Khan
18 Dresden
19 Agamemnon
20 Achilles
21 Hector
22 First head of USAF
23 Norman Schwarzkopf
24 First Lord of the Admiralty
25 Jutland

Alfred Hitchcock
1 He carries a double bass onto the train
2 *Rebecca*
3 *Marnie*
4 *Rear Window*
5 W Somerset Maugham
6 Gary Cooper
7 Salvador Dali
8 *Lifeboat*
9 Uranium ore
10 Joseph Cotten
11 *The Birds*
12 $40,000
13 James Stewart
14 *The Thirty-Nine Steps*
15 He adapted the story for the screen
16 *Saboteur*
17 Farley Granger
18 *Hamlet*
19 Honoured 1967, received 1968
20 It was the first film completed by Hitchcock
21 *The Man who Knew Too Much*
22 Shirley MacLaine
23 *To Catch a Thief*
24 *Dial M for Murder*
25 Montgomery Clift

Baddies
1 Alan Rickman
2 Richard Widmark
3 *Marathon Man*
4 *The Thirty-Nine Steps*
5 *The Hand that Rocks the Cradle*
6 'In Dreams' by Roy Orbison
7 *The Witches of Eastwick*
8 John Huston
9 Gregory Peck
10 Harry Lime (Orson Welles)
11 Robert Mitchum
12 'Buffalo Bill'
13 Bunny-boiler
14 Robert Newton
15 *One Flew over the Cuckoo's Nest*
16 'Love' and 'Hate'
17 *Single White Female*
18 Robert Shaw
19 Bonnie and Clyde
20 *Sleeping with the Enemy*
21 Lee Van Cleef
22 Cruella De Vil
23 Hannibal Lecter (spelt Lektor in the film *Manhunter*)
24 Richard Attenborough
25 *The Boston Strangler*

Africa
1 Sudan
2 Botswana
3 The Limpopo
4 Fifteen
5 The coral snake
6 Lake Victoria
7 Shoebill
8 Cairo
9 The springbok
10 The Sahara Desert
11 No, they inhabit the south and east
12 The Gulf of Aden
13 Tanzania
14 The Rift Valley
15 It is Africa's most northerly national park
16 Two (Mediterranean monk seal and Cape fur seal)
17 Greater and lesser flamingos
18 The Congo
19 Lion
20 The Nile crocodile
21 Gazelle
22 Six (Gabon, Congo, Democratic Republic of Congo, Uganda, Kenya and Somalia)
23 The Gambia
24 Tanzania
25 Giraffe

Dinosaurs
1 Terrible lizard (*deinos sauros*)
2 Warm-blooded flying reptiles related to dinosaurs
3 Stegosaurus
4 Because of its size, hence 'earth-shaking lizard'
5 Species
6 Triceratops
7 Brontosaurus
8 Its remains were first discovered in Edmonton, Canada
9 It was the first formally recognised dinosaur to be given a name
10 Tyrannosaurus rex
11 The Jurassic period
12 The Move
13 China
14 Birds
15 Oviraptor
16 Shrinkage of neck muscles after death
17 The bee hummingbird
18 Neither; they missed each other by about 42 million years
19 North America
20 Jurassic
21 Colorado
22 Water
23 The Flintstones
24 It had a short head with a parrot-like beak
25 Velociraptor

Soul Music
1 'Save Your Sweet Love Just For Me'
2 Dusty Springfield
3 James Brown
4 Sam Cooke
5 The MGs (along with Booker T Jones)
6 James Brown (they are all mentioned in Arthur Conley's 'Sweet Soul Music')
7 Curtis Mayfield
8 Saxophone
9 Aaron Neville
10 Aretha Franklin
11 Green
12 Harlem ('The Harlem Shuffle')
13 Teddy Pendergrass
14 Isaac Hayes
15 Wilson Pickett
16 Earth Wind and Fire
17 Sam and Dave
18 '. . . I'm Black and I'm Proud'
19 The Staple Singers
20 *The Blues Brothers*
21 Gamble and Huff
22 Otis Redding
23 Isaac Hayes, 'Theme from *Shaft*'
24 Jackie Wilson
25 'Isn't She Lovely'

Heavy Rock
1 Megadeth
2 Ozzy Osbourne
3 Grand Funk Railroad
4 Marilyn Manson
5 'Paranoid'
6 David Lee Roth
7 Jimmy Page
8 Leslie West
9 Eddie
10 Pearl Jam
11 Megadeth
12 Led Zeppelin
13 Blue Oyster Cult
14 Gene Simmons
15 Bruce Dickinson
16 Girlschool
17 True: it comes from the song 'The Ballad of Frankie Lee and Judas Priest'
18 'Purple Haze'
19 Frehley's Comet
20 Faith No More
21 Metallica
22 Stiltskin
23 Deep Purple
24 Slash
25 Def Leppard

Politics

1 1920s (1928)
2 Nikita Krushchev
3 Warsaw Pact
4 Bobby Sands
5 The KGB
6 To save coal resources
7 Rhodesia
8 Northern Ireland
9 Margaret Thatcher
10 Democratic Party
11 The Cultural Revolution
12 1995
13 Paris
14 Mikhail Gorbachev
15 The 'Million Man March'
16 Robben Island
17 Aneurin Bevan
18 Lord Beaverbrook
19 Fianna Fail
20 Zimbabwe African National Union
21 Michael Dukakis
22 Edward Heath
23 Nelson Mandela and F W de Klerk
24 Pol Pot
25 1958

The 1990s

1 Nelson Mandela
2 Freddie Mercury
3 The Queen and François Mitterrand
4 1990
5 1991
6 Stéphane Grappelli
7 Boris Yeltsin
8 Los Angeles
9 Michael Jackson
10 The Democratic Republic of Congo
11 Rajiv Gandhi
12 Princess Anne
13 St Petersburg
14 The United Nations
15 O J Simpson
16 1991
17 *Toy Story*
18 1997
19 The acquittal of Rodney King's police attackers
20 1996
21 Iraq invaded Kuwait
22 1994
23 The Channel Tunnel
24 Elton John
25 Yitzhak Rabin

Boxing

1 The 75th
2 James J Corbett
3 He became the first man to referee world title fights at every weight division
4 Gene Tunney, who went on to beat Jack Dempsey
5 Seventeen
6 The Marquess of Queensbury
7 Marvin Hagler
8 Jane Couch
9 Roberto Duran, 1980
10 Muhammad Ali (originally Cassius Clay)
11 Jersey Joe Walcott
12 Randolph Turpin
13 Ali v Foreman in Zaire, 1974
14 Jake LaMotta
15 It was the first world title fight to be filmed
16 Floyd Patterson, 1960
17 Chris Eubank
18 Julio Cesar Chavez
19 Thomas Hearns
20 21
21 She was the first woman to judge a world title fight (Ali v Shavers, 1977)
22 Super heavyweight
23 Mike Tyson
24 Jim Watt
25 They both won three consecutive Olympic gold medals. Papp 1948, '52 and '56; Stevenson 1972, '76 and '80.

Bad Boys & Girls

1 Stan Collymore
2 George Best
3 Ian Botham
4 Patrick Vieira
5 David Beckham
6 Moran
7 Phil Tufnell
8 Hansie Cronje
9 Ilie Nastase
10 Bjorn Borg
11 Napoli
12 A racist attack
13 Ian Wright
14 Aston Villa
15 *Addicted*
16 Brian Clough
17 Rodney Marsh
18 Jimmy Greaves
19 Graham Rix
20 Dennis Lillee
21 Carlos Mendes
22 Brooklyn
23 Evander Holyfield
24 John McEnroe
25 Eric Cantona

Animation

1 Scooby Doo
2 *King of the Hill*
3 Bam Bam
4 Bugs Bunny
5 *Family Guy*
6 *Wait 'til Your Father Gets Home*
7 Mel Blanc
8 Four
9 Schroeder
10 France/Gaul
11 Penelope Pitstop
12 Sylvester
13 Jellystone
14 Sgt Bilko
15 *Seinfeld*
16 Noo Noo
17 The name Michelangelo
18 Officer Dibble
19 Deputy Dawg
20 Bedrock
21 Mike Judge
22 The Archies
23 Mr Jinx
24 *South Park*
25 Fred Quimby

Cast List

1 Davy Crockett
2 *Falcon Crest* (Jane Wyman)
3 *Soap*
4 Guy Williams
5 *The Virginian*
6 The Addams family
7 *Twin Peaks*
8 Gary Burghoff as Radar
9 Jim Rockford
10 *Mission: Impossible* (playing Paris)
11 *Taxi*
12 *Mork & Mindy*
13 *The Mary Tyler Moore Show*
14 Johnny Weismuller
15 Martin Landau and Barbara Bain
16 William Conrad, alias Frank Cannon
17 *Batman*
18 Linda Thorson
19 *No Hiding Place*
20 *Buck Rogers in the 25th Century*
21 Dirk Benedict
22 *Marcus Welby MD*
23 *The Jack Benny Show*
24 *The Phil Silvers Show*
25 *Inspector Morse*

Brand Names

1 Ladies' underwear
2 Bovril
3 Clarence Birdseye
4 Coca-Cola
5 1960
6 The Minnesota Mining and Manufacturing Company
7 PK chewing gum
8 A fountain pen
9 Wall's ice cream
10 Toblerone
11 The Ford Motor Company
12 Samuel Colt
13 Slazenger
14 A successful racehorse
15 Ovaltine (Ovamaltine)
16 Franklin C Mars
17 Max Factor
18 Laszlo Biro
19 Unilever
20 Lego (leg godt)
21 Founder George Eastman wanted a name that started and ended with a 'k'
22 Cellophane
23 Kangol
24 Filofax
25 The Cadbury brothers

Musicals

1 *The Black Crook*, in 1866
2 Jule Styne, last of the Broadway giants
3 *The Pajama Game* (1954)
4 Catfish Row in Charleston
5 Jets and Sharks
6 *Gypsy* (1959)
7 Sholom Aleichem
8 *Whistle Down the Wind*
9 Herbert Kretzmer
10 Dave Clark's *Time* in 1986
11 Damon Runyan's
12 Stephen Fry
13 Carol Channing
14 James Fenton
15 Julie Andrews
16 'A Secretary Is Not a Toy' – *How to Succeed in Business Without Really Trying*
17 Maurice Chevalier
18 Fats Waller
19 *Half a Sixpence*
20 *King – the Musical* (1990)
21 *Mamma Mia*
22 Lionel Bart
23 *Show Boat*
24 Julie Taymor
25 Gillian Lynne

THE ULTIMATE BOOK
OF TRIVIA

QUIZ

14

1 *The Heart of the Antarctic* (1909) and *South* (1919) were written by which leader of several Antarctic expeditions who died in 1922 at Grytviken, South Georgia?

2 What colour jersey is worn by the leader of the Tour de France?

3 Who is generally regarded as the leader of the Bolshevik Revolution?

4 Who led the expedition in 1953 which culminated with Hillary and Tenzing reaching the summit of Mount Everest?

5 Who preceded Neil Kinnock as leader of the British Labour Party?

6 Who, in 1866, became principal chief of the northern hunting Sioux, with Crazy Horse, leader of the Oglala Sioux, as his vice-chief?

7 Who was the leader of 'Operation Chastise' which in 1943 caused considerable damage to dams in Germany?

8 Shaka or Chaka was the leader of which people in the early 19th century?

9 What name is given to the British government minister whose responsibility is to manage its programme of business through the House?

10 Who led the Israelites to the Promised Land?

11 How is Karim Al-Hussain Shah, the leader of the Nizari Ismailite sect of Islam, better known?

12 Robert Leroy Parker was the leader of the 'Hole in the Wall Gang', also known as the 'Wild Bunch'. How is he better known?

13 Which instrument does the leader of an orchestra play?

14 Which 1965 single by the Shangri-Las featured Billy Joel on piano?

15 Which party in Northern Ireland is led by David Trimble?

16 Dante Gabriel Rossetti was one of the leaders of which art movement?

17 With the middle name Winston, who was the deputy leader of the British Labour Party from 1980 to 1983?

18 Which brothers were the leaders of the first Jutish settlers in Britain in the 5th century AD?

19 What name is given to a Hindu or Sikh religious teacher or leader giving personal spiritual guidance to his disciples?

20 What title was assumed by Mohammed Ahmed, Sudanese military leader, who led a revolt against Egypt and captured Khartoum in 1885?

21 Who was the leader of the Gunpowder Plot who was killed while resisting arrest?

22 What was the name of the English suffragette leader who founded the militant Women's Social and Political Union?

23 Who was the leader of Solidarity, later president of Poland, who won the Nobel Peace Prize in 1983?

24 Which English king led the Third Crusade in 1191?

25 What name is given to an article offered below cost in the hope that customers attracted by it will buy other goods?

1 Who received 90 million dollars after challenging her late husband's will?

2 Which German blonde advertised French cars?

3 Which writer did Marilyn Monroe marry?

4 In which film did Marilyn star with Jack Lemmon and Tony Curtis?

5 Who said of herself 'I'm the girl who lost her reputation and never missed it'?

6 Who is the three-times German Olympic champion who won her last gold in Sydney in the long jump?

7 Which German became world champion female shot putter in 1997?

8 Which blonde starred in a 1933 monster movie that saw her paired with a gigantic gorilla?

9 Which Hollywood idol was the 'body' of the 1940s and 1950s?

10 Which blonde won Wimbledon in 1974, 1976 and 1981?

11 Which Federico Fellini film made a star of Anita Ekberg?

12 Who starred as Belle de Jour in the 1967 Luis Buñuel film of the same name?

13 Which blonde actress, along with her sister, accompanied the Beatles to India to study with Maharishi Mahesh Yogi?

14 Who played Hotlips Hoolihan in the TV series *M*A*S*H*?

15 Who did a Blonde Ambition tour?

16 Which blonde won Wimbledon in 1998?

17 Who has been linked with Prince William?

18 Which mermaid came to the West End?

19 Who is Britain's best-known woman golfer?

20 Who is Princess Anne's daughter?

21 Which diminutive blonde had her first hit with 'Genie in a Bottle'?

22 What was Blondie's breakthrough album?

23 Who is known as 'The Body'?

24 Which blonde was a folk singer in the 1970s?

25 Which blonde starred opposite Omar Sharif in *Doctor Zhivago*?

1 Who won an Oscar for his performance in *High Noon*?

2 Who or what were Ethan (John Wayne) and Martin (Jeffrey Hunter) trying to find in John Ford's *The Searchers*?

3 Who played Billy the Kid in a) *Pat Garrett and Billy the Kid*, and b) *Young Guns*?

4 Who did Errol Flynn portray in *They Died with their Boots On*?

5 Which Bob Hope comedy western featured the Oscar-winning song 'Buttons and Bows'?

6 Who played Wyatt Earp in John Ford's *My Darling Clementine*?

7 Which director and leading actor are common to the following films: *Winchester '73*, *Bend in the River*, *The Naked Spur* and *The Man from Laramie*?

8 In the 1939 movie *Jesse James*, who played the roles of Jesse and his brother, Frank, respectively?

9 In which of Clint Eastwood's films does Chief Dan George tell him that white men have been 'sneaking up on us for years'?

10 On which film was the TV series *Alias Smith and Jones* based?

11 Which film did Orson Welles credit above all others with showing him how to direct a movie?

12 Which film was a remake of Akira Kurosawa's *Shichinin no Samurai*?

13 Who directed *The Unforgiven*?

14 Who won an Oscar for his twin roles in the 1965 film *Cat Ballou*?

15 Which famous dancer and choreographer directed *The Cheyenne Social Club* in 1970?

16 Who sang 'See What the Boys in the Back Room Will Have' in *Destry Rides Again*?

17 What was the name of the one-eyed character played by John Wayne in *True Grit*?

18 Which comedy duo went *Way Out West* in 1930?

19 Who was the star of the 1953 movie *Shane*?

20 Who played opposite Clint Eastwood in *Two Mules for Sister Sara* in 1969?

21 Who became a star in Howard Hughes's *The Outlaw*?

22 Which actor 'aged' to 121 years old in *Little Big Man*?

23 What was John Wayne's final film?

24 Which Apache Indian chief was played by Chuck Connors in 1962?

25 What was Dodge City renamed in *Carry On Cowboy*?

1 In which film does Jack Lemmon star with, among others, Al Pacino, Ed Harris and Alec Baldwin as real-estate salesman Shelley 'The Machine' Levine?

2 In which 1955 film did he win his first Oscar?

3 What is his full name?

4 What was the title of Lemmon's first film, in which he co-starred with Judy Holliday?

5 With which actor does he share an apartment in *The Odd Couple*?

6 What do the Jack Lemmon movies *Some Like It Hot*, *The Apartment*, *Irma la Douce*, *The Fortune Cookie*, *Avanti!*, *The Front Page* and *Buddy Buddy* have in common?

7 In which film does he play insurance clerk C C Baxter?

8 In which country is the 1982 film *Missing* set?

9 In which film is Lemmon's character pursued by a gentleman called Osgood E Fielding III?

10 In which 1962 film does he portray an alcoholic?

11 Which British actress co-stars with him in *Avanti!*?

12 In which film of stories within a story does Lemmon appear as the grandfather of a boy hit by a car driven by Lily Tomlin?

13 In which film does he play an engineer whose quick thinking averts a catastrophe?

14 Which Neil Simon comedy pairs Jack Lemmon with Sandy Dennis in a disaster-prone trip to New York?

15 Who plays Lemmon's butler in *How to Murder Your Wife*?

16 What is the title of the 1995 follow-up to 1993's *Grumpy Old Men*?

17 In *The Fortune Cookie*, Lemmon is injured during a football game although not through playing. How does he come by his injuries?

18 For which 1973 movie did he win his second Academy Award?

19 Which actor received an Oscar nomination for the 1971 movie *Kotch*, directed by Jack Lemmon?

20 Who played Lemmon's role of Felix Ungar in *The Odd Couple* TV series?

21 For which movie did he win a British Academy Award in 1979?

22 In which of the *Airport* movies does he appear?

23 One of many performers making a cameo appearance in Robert Altman's *The Player*, what musical instrument is Jack Lemmon seen playing?

24 What is the name of his character in *Some Like It Hot* when he is not being Daphne?

25 What connects *Some Like It Hot*, *The Apartment*, *Days of Wine and Roses*, *The China Syndrome*, *Tribute* and *Missing*?

1 Of which country is Amman the capital?

2 Which modern capital is built on the site of ancient Carthage?

3 On how many hills was Rome built?

4 In which year did the Edinburgh Festival start?

5 What are the inhabitants of Madrid called?

6 What was the earliest inhabited part of Paris?

7 Where is the capital of Tibet in exile?

8 In which year did the Berlin Wall fall, precipitating the city's restoration as Germany's capital?

9 And what was the capital of West Germany before Berlin was reinstated?

10 Of which country is Kathmandu the capital?

11 What does the DC stand for in Washington, DC?

12 Which capital was confirmed on 12 December 1911 by King Emperor George V?

13 And where was this country's capital previously?

14 What capital of which country was formerly named Fort Salisbury?

15 What is the capital of Botswana?

16 Who was the last person to be imprisoned in the Palace of Westminster in 1902?

17 Which capital does the *Guinness Book of Records* credit as the world's hottest city?

18 Which capital was founded by Pedro de Valdivia on the banks of the Rio Mapocho in 1541?

19 Which city commands spectacular views of the volcano Snaefellsjokull?

20 Where is the capital of the Netherlands?

21 What is the name of the Israeli parliament?

22 On the banks of which river is Lisbon?

23 Which capital rose up against its Soviet rulers in 1956?

24 Which Asian capital's name means 'the city in the bend of a river'?

25 What is the capital of Latvia?

8

1 Which novelist born in Ghana wrote *An Ice-Cream War*?

2 Near which town was the author Thomas Hardy born?

3 Which islands are the birthplace of the giant tortoise?

4 Who was born on 9 October 1940 at the Maternity Hospital, Oxford Street, Liverpool?

5 Who is the Laoshan Mountains' most famous native philosopher?

6 Which scientist, most famous for the application of geometry to optics, was born in Ilchester in 1214?

7 In which American state was Martin Luther King, Jr born?

8 The lead singer of the group Hole was born in San Francisco. Who is she?

9 A radical philosopher of pessimism, he was born in Danzig in 1788. Who was he?

10 Where and when was William Shakespeare born?

11 Which author of *The Garden Party* and *Audience* later became the president of his native country?

12 Charles Dickens was born in a suburb of which provincial town?

13 Which British prime minister was born in West Yorkshire in 1916?

14 Which Italian astronomer, born in Pisa, renounced his greatest work in 1632?

15 Where was Thomas Edison born?

16 Archimedes was educated in Alexandria, but where was he born?

17 Which type of person is born within the sound of Bow bells?

18 Where was the birthplace of the pizza?

19 John F Kennedy died in Dallas. Where was he born?

20 James Joyce's native city was the setting for most of his work. Which city was it?

21 Where was the birthplace of the idea of parliament?

22 Where was the birthplace of Buddhism?

23 Who is the most famous person ever to have been born in Comox, British Columbia?

24 Which famous painter was born in Málaga, southern Spain, in 1881?

25 Which counter-culture music and lifestyle movement was born in Seattle?

10

1 Which lyricist worked with Richard Rodgers on such songs as 'Blue Moon', 'Where or When?' and 'My Funny Valentine'?

2 Which of Carole King's songs gave James Taylor a big hit in 1971?

3 Writer for Michael Jackson, George Benson and Michael McDonald among others, with which band did Rod Temperton first find success?

4 A hit for Elvis Costello in 1999, who wrote and had a UK number one with 'She' in 1974?

5 Who had a hit with Costello's 'Girls Talk'?

6 Whose songs have been successful for Guns N' Roses, Manfred Mann and Jimi Hendrix?

7 Which Motown artist wrote the songs 'My Guy' by Mary Wells and 'My Girl' by The Temptations?

8 Who was the first person to cover a Lennon/ McCartney song?

9 Which American songwriter co-wrote Abba's 'Ring Ring'?

10 Who has written songs with Mike Love, Tony Asher and Van Dyke Parks?

11 Which songwriters and musicians are the core of Steely Dan?

12 Which songwriting duo wrote a string of rock 'n' roll classics, including 'Hound Dog', 'Stand By Me', 'Up on the Roof' and 'Broadway'?

13 Which UK number one by Marvin Gaye was written by Norman Whitfield and Barrett Strong?

14 The song 'Evergreen' was a big hit for Barbra Streisand. Did she write the words or the music?

15 What is the surname of the brothers who wrote, among others, 'Chim Chim Cheree', 'Chitty Chitty Bang Bang' and 'The Bare Necessities'?

16 With which renowned American composer did Elvis Costello collaborate on the 1998 album *Painted from Memory*?

17 Which songwriters connect David Bowie, Chris Farlowe, Melanie, and Marianne Faithfull?

18 Who co-wrote the Band Aid single 'Do They Know It's Christmas?'?

19 Who wrote the American counterpart 'We Are the World'?

20 Who immortalised the 1969 Woodstock festival in song?

21 Which Henry Mancini/Johnny Mercer song was 'sung' by Audrey Hepburn in *Breakfast at Tiffany's*?

22 A huge hit for Whitney Houston, who wrote 'I Will Always Love You'?

23 Which team, later married, wrote 'Ain't No Mountain High Enough', 'Reach Out and Touch' and 'You're All I Need to Get By'?

24 Which song was George Harrison accused of plagiarising for his hit 'My Sweet Lord'?

25 Whose songs were recorded by a variety of artists on the album *Red Hot and Blue*?

1 Elvis Presley's twin brother died at birth. What was his name?

2 Where did Buddy Holly play his final show before taking off on that ill-fated flight?

3 Name the band that lost four members in the plane crash that killed Otis Redding.

4 Jim Morrison was found dead in what?

5 Who died in the same air crash as Cowboy Copas and Hawkshaw Hawkins?

6 Who fell to his death from an Amsterdam window in 1988?

7 He died playing Russian roulette and has since been celebrated in song by Paul Simon. Who was he?

8 Whose body was stolen and cremated in the desert?

9 Name the singer whose body was found in a Hollywood hotel room on 4 October 1970, eighteen hours after she died.

10 Name the legendary British producer who first shot his landlady before shooting himself.

11 What did Ron 'Pigpen' McKernan, Keith Godcheaux and Brent Myland all have in common?

12 His recording of 'I'll Never Get Out of This World Alive' charted just a few days before his death in January 1953. Name the country star.

13 Gene Vincent was injured in a 1960 car crash. But who was killed in that same crash?

14 He was born Robert Walden Cassotto, suffered from a weak heart all of his life and died aged 37. Who was he?

15 He was killed when a car driven by his girlfriend, Gloria Jones, crashed into a tree on Barnes Common. Name him.

16 'Three Stars', a hit for Ruby Wright in Britain and Tommy Dee in the States, relates to the death of which singers?

17 Ever glamorous, she died, aged 34, on 26 October 1966 and Ian Dury later called her 'the greatest popular singer Britain has ever had'. Who was she?

18 He flew his own single-engine aircraft but crashed into Monterey Bay in October 1997. What was the stage name of the man born Henry John Deutschendorf, Jr?

19 Name the musical major whose plane disappeared somewhere over the English Channel in December 1944.

20 Who was the reggae legend who died from cancer in Miami, Florida on 11 May 1981?

21 She was the greatest of all blues singers but nobody placed a headstone on her grave until Janis Joplin helped fund a memorial many years after her death. Who was she?

22 How did several Spinal Tap drummers perish, prior to the arrival of Mick Shrimpton?

23 Name John Lennon's killer.

24 Tammi Terrell died from a brain tumour three years after collapsing on stage in the arms of another Motown singer. Who was he?

25 Name the former Beatle bass player who died in 1962.

1 Which aerial form of transport did Louis Lenormand invent in 1783?

2 When did the *Mayflower* arrive in America?

3 When did Julius Caesar cross the Rubicon?

4 When did Adolf Hitler become German chancellor?

5 When was Louise Brown, the first 'test-tube baby', born?

6 When was the Battle of Hastings?

7 When was the Maastricht Treaty signed?

8 When did Magellan's expedition achieve the first circumnavigation of the globe?

9 When were the first Winter Olympic games held?

10 When did Albinus introduce coffee to Europe?

11 When was the state of Israel founded?

12 In which year was King Charles I executed?

13 When did Einstein first publish his theory of relativity?

14 When did India become independent?

15 When was the unification of Italy formally declared?

16 In which year was John F Kennedy assassinated?

17 When did Rome become a republic?

18 In which year was San Francisco devastated by a great earthquake?

19 When did Sigmund Freud first coin the word 'psychoanalysis'?

20 When did Copernicus state that the planets went round the sun?

21 When did Neil Armstrong set foot on the moon?

22 When was the Chernobyl disaster?

23 When did the Spanish cede Gibraltar to Britain?

24 When did Marx and Engels publish the *Communist Manifesto*?

25 When did Martin Luther nail his 95 theses to a door in Wittenberg, heralding the Reformation?

1 In which country were Europe's first banknotes issued?

2 The first reusable spacecraft, the Space Shuttle, made its inaugural flight in 1981. What was it called?

3 Which were the first animals, apart from insects, to live on land?

4 Mrs Sirimavo Bandaranaike became the world's first woman prime minister on 21 July 1960. Of which country was she head of government?

5 Where was the first fire insurance policy organized?

6 When was the first National Lottery draw held in Britain?

7 Captain James Cook's ship *Resolution* became the first to cross what during its voyage of January 1773?

8 In 1997 the first cloned sheep was 'born'. What was her name?

9 When did Diner's Club introduce the first credit card?

10 Where was the world's first purpose-built covered theatre, opened in 1585?

11 Which country's national beauty won the first Miss World contest in 1951?

12 Who first introduced potatoes to Europe in 1586?

13 Which was the Marx Brothers' first film?

14 Which airliner had its first flight in March 1969?

15 Where was the first purpose-built observatory constructed in 1576?

16 Which city became the first to install electric traffic lights in 1914?

17 Who was the first owner of a zoo?

18 When were women in Switzerland given the right to vote for the first time?

19 Why was the birth of Louise Brown on 25 July 1978 so significant?

20 Which operation was a world first for Dr Christian Barnard in December 1967?

21 The magnetic compass was first used by whom?

22 Who became the first US president to resign from the post?

23 Who became the first woman to fly solo from England to Australia in 1930?

24 Where was the world's first skyscraper?

25 Yuri Gagarin became the first spaceman while his *Vostok* craft made how many orbits of the Earth on 12 April 1961?

1 Which team didn't collect the trophy in the first FA Cup final in 1872?

2 In the final of which indoor sport's world championship was Mervyn King beaten in January 2002?

3 Who were the beaten finalists in the 1991 Rugby Union World Cup, held in England?

4 Who was beaten in consecutive Wimbledon singles finals in the 1980s by Boris Becker and Pat Cash?

5 Although arguably the greatest 800 metres runner of all time, who managed only silver medals in the event at the Moscow and Los Angeles Olympics?

6 Which country contested three of the first four European Football Championship finals, losing them all?

7 Who has lost in all six of his World Professional Snooker Championship finals?

8 Which team lost two consecutive Worthington Cup finals in the 1990s?

9 What connects Garrison Savannah in 1991, Party Politics in 1995 and Blue Charm in 1999?

10 Who came second in an athletics race at the Seoul Olympics and took home the gold medal?

11 Who were beaten by Australia in the final of the 1999 Cricket World Cup?

12 Which footballing nation has been beaten in three World Cup finals?

13 Who were runners-up in the FA Carling Premiership in 1994/95 and 1997/98 ?

14 Who lost to John Daly in the play-off for the 1995 Open Golf Championship, after sinking an incredible putt on the 72nd hole to tie the scores?

15 Who reached three Wimbledon finals in the 1990s and was thwarted first by Andre Agassi and then twice by Pete Sampras?

16 Who were the first runners-up in the Football League Cup in 1961, in the days before many top teams were involved?

17 Despite winning more races than champion Mike Hawthorn, who was runner-up in the 1958 Formula One season?

18 A Wimbledon champion three times, in how many other finals was Boris Becker on the receiving end?

19 Which rugby union side was beaten by Toulouse in the first Heineken European Cup final in 1996?

20 Which American football team were beaten finalists in four consecutive Superbowls in the 1990s?

21 What do Ilie Nastase, Jimmy Connors, Roscoe Tanner and John McEnroe have in common?

22 Who were runners-up in the University Boat Race in 2002?

23 The United States topped the medal table at the first modern Olympics at Athens in 1896. Which nation came second?

24 In *Wisden*, the bible of cricket, a panel of 100 experts voted Sir Donald Bradman player of the century. Who came second in the poll?

25 Old Etonians were first in 1875 and Sheffield Wednesday the most recent in 1993 – to do what?

1 Which Liverpool player moved to Juventus in the 1980s?

2 How many Italian clubs did David Platt play for?

3 Who did Gary Lineker play for?

4 Which English manager led Barcelona to the championship?

5 Who bought Robbie Keane from Coventry?

6 Who bought Gazza for five million?

7 How many teams did Bobby Robson manage abroad?

8 Which was the first Italian team Roy Hodgson managed?

9 Which country does Muzzy Izzet play for?

10 Who did Luther Blisset play for?

11 Where did Steve Archibald move to?

12 How many overseas teams did Mark Hughes play for?

13 Who moved from Liverpool to Real Madrid in 1999?

14 Which Welshman managed Real Madrid?

15 Who did Kevin Keegan play for?

16 Who is the only Brit to win the European player of the year award?

17 Where did Paul Lambert play?

18 Who did John Collins play for?

19 Who did Chris Waddle play for?

20 Who did Glenn Hoddle play for?

21 Who managed Hoddle at Monaco?

22 Who did Joe Jordan play for?

23 Who did Liam Brady first play for in Italy?

24 Which European international team did Roy Hodgson manage?

25 Which did Jimmy Greaves move from to go abroad?

12

14 Where did the word 'robot' first appear?

15 Who was 'the modern Prometheus'?

16 Who coined the phrase 'cyberpunk'?

17 Which evil creature did Terry Nation create in 'The Hidden Planet'?

18 Which half-policeman, half-robot did Paul Verhoeven create in 1987?

19 Which SF writer was born in Shanghai and interned in a Japanese POW camp as a child?

20 From which play was the title *Brave New World* a quotation?

21 Whose *Neuromancer* was a cult hit cyber novel?

22 What gets systematically sought out and destroyed in *Fahrenheit 451*?

23 What is the name of the Sigourney Weaver character in *Alien*?

24 Name the author of *Stranger in a Strange Land*.

25 Where did the invaders in H. G. Wells's *War of the Worlds* finally expire?

1 One of the two founding fathers of science fiction is H G Wells. Who is held to be the other?

2 Which former chairman of the British Interplanetary Society has lived in Sri Lanka since 1956?

3 What is the term for the 1980s horror films that display gore and mutilation?

4 Which pop singer had a small but significant role in David Lynch's film version of *Dune*?

5 Which US television series ran for 156 episodes between 1959 and 1964, one of which starred Lee Marvin as a robot boxer?

6 Who created *Star Trek*?

7 Which US illustrator helped develop Captain America and was known as the 'King of the Airbrush'?

8 Which 1955 film concerned a spaceman who turns into an amorphous blob in Westminster Abbey?

9 In *2001: A Space Odyssey*, what was the heuristically programmed algorithmic computer better known as?

10 George Méliès's *A Trip to the Moon* is generally regarded as the first film with a science-fiction theme. In what year was it made?

11 Whose first major novel divides the human species into the gentle Eloi and the bestial Morlocks?

12 *Do Androids Dream of Electric Sheep* became which film?

13 Which Russian-born US writer discovered SF through magazines in his dad's candy store?

1 In which century did the Renaissance begin?

2 In which museum is Leonardo da Vinci's *Mona Lisa*?

3 Where did the Renaissance begin?

4 The decoration of which chapel ceiling was commissioned by Pope Julius II in 1508?

5 Which Italian city was the centre of the Renaissance?

6 'Renaissance' means 'rebirth'. To whose values did its followers want to return?

7 Which great artist did François I bring from Italy to Amboise in France?

8 Which family of bankers dominated Florence during the Renaissance?

9 What was the title of Niccolo Machiavelli's famous book published in 1532?

10 Which palace was the centre of Renaissance art in France?

11 What was Filippo Brunelleschi's profession?

12 Which emperor commissioned most of Titian's work?

13 Who designed the dome of St Peter's Cathedral in the Vatican?

14 What was Donatello's profession?

15 Who became the official painter to Popes Julius II and Leo X?

16 Who, most famously, sculpted a marble David?

17 In which city did Il Correggio live and work?

18 In which part of France are most of the Renaissance chateaux?

19 In Carol Reed's *The Agony and the Ecstasy*, who plays Michelangelo?

20 Whose *Lives of the Artists* is the main contemporary source of information on the Italian Renaissance?

21 Who made it his life's mission to transplant the Renaissance onto German soil?

22 Leonardo da Vinci and Michelangelo were simultaneously employed to decorate different parts of which room?

23 Which architect designed the great Florence cathedral dome?

24 Which technique for representing three-dimensional space on a flat surface was one of the key artistic achievements of the Renaissance?

25 Whose birth in a shell was depicted by Botticelli?

1 In which decade of the 19th century did Conservative Judaism separate from Reform in the United States?

2 Who in 1534 proclaimed himself head of the Church of England?

3 What does the Arabic word 'Islam' mean?

4 Which religion developed in ancient Persia more than a thousand years before Islam?

5 Which branch of Christianity was pioneered by the brothers John and Charles Wesley and George Whitefield in the late 1720s?

6 Which tradition originated at the end of the 15th century in northern India?

7 A Bar Mitzvah ceremony celebrates a boy's coming of age at thirteen. What is the ceremony called when a girl reaches that age?

8 By what nickname are followers of the Holy Spirit Association for the Unification of World Christianity better known?

9 What do Buddhists call the state of final and definitive enlightenment?

10 The swastika symbol is sacred to the Jain tradition. What is meant by the Sanskrit word 'svastika'?

11 In which year was Pakistan formed as an Islamic state?

12 Which branch of Christianity holds meetings in Kingdom Halls?

13 Which order was founded in Boston, Massachusetts in 1879 by Mary Baker Eddy after receiving help from a healer for her spinal condition?

14 'Kippah' is the Hebrew word for the skullcap worn by Jews. What is the equivalent Yiddish word?

15 In which country do people worship nature deities and spirits in a tradition called Shrine Shinto?

16 In which century did the Dalai Lamas become rulers of Tibet?

17 The *Bhagavad-Gita* is a holy book of which religion?

18 What is Rosh Hashanah?

19 Of which religion is Sufism a branch?

20 Which order is referred to as 'fire worshippers' by its detractors?

21 What occasion in the Christian calendar is the first Sunday after the first full moon after the spring equinox?

22 In which Asian capital city is the Temple of Heaven?

23 What is the meaning of the word 'Shinto'?

24 Which religion has a doctrine of the 'three bodies', consisting of the Appearance or Transformation Body, the Body of Bliss and the Dharma Body?

25 What name is given to the Islamic period of fasting?

1 From where, on 4 October 1957, was the first man-made satellite launched into space?

2 With which sport is Edwin Hubble, of telescope fame, associated?

3 By what term is a 'lunar roving vehicle' better known?

4 Who was the first American to go into orbit in space?

5 How long did he take to complete one orbit of the earth?

6 In April 1970, who said 'Houston, we have a problem'?

7 Who was the first man to set foot on the moon?

8 And in which year did this happen?

9 From where do the European 'Ariane' rockets lift off?

10 Which Soviet artificial satellite was launched in October 1957?

11 Where was the launch pad of the Space Shuttle?

12 What is the reusable part of a Shuttle called?

13 Where is Mission Control Center?

14 What is the name of the Russian space station, sent into orbit in 1986?

15 What happened to Laika the dog?

16 What speed did *Saturn V* have to reach to escape Earth's gravitational pull?

17 Which Space Shuttle exploded on 28 January 1986?

18 Who holds the record for the longest period spent in space?

19 How long did he stay in space?

20 What is ARECIBO?

21 Which robotic probe accomplished the first mission to Mars in 1976?

22 Between 1969 and 1972, how many men went to the moon?

23 In which year did the last manned expedition to the moon take place?

24 Whose book about the history of America's first space programme was called *The Right Stuff*?

25 What distinction did Sally Ride achieve?

ANSWERS TO QUIZ 14

Leaders
1 Sir Ernest Shackleton
2 Yellow
3 Vladimir Ilyich Lenin
4 Sir John Hunt
5 Michael Foot
6 Sitting Bull
7 Guy Gibson
8 Zulu
9 Leader of the House
10 Moses
11 Aga Khan
12 Butch Cassidy
13 Violin
14 'Leader of the Pack'
15 Ulster Unionists
16 Pre-Raphaelite Brotherhood
17 Dennis Healey
18 Hengist and Horsa
19 Guru
20 The Mahdi
21 Robert Catesby
22 Emmeline Pankhurst
23 Lech Walesa
24 Richard I (Coeur de Lion)
25 Loss leader

Blondes
1 Anna Nicole Smith
2 Claudia Schiffer
3 Arthur Miller
4 *Some Like It Hot*
5 Mae West
6 Heike Drechsler
7 Astrid Kumbernuss
8 Fay Wray
9 Rita Hayworth
10 Chris Evert (in 1981 she was known as Chris Evert-Lloyd)
11 *La Dolce Vita*
12 Catherine Deneuve
13 Mia Farrow
14 Loretta Swit
15 Madonna
16 Jana Novotna
17 Britney Spears
18 Daryl Hannah
19 Laura Davies
20 Zara Phillips
21 Christina Aguilera
22 *Parallel Lines*
23 Elle McPherson
24 Joni Mitchell
25 Julie Christie

Westerns
1 Gary Cooper
2 Ethan's niece, Debbie (Natalie Wood)
3 a) Kris Kristofferson, b) Emilio Estevez
4 General George Armstrong Custer
5 *The Paleface*
6 Henry Fonda
7 Anthony Mann and James Stewart
8 Tyrone Power and Henry Fonda
9 *The Outlaw Josey Wales*
10 *Butch Cassidy and the Sundance Kid*
11 John Ford's *Stagecoach*
12 *The Magnificent Seven*
13 John Huston, 1960 (Clint Eastwood's film is called *Unforgiven*)
14 Lee Marvin
15 Gene Kelly
16 Marlene Dietrich
17 Rooster Cogburn
18 Laurel and Hardy
19 Alan Ladd
20 Shirley MacLaine
21 Jane Russell
22 Dustin Hoffman
23 *The Shootist*
24 Geronimo
25 Stodge City

Jack Lemmon
1 *Glengarry Glen Ross*
2 *Mister Roberts*
3 John Uhler Lemmon III
4 *It Should Happen to You*
5 Walter Matthau
6 They were all directed by Billy Wilder
7 *The Apartment*
8 Chile
9 *Some Like It Hot*
10 *Days of Wine and Roses*
11 Juliet Mills
12 *Short Cuts*
13 *The China Syndrome*
14 *The Out-of-Towners*
15 Terry-Thomas
16 *Grumpier Old Men*
17 He is a touchline cameraman flattened by a running back
18 *Save the Tiger*
19 Walter Matthau
20 Tony Randall
21 *The China Syndrome*
22 *Airport '77*
23 The piano
24 Jerry
25 He was nominated for Oscars in all of them

Capitals
1 Jordan
2 Tunis
3 Seven
4 1947
5 Madrileños
6 The Ile de la Cité
7 Dharamsala, India
8 1989
9 Bonn
10 Nepal
11 District of Columbia
12 Delhi
13 Calcutta
14 Harare, Zimbabwe
15 Gabarone
16 Emmeline Pankhurst
17 Bangkok
18 Santiago de Chile
19 Reykjavik
20 The Hague
21 The Knesset
22 River Tagus
23 Budapest
24 Hanoi, Vietnam
25 Riga

Birthplaces
1 William Boyd
2 Dorchester, Dorset
3 Galapagos Islands
4 John Lennon
5 Confucius
6 Roger Bacon
7 Georgia
8 Courtney Love
9 Arthur Schopenhauer
10 Stratford-upon-Avon in 1564
11 Vaclav Havel
12 Portsmouth
13 Harold Wilson
14 Galileo Galilei
15 Milan, Ohio
16 Syracuse, Sicily
17 A genuine cockney
18 Naples, Italy
19 Brookline, Massachusetts, in 1917
20 Dublin
21 The oldest known parliament was at Althing near Thingvellir, Iceland
22 It evolved from the teachings of Siddhartha Gautama in northern India in the 5th century
23 Pamela Anderson
24 Pablo Picasso
25 Grunge

Songwriters
1 Lorenz Hart
2 'You've Got a Friend'
3 Heatwave
4 Charles Aznavour
5 Dave Edmunds
6 Bob Dylan
7 Smokey Robinson
8 Kenny Lynch with 'Misery'
9 Neil Sedaka
10 Brian Wilson
11 Walter Becker and Donald Fagen
12 Jerry Leiber and Mike Stoller
13 'I Heard It Through the Grapevine'
14 Music
15 Sherman (Richard M and Robert R)
16 Burt Bacharach
17 Mick Jagger and Keith Richards
18 Bob Geldof and Midge Ure
19 Michael Jackson and Lionel Richie
20 Joni Mitchell
21 'Moon River'
22 Dolly Parton
23 Nickolas Ashford and Valerie Simpson
24 'He's So Fine'
25 Cole Porter

Music Deaths
1 Jesse Garon
2 Clear Lake
3 The Bar-Kays
4 A bath
5 Patsy Cline
6 Chet Baker
7 Johnny Ace
8 Gram Parsons
9 Janis Joplin
10 Joe Meek
11 All were keyboardists who died while with The Grateful Dead
12 Hank Williams
13 Eddie Cochran
14 Bobby Darin
15 Marc Bolan
16 Buddy Holly, Big Bopper and Ritchie Valens
17 Alma Cogan
18 John Denver
19 Glenn Miller
20 Bob Marley
21 Bessie Smith
22 They spontaneously combusted
23 Mark Chapman
24 Marvin Gaye
25 Stuart Sutcliffe

Dates
1 The parachute
2 1620
3 49 BC

4 1933
5 25 July 1978
6 1066
7 1992, in Chamonix
8 1522
9 1924
10 1580
11 1948
12 1649
13 1905
14 15 August 1947
15 February 1861
16 1963
17 509 BC
18 1906
19 1896
20 1543
21 21 July 1969
22 1986
23 1713
24 1848
25 31 October 1517

Firsts

1 In Sweden by the Bank of Stockholm in 1661
2 *Columbia*
3 Amphibians
4 Ceylon (Sri Lanka)
5 Hamburg, on 3 December 1591
6 19 November 1994
7 The Antarctic Circle
8 Dolly
9 May 1950
10 Vicenza, northern Italy
11 Miss Sweden (Kiki Haakonson)
12 Sir Thomas Harriot
13 *Coconuts*
14 Concorde
15 Uraniborg, in Denmark
16 Cleveland, Ohio
17 Queen Hatshepsut of Egypt, *c.*1500 BC
18 7 February 1971
19 She was the world's first test-tube baby
20 The first human heart transplant operation, in Cape Town, South Africa
21 The Chinese
22 Richard Nixon
23 Amy Johnson
24 Chicago, in 1883
25 One

Runners-Up

1 Royal Engineers (they lost the next two as well)
2 Darts (he lost to Tony David)
3 England
4 Ivan Lendl

5 Sebastian Coe
6 Yugoslavia
7 Jimmy White
8 Middlesbrough
9 They all came second in the Grand National
10 Carl Lewis (after Ben Johnson's disqualification)
11 Pakistan
12 West Germany (1966, 1982 and 1986)
13 Man Utd
14 Costantino Rocca
15 Goran Ivanisevic
16 Rotherham United (lost 3-2 to Aston Villa)
17 Stirling Moss
18 Four
19 Cardiff
20 Buffalo Bills
21 They were all beaten in Wimbledon finals by Borg
22 Cambridge
23 Greece
24 Sir Garfield Sobers
25 They lost the FA Cup final after a replay

Soccer Exports

1 Ian Rush
2 Three
3 Barcelona
4 Terry Venables
5 Inter Milan
6 Lazio
7 Three
8 Inter Milan
9 Turkey
10 A C Milan
11 Barcelona
12 One
13 McManaman
14 Toshack
15 Hamburg
16 Keegan
17 Bayern
18 Monaco
19 Marseille
20 Monaco
21 Arsene Wenger
22 A C Milan/Verona
23 Juventus
24 Switzerland
25 Spurs

Science Fiction

1 Jules Verne
2 Arthur C Clarke
3 Splatter movies
4 Sting
5 *The Twilight Zone*
6 Gene Roddenberry
7 Alex Schomburg

8 *The Quatermass Experiment*
9 HAL
10 1902
11 H G Wells – *The Time Machine*
12 *Blade Runner*
13 Isaac Asimov
14 In Karel Capek's play *R.U.R. Robota* is the Czech work for statute labour
15 *Frankenstein* by Mary Shelley
16 Bruce Bethke in his 1983 short story 'Cyberpunk'
17 The Daleks – it was a 1963 episode of *Doctor Who*
18 *Robocop*
19 J G Ballard
20 Shakespeare's *The Tempest*
21 William Gibson
22 Books
23 Ripley
24 Robert Heinlein
25 Primrose Hill

The Renaissance

1 The 15th century
2 The Louvre, Paris
3 Italy
4 The Sistine Chapel
5 Florence
6 The values of Greco-Roman antiquity
7 Leonardo da Vinci
8 The Medici family
9 *The Prince*
10 Fontainebleau
11 Architect
12 Charles V
13 Michelangelo
14 Sculptor
15 Raphael
16 Michelangelo Buonarroti
17 Parma
18 The Loire Valley
19 Charlton Heston
20 Giorgio Vasari
21 Albrecht Dürer
22 The Council Chamber in the Palazzo Vecchio, Florence
23 Brunelleschi
24 Perspective
25 *The Birth of Venus* (1485)

Religion

1 The 1880s (1889)
2 Henry VIII
3 Submission or surrender
4 Zoroastrianism
5 Methodism
6 The Sikh tradition
7 Bat Mitzvah

8 Moonies
9 Nirvana
10 Well-being
11 1947
12 Jehovah's Witnesses
13 The Church of Christ, Scientist
14 Yarmulke
15 Japan
16 17th
17 Hinduism
18 Jewish New Year
19 Islam
20 Zoroastrians
21 Easter
22 Beijing
23 The way of the gods
24 Mahayana Buddhism
25 Ramadan

Man in Space

1 Baikonur Kosmodrome, Kazakstan
2 Boxing – he was once offered the role of 'Great White Hope' in a match against world heavyweight champion Jack Johnson
3 Moon buggy
4 John Glenn, on 20 February 1962
5 108 minutes
6 Jim Lovell on *Apollo 13*
7 Neil Armstrong
8 1969
9 French Guyana, South America
10 *Sputnik 1*
11 Cape Canaveral in Florida
12 The Orbiter
13 Houston, Texas
14 *Mir*
15 The first animal in space died during the flight
16 40,000 km/h
17 *Challenger*
18 A Russian doctor called Valery Poliakov
19 438 days on *Mir*
20 The largest telescope dish in the world (305 metres, in Puerto Rico)
21 *Viking*
22 Twelve
23 1972
24 Tom Wolfe
25 On 18 June 1983 she became the first American woman to orbit Earth

Photographs reproduced by kind permission of Ardea Ltd, Empics, Oroñoz Ltd, Pictorial Press.

The author and publishers have made every reasonable effort to contact all copyright holders. Any errors that may have occurred are inadvertent and anyone who for any reason has not been contacted is invited to write to the publishers so that a full acknowledgement may be made in subsequent editions of this work.